D1590707

RADIX 2022

Also by Edward Dutton

Meeting Jesus at University: Rites of Passage and Student Evangelicals (2008)

The Finnuit: Finnish Culture and the Religion of Uniqueness (2009)

Culture Shock and Multiculturalism (2012)

Religion and Intelligence: An Evolutionary Analysis (2014)

The Ruler of Cheshire: Sir Piers Dutton, Tudor Gangland and the Violent Politics of the Palatine (2015)

How to Judge People By What They Look Like (2018)

J. Philippe Rushton: A Life History Perspective (2018)

The Silent Rape Epidemic: How the Finns Were Groomed to Love their Abusers (2019)

Race Differences in Ethnocentrism (2019)

Churchill's Headmaster: The "Sadist" Who Nearly Saved the British Empire (2019)

Making Sense of Race (2020)

Islam: An Evolutionary Perspective (2021)

With Bruce Charlton

The Genius Famine: Why We Need Geniuses, Why They're Dying Out and Why We Must Rescue Them (2015)

With Richard Lynn

Race and Sport: Evolution and Racial Differences in Sporting Ability (2015)

With Michael Woodley of Menie

At Our Wits' End: Why We're Becoming Less Intelligent and What It Means for the Future (2018)

SPITEFUL MUTANTS

EVOLUTION, SEXUALITY, POLITICS, AND RELIGION IN THE 21ST CENTURY

EDWARD DUTTON

Radix & Washington Summit Publishers
734 Clearwater Dr.
Whitefish, MT 59937

email : hello@RadixJournal.com
web: www.RadixJournal.com

Cataloging-in-Publication Data is on file with the Library of Congress

hardback: 978-1-59368-082-4
paperback: 978-1-59368-083-1
eBook: 978-1-59368-084-8
audio: 978-1-59368-085-5

Printed in the United States of America
10 9 8 7 6 5 4 3 2 1

CONTENTS

VII   ACKNOWLEDGMENTS

CHAPTER 1

5   **THE ENEMY IS ... US?**
The Zombie As Modern Myth

CHAPTER 2

25   **MAKING SENSE OF SPITEFUL MUTATIONS**
The Breakdown of Darwinian Selection

CHAPTER 3

83   **THE RETURN OF HERESY**
The Faith of the Social Justice Warrior

CHAPTER 4

111   **THE NEXT GREAT AWAKENING**
The Black Lives Matter Movement

CHAPTER 5

145   **TRUSTING THE PLAN**
Conspiracy Theories and the American Right

CHAPTER 6

181   **THE EVOLUTION OF A TABOO**
Homosexuality and Civilization

CHAPTER 6

235   **BORN AGAIN**
Gender Dysphoria and Alienation As Identity

CHAPTER 8

285   **THE END OF LOVE**
Herbivore Men and the Decline of Sex

CHAPTER 9

329   **HIDING IN PLAIN SITE**
The Normalization of Pedophilia

CHAPTER 10

351   **THE FUTURE PAST**
Our Social Apocalypse

367   **INDEX**

377   **ABOUT THE AUTHOR**

ACKNOWLEDGMENTS

The topical chapters of this book first appeared as essays, published in *Radix Journal*, across 2020-21. They were written as stand-alone pieces, and thus the expanded final product has somewhat the feel of an "essay collection." In preparing the volume, I found that editing the essays too much meant that they didn't really flow. Thus, readers may encounter some repetition across chapters, especially with regard to key theoretical issues. That said, though *Spiteful Mutants* is episodic—taking on various contemporary issues, from BLM to QAnon—it is essentially about *one thing*, namely, the evolutionary and social implications of the industrial revolution. It is thus a monograph, which examines phenomena, various and sundry, from one perspective.

Some sections of theoretical chapters first appeared in previous books of mine: *At Our Wits' End* (with Michael Woodley of Menie, 2018), *The Silent Rape Epidemic* (2019), *Race Differences in Ethnocentrism* (2019), and *Witches, Feminism, and the Fall of the West* (2021).

I am grateful to all those who helped me complete this project. Dr. Frank Salter read and commented on the entire manuscript. In developing the essays, I have benefited from discussions with Dr. Michael Woodley of Menie, J.O.A. Rayner-Hilles, Esq., Prof. Ray Blanchard, Prof. Dimitri van der Linden, Prof. Paul Gottfried, Mr. Richard Grannon, and Mr. Josh Neal. I also extend my thanks to Mrs. Susanna Sanlon for her assistance on English religious revivals. I would additionally like to thank Dr. Stephen Laker of Kyushu University, Japan, for reading over the sections related to Japan. Mr. Richard Spencer commissioned the original articles and has brought the final product to its completion.

Edward Dutton
April 2022

SPITEFUL MUTANTS

In the breeding of domestic animals, the elimination of those individuals, though few in number, which are in any marked manner inferior, is by no means an unimportant element toward success. This especially holds good with injurious characters which tend to reappear through reversion, such as blackness in sheep; and with mankind some of the worst dispositions which occasionally without any assignable cause make their appearance in families, may perhaps be reversions to a savage state, from which we are not removed by very many generations.

Charles Darwin, *The Descent of Man* (1871)

CHAPTER 1

THE ENEMY IS ... US?

The Zombie As Modern Myth

I n the "cult classic" *28 Days Later* (2002), we are thrown into an apocalyptic dystopia of the not-too-distant future.[1] In an opening scene, animal-rights protesters have broken into a Cambridge laboratory, intending to release a group of chimpanzees, which, according to them, are tortured victims of systemic oppression. These animals have, in fact, been infected with a highly-contagious and extremely dangerous new virus, which instills them with uncontrollable rage. As the breakout ensues, one of the chimps bites a female activist, and she promptly becomes a convulsing, murderous maniac. After jumping from chimp to human, the virus quickly spreads throughout the global population, turning millions into zombies who seek out non-infected humans to bite, and so create yet more savage automatons. The social order collapses.

28 Days Later—directed by Danny Boyle and produced on a small budget—became a runaway success in Britain. Since then, it has remained a standard in the burgeoning "zombie" genre. The first example of such a film was produced in 1932, though the style became especially prominent in the wake of George Romero's (1940-2017) *Night of the Living Dead* from 1968.[2] The

---

1—Danny Boyle (dir.), *28 Days Later*, Fox Searchlight Pictures, 2002.

2—George Romero (dir.), *Night of Living Dead*, Continental Distributing, 1968.

storylines are always very similar: a group of "normal" people, who have escaped infection, struggle to survive, avoid the hoards of the mindless, violent "living dead," and rebuild some semblance of civilization. The zombie genre is so popular—and culturally salient—that it has generated numerous spoofs, such as the British comedy *Shaun of the Dead* (2004),[3] and even real-world "zombie walks." Hundreds of citizens will don gory makeup and tattered costumes and march—or rather lurch and moan—through city centers, usually as part of a "pub crawl" or in the name of some charitable cause.[4]

The idea of the zombie can be traced back to the voodoo religion of Haiti and, ultimately, to the religious beliefs of Benin, from which many African slaves hailed. The "zombie" of that tradition is a monster or evil spirit. According to one ethnographer, only "deviant" people are made into zombies. It is unclear how this developed into the idea of the malevolent "walking corpse," but it has become so ubiquitous in Western popular culture that the zombie has been termed "the only modern myth."[5]

Why should the zombie be so popular? One possibility is that, as with traditional fairy tales, the genre taps into something that we fear might be happening to us. It thus provides us with advice on how to negotiate this trauma, doing so by means of a story, such that we can better absorb

---

3—Edgar Wright (dir.), *Shaun of the Dead*, Universal Pictures, 2004.

4—*Euro News*, "Mexico City's Zombie Walk Attracts Tens of Thousands," (5th November 2017), https://www.euronews.com/2017/11/05/mexico-citys-zombie-walk-attracts-tens-of-thousands.

5—Christopher Moreman and Cory Rushton, "Introduction: Race, Colonialism and the Evolution of the 'Zombie,'" in *Race, Oppression and the Zombie: Essays on the Cross-Cultural Appropriations of the Caribbean Tradition*, edited by Christopher Moreman and Cory Rushton (Jefferson: McFarland & Company, 2011).

the necessary information. Evolutionary psychologists, those who study the evolution of the human mind, generally concur that a vital component of fairy tales is "transmitting practical information on such adaptively important matters as resource acquisition, predator avoidance, and social interaction."[6] Literature of this kind, as well as the oral tradition that precedes it, should be understood as an "information acquisition strategy." "Little Red Riding Hood," for instance, "packs a double emotional wallop by combining our evolved fear of being harmed by animals with our evolved fear of being harmed by strangers."[7] The child is better able to take in this crucial, adaptive information due to it being presented in the form of an escapist fantasy, with its assorted surreal elements. Children are better able to imbibe information—that is, better able to learn—if it is dispensed together with imagination-stimulating elements, rather than simply explained in a matter-of-fact way.[8] Also, these stories have been vetted across generations to be maximally informative and engaging, meaning that they are likely to be very useful guides to life.[9]

In many ways, "myths" can be argued to be fairy tales for adults. Their evolutionary function can be understood as being to "validate and justify, conserve and safeguard the fundamental realities and values, customs and beliefs on which depend the stability and continuance of a given

6—Joseph Carroll, *Literary Darwinism: Evolution, Human Nature, and Literature* (London: Routledge, 2004), 38.

7—*Ibid.*

8—Deena Skolnick Weisberg, Hande Ilgaz, Kathy Hirsh-Pasek, *et al.*, "Shovels and Swords: How Realistic and Fantastical Themes Affect Children's Word Learning," *Cognitive Development*, 35 (2015): 1-14.

9—A point made by Jordan Peterson in *Maps of Meaning: The Architecture of Belief* (London: Routledge, 2015).

way of life," as one anthropologist put it.[10] Myths, in other words, are the distillations of centuries of experience, under conditions of Darwinian selection, on how best to act in certain situations, including those we most fear. One of those situations is, of course, being invaded by another group, such that most of your own group is killed and a small band of you, surrounded by enemies, are left to survive on your own.

Zombie movies are eye-opening because they do not involve a foreign invasion. They are centered-around "intra-vasions," as it were. The vast majority of your own people are "losing their minds"—destroying civilization, creating chaos and bloodshed, and making other people zombies, just like themselves. This kind of myth may well be particularly popular in the modern West, as we, on a gut level, fear that this is exactly what is happening. In George Romero's famous series of films, the nature of zombification is ambiguous: no clear cause is given, and some characters speculate it might be the result of radiation from a NASA space probe, thus affecting everyone on Earth. Indeed, everyone who perishes in the apocalypse transforms into a zombie, whether they have been bitten or not. The only escape from the horror is death through massive cranial hemorrhaging (the "head shot"). Romero's zombies are passive and sometimes peaceful. They return to familiar places—most notably a shopping mall in *Dawn of the Dead* (1978)—and rehearse their former lives by rote, in what has generally been taken as a critique of "mindless" consumer capitalism.[11]

10—E. O. James, "The Nature and Function of Myth," *Folklore*, 68 (1957): 474-482.

11—George Romero (dir.), *Dawn of the Dead*, United Film Distribution, 1978.

As these films developed, and began to take hold of the public imagination, the zombies became faster, deadlier, more aggressive, and, seemingly, *intentioned* in their riotous violence. As one survivor will invariably relay to another at some point in these films: "*Maybe they're coming for us!*" Zombies thus serve as a mask on traumatic—and often "politically incorrect"—fears infecting contemporary mass society. In Zach Snyder's remake of *Dawn of the Dead* (2002), which was produced shortly after the events of September 11th, the zombies were Islamic fanatics living in Western countries: the title sequence includes images of Muslims at prayer and "found footage" of journalists being overwhelmed while reporting from the Middle East.[12] The "normals" congregate at a shopping mall as their home base. Snyder's remake seems less a critique of capitalism than a Bush-era, right-wing call to "defend our way of life." In *World War Z* (2013), zombies form massive pyramids of bodies to scale the border walls surrounding Israel, seemingly a metaphor for mass immigration, demographic displacement, and the Jewish state's precarious position in the Middle East.

Might our fears, which play out vividly on the silver screen, be justified? My answer is "yes," and that is what this book is about. The "zombie" is attempting to destroy humanity and, more immediately, to annihilate its own group. This is, without any exaggeration whatsoever, what "Woke" culture writ large is trying to do. Many of you reading this book might be part of distantly connected bands of the uninfected, who want to see another day.

12—Zack Snyder (dir.), *Dawn of the Dead*, Universal Pictures, 2004.

In the words of the ill-fated lab attendant in *28 Days Later*, "In order to cure"—or, we would add, just survive—"you must first understand." And we do seek to understand. Countless books, videos, and articles have been published denouncing, ridiculing, or lamenting homosexuality, transsexuality, Wokeism and "cancel culture," "Social Justice Warriors" (SJWs), and the rest. If you are unfamiliar with this literature, a quick internet search with these key words will unearth it. Few of these explorations have advanced our understanding of the phenomena. They fail to answer *why* these things are occurring; *how* they came about; and *how* and *why* the ideology surrounding them has become prominent and, indeed, *dominant*, in our world. Moreover, a full analysis of contemporary morals, *mores*, and trends—"*décadence*," as it was once widely known—helps us understand how societies function, can thrive and expand, and be brought crashing down.

We will thus treat highly controversial topics with rationality and objectivity—and also *sympathy*. Zombies are not "evil" on a personal level; they are, in fact, "innocent" of their crimes. They have been infected with mind viruses and mutations, and, outside their control, enlisted in a nihilistic campaign. Condemning leftists and sexual deviants might purge pent-up frustration and revulsion, but it also overlooks a key component of their mindset, at least in many cases. We must remember that the most extreme sexual deviant and most obnoxious SJW could genuinely believe that what they are engaging in is "right" and "moral"—and, in turn, that traditional *mores* and morals are "evil," "harmful," and "Fascist." This has something to do with the political ideologies of "liberation" that have developed since the 18th century and the Age of Revolution. But Woke morals have emerged as a mutation—and thus evolution—of religion in the Western world. In other words, *I am Woke—and you must be Woke, too! The world must be Woke!*" Cries of "*Just leave me alone!*" will be about as effective as requesting a diplomatic parlay with an advancing zombie mob. The power of belief is at the core of these ideologies, and they might be best understood as part of an evolution of Christianity itself. It is "heretical" Christianity, perhaps, but heresy has a tendency of becoming dogma. And in contradistinction to most heresies, Woke ideology aggressively disrupts identity and productive sexuality—and thus threatens the existence of humanity itself.

So where is all this coming from? This book is based on a critical insight about the most existential of subjects: *who lives, who dies, who passes on their genes,* and *who doesn't.* Once upon a time, the crucible of evolution was child mortality. Until 1800, the child mortality rate was approximately 50 percent; that is, every other baby didn't make it into adulthood. Only the healthiest children—those with the lowest "mutational load," that is, the fewest "mutant genes," which made them less fit—survived childhood diseases and grew up to have a legacy.[13] Warfare also played a role. Groups would fight each other, and the group that was better able to triumph in these battles and invasions would be more likely to advance their culture.

Following the Industrial Revolution, the world became immensely wealthier, healthier (in the sense of

---

13—Anthony Volk and Jeremy Atkinson, "Is Child Death the Crucible of Human Evolution?" *Journal of Social, Evolutionary, and Cultural Psychology,* 2 (2008): 103-116.

the development of inoculation and effective medicine), and more comfortable, and the harsh Darwinian selection pressures that characterized previous ages subsided. One of the most impactful consequences of this is the dramatic decrease in childhood mortality, which has fallen to below one percent in most advanced countries.[14] Thus, millions of people with high levels of mutation, who would not have survived childhood in previous times, walk among us in the postmodern age. The brain is roughly 84 percent of the genome—that is, 84 percent of genes relate to brain development—rendering it a massive target for mutation. Thus, if you have high mutational load of the body, you will certainly have high mutational load of the mind. In fact, the two have been proven to be comorbid, that is, to go together.[15] To the extent that they behave like zombies, destroying the genetic interests of their group, these people are what have been termed "Spiteful Mutants,"[16] a concept we will dissect below.

Due to the highly sociable nature of humanity, we are evolved to be around other genetically healthy people, who believe and espouse ideas that are fitness-elevating. Furthermore, humans are highly environmentally plastic. Less complex organisms are born ready to get on with

---

14—*Centers for Disease Control and Prevention*, "Mortality in the United States, 2018," NCHS Data Brief No. 355, January 2020, https://www.cdc.gov/nchs/products/databriefs/db355.htm.

15—See, Matthew Sarraf, Michael Woodley of Menie, and Colin Feltham, *Modernity and Cultural Decline: A Biobehavioral Perspective* (Basingstoke: Palgrave Macmillan, 2019).

16—Michael Woodley of Menie, Matthew Sarraf, Robert Pestow, *et al.*, "Social Epistasis Amplifies the Fitness Costs of Deleterious Mutations, Engendering Rapid Fitness Decline Among Modernized Populations," *Evolutionary Psychological Science,* 3 (2017): 181-191.

life, following their instincts. More complex organisms, often evolved to a harsher but more predictable ecology, benefit from having a "childhood," in which they are able to learn about their world and so be more likely to thrive. Accordingly, they are born helpless and relatively low in instinct. They learn adaptive behaviors from their parents and from their broader group. They are socialized into the most adaptive possible ways to behave; directed to follow a road map of life that will make them the most likely to survive, to develop optimally, and pass on their genes. In addition, this "road map" directs them to optimally thrive in the very specific and narrow environment to which their species, or sub-species, has long been adapted, and any instincts they have will be highly useful to them. Thus, if the environment rapidly changes, members of such a species may experience an "evolutionary mismatch," resulting in their behaving in maladaptive ways. This will be mediated, in part, by the way in which such a mismatch induces a sense of dysphoria and depression.

We are evolved to compete to survive, every day, and, suddenly, we don't have to. Congruous with this, it has been found that "mortality salience"—the fear of danger, death, and deprivation—predicts a desire to have children, as we are evolved to ensure that our genes are passed on in the context of imminent destruction.[17] Take away mortality salience, and we may heavily limit our fertility and even, maladaptively, reason ourselves into not having children at all. This is especially so as mortality salience elevates religiosity, something that in turn tends to promote

---

17—Immo Fritsche, Eva Jonas, Peter Fischer, *et al.*, "Mortality Salience and the Desire for Offspring," *Journal of Experimental Social Psychology*, 43 (2007): 753-762.

natalism, and other adaptive traits, as "God's will."[18] And if the nature of the group changes—such that it ceases to be composed overwhelmingly of genetically healthy people—then it will cease to socialize its offspring properly, resulting in more and more of them adopting fitness-reducing behavior or even developing abnormal sexuality.

SPITEFUL MUTANTS

We will see that when there are too many Spiteful Mutants in the population, their anti-adaptive ways of thinking can spread like a virus, unless we are extremely genetically healthy ourselves and thus resistant to them. Let us be clear by what we mean by "Spiteful Mutants." They can be understood as manifesting in three inter-related forms, all of which we will explore in this book: leftist individualists (Machiavellians and Narcissists), psychopaths, and people with low IQ. As we will explore, leftist individualists, due to runaway individualism, eventually direct the group to destroy itself and not to place its children on the adaptive road map of life. Psychopaths and those with low IQ, who share psychopathic traits such as selfishness, help to create a dangerous, chaotic and disunited society which, as we will see, tends to be displaced by a more united one. These Spiteful Mutants, and especially the former type, heighten or bring about a series of partly genetically-mediated conditions which we will also explore such as homosexuality, gender dysphoria, pedophilia and sexual dysfunction.

Until recently, we were selected to be relatively group-oriented. This is because, under harsh selection pressures,

18—Ara Norenzayan and Azim Shariff, "The Origin and Evolution of Religious Pro-Sociality," *Science*, 322 (2008): 58-62.

the group that is highest in "positive ethnocentrism" (internal cooperation) and "negative ethnocentrism" (external aggression) tends to predominate, all else being equal, as computer models have shown. In these studies, ethnocentric groups always dominated the computer grid after many generations when they battled those that cooperate with nobody, cooperate with everybody, or only cooperate with members of another group.[19]

As pack animals, we need to be group-oriented, but we also need to climb the hierarchy of the group, because those with more resources tend to disproportionately pass on their genes by ensuring their own survival and the survival of more of their offspring. Thus, we were selected—and our group was selected—to have a balance between "binding" and "individualizing" foundations. "Binding" means group-orientation: obedience to authority, in-group loyalty, and a regard for sanctity, that is, strong feelings of disgust to what is maladaptive. "Individualizing" refers to a regard for equality and harm avoidance: the individual is sacred and sovereign and nothing should constraint or (de-)form him, or prevent him from climbing to the top.[20] We will explore these "foundations" in more detail later, but it's important to understand that these are largely "instinctive" or "hardwired;" they are not entirely the result of nurturing or education. Moreover, we were also under selection pressure for intelligence: the ability to solve cognitive problems. All else being equal, groups that are more intelligent will

---

19—Ross Hammond and Robert Axelrod, "The Evolution of Ethnocentric Behavior," *Journal of Conflict Resolution*, 50 (2006): 1-11.

20—Jonathan Haidt, *The Righteous Mind: Why Good People Are Divided By Politics and Religion* (London: Penguin, 2012).

dominate those who are less intelligent, through superior weapons and planning. Under harsh conditions, people with high intelligence will attain higher social status, leading to more resources and more of their offspring surviving.[21] The richer half of early 17th-century English populations had as much as double the completed fertility as the poorer half.[22] In that all these traits were being selected for, as was genetic physical and mental health, we would expect all of these traits to correlate. In other words, there is a general "fitness factor" that was being selected for. Intelligence correlates with genetic health,[23] as does traditional religiosity, something which tends, itself, to be highly group oriented.[24]

We can understand all of these "instincts of the mind"—and deviations from them—in terms of the values that predominate among societies and individuals that compose them. Any deviation from this optimum can be expected to be associated with evidence of mutation. This can be expected to be the case with leftism, as this is characterized, as we will see, by extreme individualism. Leftists are concerned with the "individualizing" foundations of equality (as pulling everyone else down

21—Edward Dutton and Michael A. Woodley of Menie, *At Our Wits' End: Why We're Becoming Less Intelligent and What It Means for the Future* (Exeter: Imprint Academic, 2018).

22—John F. Pound, "An Elizabethan Census of the Poor," *University of Birmingham Historical Journal,* 7 (1972): 142160.

23—David Hugh-Jones and Abdel Abdellaoui, *Natural Selection in Contemporary Humans is Linked to Income and Substitution Effects* (School of Economics, University of East Anglia, 2021).

24—Edward Dutton, Guy Madison, and Curtis Dunkel, "The Mutant Says in His Heart, "There Is No God": The Rejection of Collective Religiosity Centred Around the Worship of Moral Gods is Associated with High Mutational Load," *Evolutionary Psychological Science,* 4 (2018): 233-244.

gets you relatively more power) and "harm avoidance" (as avoiding harm to all avoids harm to you).[25] Leftists signal their concern with these foundations because they always perceive themselves as lacking power, which makes them strive for ever more power. For individualists, there's always someone out there more powerful than they are, real or imagined. Perceiving themselves as weak, they cannot risk overtly playing for status—by signaling their power—as they will fear being harmed. Thus, they must "disguise" their attempts to attain status, only playing for it covertly. "Virtue-signaling" is a covert competitive strategy. It is less likely to provoke direct conflict than signaling bravery or toughness, as it will make the signaler seem kind. This tactic has been noted to be more prominent among females than among males.[26]

Individualism is also found with the most extreme elements of the Right. Such people have been shown to be high in psychopathic traits; in other words, they are extremely low in concern about harm-avoidance and are thus belligerent.[27] Leftism gives us the evolutionary mismatch of insufficient concern with "binding" values; the extreme Right will take us in the other direction, to perpetual war, or at least to fantasies of "civil war" fought in the streets or various "days of reckoning" like

25—Jesse Graham, Jonathan Haidt, and Brian Nosek, "Liberals and Conservatives Rely on Different Sets of Moral Foundations," *Personality Processes and Individual Differences,* 96 (2009): 1029-1046.

26—Joyce Benenson, "The Development of Human Female Competition: Allies and Adversaries," *Philosophical Transactions of the Royal Society B,* 368 (2013): 2013007920130079.

27—Jordan Moss and Peter O'Connor, "The Dark Triad Traits Predict Authoritarian Political Correctness and Alt-Right Attitudes," *Heliyon,* 6 (2020): e04453.

we saw on January 6, 2021. In that the "Alt-Right" is currently "dissident," psychopaths may also be attracted to it simply because they like danger and offending people. Libertarians—often classified as on the right— are concerned with no moral foundations at all; they are amoral, something also associated with psychopathology.[28]

Finally, those who have low intelligence will be low in conformism to the dominant set of values, because low IQ, as we will see, correlates with the inability to understand what these are and the inability to force oneself to believe them.[29] Low intelligence also correlates with low trust, and thus skepticism of democracy and civic life, because less intelligent people are more likely to be conned, so it pays to trust nobody. It is further correlated with rigid, black-and-white thinking. The result is a tendency for those with low IQ to be attracted to extreme conservatism and conspiracy theories.[30] Such beliefs can also be attractive to those with depression and anxiety. These ailments can make people paranoid and make the world seem like an evil place with evil forces behind it. Conspiracy theories can make sense of a chaotic world. Famously, those with schizophrenic tendencies are prone accepting the most outlandish notions.[31] Psychopathology, perhaps due to

28—Ravi Iyer, Spassena Koleva, Jesse Graham, *et al.*, "Understanding Libertarian Morality: The Psychological Dispositions of Self-Identified Libertarians," *PLOS ONE*, 7(2012): e42366.

29—Michael A. Woodley of Menie and Curtis Dunkel, "Beyond the Cultural Mediation Hypothesis: A reply to Dutton (2013)," *Intelligence*, 49 (2015): 186-191.

30—Viren Swami, Martin Voracek, Stefan Stieger, *et al.*, "Analytic Thinking Reduces Belief in Conspiracy Theories," *Cognition*, 133 (2014): 572-585.

31—Neil Dagnall, Kenneth Drinkwater, Andrew Parker, *et al.*, "Conspiracy Theory and Cognitive Style: A Worldview," *Frontiers in Psychology*, 6 (2015):

the paranoia involved, independently predicts belief in conspiracy theories.[32]

It seems that when these mental conditions come along with Machiavellianism, people are left-wing—attacking group-oriented foundations to attain personal power. When they are found with psychopathology, which makes people more openly aggressive and unconcerned about what others think of them, they adopt certain forms of the extreme Right; they do not virtue-signal, and they are not concerned about fairness or equality: they simply desire conflict. Extreme leftism is also associated with Narcissism, desiring love and praise.[33] It may be that the relationship between this trait (and to some extent Machiavellianism) and political orientation varies according to whether leftist or rightist values are dominant in the society. But in that these perspectives are associated with both low intelligence and psychological disorders, they can be understood as expressions of mutation.

SPITEFUL IDEAS

In that we were selected to be strongly group-oriented, we might expect much of the deviation from

206; David De Coninck, Thomas Frissen, Koen Matthijs, *et al.,* "Beliefs in Conspiracy Theories and Misinformation About COVID-19: Comparative Perspectives on the Role of Anxiety, Depression and Exposure to and Trust in Information Sources," *Frontiers in Psychology,* (2021), https://doi.org/10.3389/fpsyg.2021.646394.

32—Evita March and Jordan Springer, "Belief in Conspiracy Theories: The Predictive Role of Schizotypy, Machiavellianism, and Primary Psychopathy," *PLoS ONE,* 14(2019): e0225964.

33—Moss and O'Connor, "The Dark Triad Traits Predict Authoritarian Political Correctness and Alt-Right Attitudes," *op cit.*

preindustrial norms to involve the manifestation of more and more selfish, individualistic people, adapted to an environment that is not harsh and selective but, rather, easy and unpredictable. Such an easy environment does not require great cooperation, because basic needs are met, meaning that mental instability is not selected out. It is quite feasible, in such an easy ecology, to withdraw into yourself if something bad happens—to suffer from a period of depression, in which you work out what occurred and why—and still survive. Confronted with an environment that is stable, such people can be expected to actively try to create chaos, because that is the ecology to which they are evolved. They are adapted to intra-group or inter-group warfare, not to the stability that has selected for an optimum balance between the moral foundations, that is, conservatism.

Now, the ideas that emanate from such people can be seen to spread, in the same way that depressive ways of thinking can spread. An example of this is the way that depression—and the nihilistic, suicidal ideas associated with it—can spread from people who are depressed for primarily genetic reasons to their friends and colleagues.[34] It might be averred that, strictly-speaking, these mutations are not "spiteful," as "spite" implies needless malice, which doesn't benefit the person being spiteful.[35] It can be responded, however, that, in an evolutionary sense, everyday "spiteful" behavior may be adaptive on

---

34—T.E. Joiner, "Contagious Depression: Existence, Specificity to Depressed Symptoms, and the Role of Reassurance Seeking, *Journal of Personal and Social Psychology*, 67 (1994): 287-296.

35—William Hamilton, "Selfish and Spiteful Behaviour in an Evolutionary Model," *Nature*, 228 (1970): 1218–1220.

some level: it is damaging an evolutionary competitor and his prospects, even if only mildly. So, in a sense, a spiteful mutation—even if it causes the carrier to kill himself—could be adaptive by helping to create chaotic conditions in which people who are genetically similar to him might better thrive. But from the perspective of group-oriented people, he is a Spiteful Mutant, who infects other people with maladaptive inclinations, such as the inclination to abandon reproduction.

It has been mathematically shown that this is plausible when organisms are bunched together and cannot escape each other—this being the modern condition to a great extent.[36] In such conditions, a Spiteful Mutant, in a position of societal influence, could infect a whole society with depression, by creating dysphoria as an out-working of their dark and despondent worldview. And this would be more likely if there were growing numbers of mutant, depressed people. This, along with related processes that we will explore, is what has happened, such that the majority of people, to varying degrees, are now infected with a virus of the mind that causes them not to want to pass on their genes to any significant extent, and even to directly, and indirectly, dissuade others from doing so.

Spiteful Mutants, as we will see, have interfered with the ability of the group to direct its offspring along an adaptive path—by undermining institutions that did so, such as the family and traditional religiosity—helping to create more and more maladaptive people who have lost the desire to breed, to aid their group's genetic interests, or even live at all. Some Spiteful Mutants, it will be argued,

36—See Francisco Dionisio, "Selfish and Spiteful Behavior Through Parasites and Pathogens," *Evolutionary Ecology Research,* 9 (2007): 1199-1210.

have managed to bring about the collapse of traditional religion, ethnic pride, and everything that is associated with mental and physical health and evolutionary success. Up is down, right is left, and, as it were, the dead walk the earth. Others, those who completely lack "individualizing" values, also help to sow chaos, pushing us towards a situation of war, in which they can thrive. These are leaders of extreme conservative cults, such as David Koresh (1959-1993) of the Branch Davidians of Waco, Texas, and similar paranoid, bellicose types, who may be, for example, very high in "sanctity" but low in the other moral foundations.[37] Such societies collapse into chaos and are displaced by societies that are more balanced.

Many genetically healthy people can be infected with these ideas and especially, in our current society, with left-wing ideas. Even under harsh selection pressures, there was always a balance in the group between "binders" and "individualists," leading to genetically healthy individualists who were kept in check by a group-oriented culture. With this switch to an individualistic culture, many healthy group-oriented people—being conformist—can be induced to be individualist while individualists are in their element. That said, it is the rise in individualists, due in part to mutation, and the extent of their individualism that has precipitated this transformation.

LA RÉSISTANCE

The silver lining of the Zombie Apocalypse is that the mentally unhealthy are in the process of removing

---

37—Rebecca Frey, *Fundamentalism* (New York: Facts On File, 2007), 4.

themselves from the gene pool. In this way, Wokeness can be considered the new child mortality. If you can overcome the dysphoria, nihilism, and individualism that it induces and breed anyway, then your genes will survive. Zombies spread a virus of Wokeness—that induces you not to pass on your genes—and only certain kinds of people, those who are genetically resistant to Woke ideas, will leave a legacy.

The result, as we will explore below, will eventually be the return to something like the society that existed before the Industrial Revolution—at the very least to a society that is traditionally religious and that promotes, as part of this religiosity, adaptive traits such as pro-natalism. In the meantime, we have an evolutionary trial not by "warfare," as in days of old, but by "Wokefare." We will explore a number of the most salient results of this new evolutionary situation, a number of expressions of the influence of Spiteful Mutants. Specifically, we will look at the evolutionary dimensions behind the rise of Social Justice Warriors, the Black Lives Matter protests of the summer of 2020, right-wing conspiracies such as QAnon, trans-sexuality, homosexuality, celibate males, and related issues such as feminism and pedophilia. But before looking at exactly how Spiteful Mutants operate, however, there are a number of scientific concepts with which we need to familiarize ourselves.

CHAPTER 2

MAKING SENSE OF SPITEFUL MUTATIONS

The Breakdown of Darwinian Selection

One of the consequences of social media is that we are aware of how the lives of one-time friends and acquaintances, with whom we would otherwise have completely lost touch, have panned out. I was born in 1980 and did my undergraduate degree at Durham University between 1999 and 2002. Durham is a small, Medieval Cathedral city in the northeast of England. Its highly traditional university has been described as a "dreamy mini-Oxford,"[1] dominated by privately educated students, many of whom are Oxford or Cambridge rejects.[2] As they've entered their 40s at the time of writing, if my female university acquaintances have not had children, they are unlikely to have any. If they have one child, then they are not likely to have any more, meaning they will operate at below replacement fertility.

As I will discuss in more detail later, I knew many females at university who were members of "DICCU":

1—Jonathan Margolis, "Party for Jesus," *The Guardian,* September 22, 1999, https://www.theguardian.com/education/1999/sep/22/highereducation.

2—Sunniva Carlsen, "We Asked Students at Other Unis What They Really Think of Durham," *The Tab,* November 8, 2017, https://thetab.com/uk/durham/2017/11/08/we-asked-students-at-other-unis-what-they-really-think-of-durham-37656.

the Durham Inter-Collegiate Christian Union. This was a fundamentalist, evangelical Christian group that eschewed drinking, premarital sex, and, indeed, all of the hedonism that tended to characterize undergraduate life.[3] As far as I am aware, all of the females I knew in this group have married and have had children, in most cases two or more. By contrast, a girl whom I knew who was cold, nihilistic, anti-religious and spent her undergraduate years doing little other than drinking and bitching about thinner girls, has definitely not married nor reproduced. Another woman, whom I lived close to as a First Year, was a public school girl—a "public school" is a prestigious, private school at which pupils usually board—who was heavily involved in the Labour Party. We got on well, despite our political differences—I was involved in the Conservative Party—in those less polarized times. She has married, but has no children. The same is true of the proto-Woke women with whom I studied; in many cases, they remain single as well. This is Darwinian selection in action.

There are four essential kinds of selection: natural, sexual, kin, and group. *Natural selection* is the process whereby an organism is adapted, both physically and mentally, to a particular kind of ecology. In the process of procreation, an infant inherits copies of genes. Each gene is composed of two alleles, with one allele inherited from each parent. Sometimes something goes awry, and these alleles do not copy correctly. This leads to mutation. Under the brutal conditions of natural selection, organisms are fine-tuned to their environment, so the mutations almost always make them less well-adapted to it. Accordingly,

---

3—See Edward Dutton, *Meeting Jesus at University: Rites of Passage and Student Evangelicals* (Aldershot: Ashgate, 2008).

the carriers of these mutations will be selected against, and they won't pass on their genes, or they won't pass them on to any significant extent. Sometimes, a mutation actually gives the carrier an advantage in its particular environment. Blue eyes, for example, would have given the first blue-eyed person an edge, as he or she would have been able to absorb more sunlight and convert it into Vitamin D, in an environment where it was relatively dark for much of the year. This would especially be so due to blue eyes tending to be accompanied by pale skin, which also allows the absorption of more sunlight.[4] When this kind of mutation happens, the allele would be selected for and the carrier would end up with a larger number of descendants. That said, in general, mutation is selected against.

SEXUAL SELECTION

The second form of selection highlighted by Darwin was *sexual selection*. Darwin observed, "It is certain that among all animals there is a struggle between the males for possession of the female."[5] In most animal species, males fight to mate with as many females as they can. In winning these fights, they establish who among them is the strongest, who is the healthiest, and who, therefore, has very few mutant genes. Females are sexually attracted to males who are successful in these fights. The dominant male, as far as the females are concerned, will provide them with healthier children, and these children are more

4—See Gregory Cochran and Henry Harpending, *The 10,000 Year Explosion: How Civilization Accelerated Human Evolution* (New York: Basic Books, 2009).

5—Charles Darwin, *The Descent of Man* (London: John Murray, 1871), II, 239.

likely to survive the rigors of natural and sexual selection themselves. This means that the female's own genes are more likely to be passed on. The population remains healthy and strong, in part because those who lack genetic health, those with a high percentage of mutant genes, find that the females do not want to have sex with them. The females aggressively fight off any attempt by an unattractive male (a male who is high in mutational load) to breed with them.

Throughout animal species, males compete for territory; or, in the case of the social animals, such as humans, the group competes for territory, with each male competing for a position within the status hierarchy of the group. Only those who are successful in getting territory or attaining high status are attractive to the females. And the males ultimately attract the females through winning fights. Something like rape generally occurs as a last resort, when a desperate and unattractive male forces a relatively attractive female into sexual relations with him, failing to win her on his own.[6]

In addition, females are generally attracted to the kinds of qualities that lead to the males obtaining status in the first place. In a society where status is, effectively, achieved through fighting, these will be markers of physical strength and genetic health: muscles, size, a nice furry mane as an indicator of the healthy genes necessary to successfully grow one, and so on. Males showcase these desirable qualities through fighting in front of the females and also by what is known as "strutting." They walk around advertising their genetic quality. A good example of this

---

6—See Randy Thornhill and Craig Palmer, *A Natural History of Rape: Biological Causes of Sexual Coercion* (Cambridge: MIT Press, 2000).

is the peacock's tail. As American psychologist Geoffrey Miller has noted, only a genetically healthy peacock has sufficient resources left over to grow a large and colorful tail. A less healthy peacock must invest more of his bio-energetic resources into fighting off disease, leading to the production of a gaudy, asymmetrical, or small tail.[7] Chimpanzees deliberately display their erections, conveying to the females that they are genetically healthy enough to be able to direct resources into growing a large penis.[8] The human male will stereotypically display his (supposed) wealth and, by implication, his relatively high place in the hierarchy. He has the resources left over for the designer shirt and the sports car, or, at least, he wants the females to think he does.

Males and females are evolved to operate different selection strategies. The male has nothing to lose from a sexual encounter. As such, he is evolved to want to have sex with as many females as he can. To the extent that he is picky, he will select for indicators of fertility. Accordingly, he will be attracted to "youth" (as younger females tend to be more fertile) and to "beauty." He will regard as "beautiful" a woman who is symmetrical, because this implies low mutational load. She has managed to maintain a symmetrical phenotype in the face of disease, and she has inherited few mutations. He will also be attracted to feminine features, as these also imply fertility. As such, women tend to "doll themselves up" in order to make themselves appear younger, more

---

7—Geoffrey Miller, *The Mating Mind: How Sexual Choice Shaped the Evolution of Human Nature* (New York: Anchor Books, 2000).

8—Alan Dixson, *Primate Sexuality: Comparative Studies of the Prosimians, Monkeys, Apes, and Humans* (Oxford: Oxford University Press, 2012).

feminine, and more beautiful. The female has a lot to lose from the sexual encounter, as she can become pregnant. This makes her picky. Accordingly, she selects, to a greater extent than the male, for status or evidence of the ability to attain it. A high-status male will be better able to invest in her and her offspring, meaning that both are more likely to survive. Thus, females tend to marry socially "hypergamously," that is, "upwards."[9] This means that males are very concerned with status and attempting to convey their status, as a means of picking up high-quality female partners.

PASSING ON YOUR GENES INDIRECTLY

The third form of selection highlighted by Darwin is *social selection.* This relates to how a group treats its various members and the impact this has on whether they pass on their genes. For example, does the group execute most of its criminals or not? If it does, it acts to remove whatever genes relate to criminality from the gene pool, so this will be social selection in action. When two groups that adopt different forms of social selection come into conflict, there is *group selection*, with one group tending to replace the other group and its genes.

It should be noted that there is considerable debate over the utility of group selection as a construct. American evolutionary biologist David Sloan Wilson has advocated the *Multi-Level Selection Theory.*[10] He argues

9—Edward Dutton, "Women Marry Up," in *Encyclopedia of Evolutionary Psychological Science,* eds. Todd Shackelford and Vivian Shackelford-Weekes (New York: Springer, 2018).

10—David Sloan Wilson and Elliot Sober, "Reintroducing Group Selection

that once cooperative groups develop within a species then selection acts to promote those groups that possess the optimum level of certain qualities that permit them to out-compete other groups. Thus, selection still operates on individuals within a group, but can also be seen to operate on groups themselves, as collections of individuals (who identify as such and create group borders) and, in some circumstances, can shift away from individual and towards group selection. This model, as we will now see, helps to explain, for example, the development of altruistic tendencies. Indeed, it can be conceived as a logical extension of something that most evolutionary biologists happily accept, *kin selection.*

British biologist William Hamilton (1936-2000) developed the concept of "inclusive fitness."[11] This is the idea that there are a number of ways in which you can pass on your genes; it doesn't have to only be through direct descendants. Hamilton argued that we all follow a process of "kin selection," where we invest in people who are not our children but still closely related to us. Thus, uncles and aunts will invest in their nieces and nephews, with whom they share 25 percent of their genes. Cousins will help each other out, sharing 12.5 percent of their genes, and this may even extend to cousins once removed, with the older one treating the younger one as a *de facto* niece or nephew. This process is why the spinster aunt, who has no children of her own, give presents to her siblings' children. In doing so, she

to the Human Behavioral Sciences," *Behavioral and Brain Sciences*, 17 (1994): 585–654.

11—William Hamilton, *The Narrow Roads of Gene Land* (Oxford: Oxford University· Press, 1996); William Hamilton, "The Genetical Evolution of Social Behavior: I and II," *Journal of Theoretical Biology*, 7 (1964): 1-52.

is not simply being altruistic, because if she were, she could just give money to charity. She is helping to pass on her own genes, a quarter of which are carried by each nephew or niece. For this reason, in some circumstances, it would make sense, in terms of inclusive fitness, to lay down your life if a large number of your cousins were under mortal threat, especially if you had already had children yourself. According to Hamilton, people will act altruistically if the benefit to their inclusive fitness is greater than the fitness cost of the act—something known as "Hamilton's Rule." It would make sense for a menopausal mother to lay down her life to save her only child. This would not make so much sense if the mother, aged 21, was told to make a choice between her unborn baby's life and her own, as she could go on to have many more children. In these circumstances, we would expect her to choose her own life.

The idea of kin selection can be extended to group selection. It is a genetic fact that ethnic groups are genetic clusters. English and Danish genes are so similar, that the average Englishman is only slightly genetically similar to the next average Englishman *relative* to the average Dane, based on genetic assay data. Australian political psychologist Frank Salter has calculated that if the world were divided between only English and Danes, then the relationship between two average English people would have a kinship coefficient of 0.0021, where it would be zero for an Englishman and a Dane. This coefficient would be the equivalent of sharing a set of great-great-great-great-great-great grandparents, or being 7th cousins. Despite the similarity of English and Danes, from a genetic perspective, it could still be adaptive for an Englishman to fight to protect his ethnic group from Danes, even if it risked his having no children at all. If his actions saved 120 of his own people, this would compensate for the loss of his family of two children.[12] The soldier, who laid down his life in this way, would be operating at the level of group selection.

Indeed, computer models show that the more ethnocentric group—the group whose members are more inclined to repel outsiders and make sacrifices for the good of the group—always eventually dominates in the battle of group selection, all else being equal. This group triumphs over groups composed of members who will cooperate with the enemy but not the in-group members, cooperate with everyone or cooperate with nobody.[13] This, of course, means that it is adaptive for a group to be highly ethnocentric and, yet, for its members to actively encourage individualism— low ethnocentrism—in rival groups.[14]

So group selection is simply a logical extension of kin selection, as ethnic groups are extended kinship groups, as has been demonstrated with genetic assay data.[15] The important qualification to this model is that people will only engage in altruistic behavior if the genetic payoff outweighs the sacrifice. This means that it is more difficult for them to be exploited by selfish "free-riders." They are altruistic, but only within certain limits. Group selection,

---

12—Frank Salter, *On Genetic Interests: Family, Ethnicity and Humanity in an Age of Mass Migration* (New Brunswick: Transaction Publishers, 2007), 70, Table 3:4.

13—Ross Hammond and Robert Axelrod, "The Evolution of Ethnocentric Behavior," *Journal of Conflict Resolution,* 50 (2006): 1-11.

14—For further discussion of this process, see Kevin MacDonald, *The Culture of Critique: An Evolutionary Analysis of Jewish Involvement in Twentieth-Century Intellectual and Political Movements* (Westport: Praeger, 1998).

15—Salter, *On Genetic Interests, op cit.*

nevertheless, raises criticism from certain researchers, which we outline in the next section.

One of the reasons for this seems to be little more than a misunderstanding of what is meant by the term. When modern evolutionary psychologists talk about "group selection," they mean "Multi-Level Selection" or "New Group Selection." The original model of group selection argued that altruism developed because more co-operative groups were more likely to survive. The major weakness with this model was "subversion from within." Any group of altruists would be exploited by selfish free-riders, who would manifest by genetic chance, and these would then out-breed the altruists.[16] This is not, however, what New Group Selection is arguing. As we have already noted, New Group Selection is simply extending kin selection to a very distant level of kin—the ethnic group. It distinguishes between "kin" and "ethnic group," because most people would not necessarily conceive of their ethnic group as genetic kin. So there is a nuanced difference between New Group Selection and kin selection.

CRITICISMS OF GROUP SELECTION

"Group selection" (meaning "New Group Selection") has been criticized in depth by Canadian psychologist Steven Pinker, in an essay entitled "The False Allure of Group Selection."[17] His key points are as follows:

16—Samir Okasha, "Biological Altruism," in *The Stanford Encyclopedia of Philosophy*, ed. Edward Zalta, https://plato.stanford.edu/archives/fall2013/entries/altruism-biological/.

17—Steven Pinker, "The False Allure of Group Selection," *The Edge*, June 18, 2012, www.edge.org/conversation/the-false-allure-of-group-selection.

1. "Group selection" deviates from the "random mutation" model inherent in evolution.

2. We are clearly not going to be selected to damage our individual interests, as group selection implies.

3. Human altruism is self-interested and does not involve the kind of self-sacrifice engaged in by sterile worker bees.

Each of these points can be rebutted. Firstly, if the group selection model is building on the individual selection model then it is bound to present a slightly different metaphor. To dismiss it on these grounds seems to betoken nothing more than a fervent attachment to the original metaphor. Secondly, the group-selection model merely suggests that a group will be more successful if there is genetic diversity, meaning that an optimum percentage of its members are inclined to sacrifice themselves for their group. Thirdly, it is clearly the case that a small percentage, in many groups, is, indeed, prepared to sacrifice itself for the group, sometimes damaging their individual genetic interests; otherwise, we'd lack the great store of poetry honoring fallen heroes. So, it seems to me that it is reasonable to accept multi-level selection. Furthermore, as noted, computer modeling has shown that groups that are internally cooperative, but harsh to members of other groups, tend to eventually win in the battle of group selection.[18] That said, in general, social selection is simply the effect that the culture of the group has on somebody's chances of survival.

18—Hammond and Axelrod, "The Evolution of Ethnocentric Behavior," *op cit.*

It is also worth noting the language that Pinker employs in criticizing group selection. He refers to it as having a "false allure," terms it a "dust bunny" and a "hairy blob" that apparently "bleeds outwards to a motley collection of other, long-discredited versions." It has, claims Pinker, "placed blinkers on psychological understanding by seducing many people." This is emotionally manipulative language, which attempts to compel the reader to associate group selection with being seduced, with stupidity, with beasts of burden, and with the word "discredited." It is the fallacy of the "poisoning of the well," and the fact that Pinker engages in this tends to imply cognitive dissonance: that he rejects group selection for his own personal reasons; realizes that the model is likely reasonable; and is thus triggered to react in an emotional fashion.

Group selection has also been criticized by American physicist Gregory Cochran, who claims it is vanishingly unlikely to ever manifest, "almost impossible."[19] We can respond that given the millions of different species on Earth, it would have come about eventually. If it is the simplest explanation for available data on how humans behave, then it is most likely true. Group selection is real and necessary to explain evolution, but its mechanisms are not yet fully understood.[20]

Additionally, it has been argued that early human groups were too small and sparse for group selection,

19—Gregory Cochran, "Group Selection (and Homosexuality)," *West Hunter,* January 13, 2013, https://westhunt.wordpress.com/2013/01/10/group-selection-and-homosexuality/.

20—For further exploration, see Bruce Charlton, "Reconceptualizing the Metaphysical Basis of Biology: A New Definition Based on Deistic Teleology and a Hierarchy of Organizing Entities," *The Winnower,* 6 (2016): e145830.07350.

but this has been comprehensively refuted by abundant evidence of genocide among such groups, with genocide levels increasing with adoption of agriculture, and separated clans seeming to form large groups in order to repel invaders from different tribes.[21]

Moreover, detailed modeling has found that group selection is a reality, researchers terming it "cultural group selection." According to this model, groups of humans adopt and enforce sets of social rules, which then select for genes. In this way, the rules become part of the environment. Groups with superior rules out-compete other groups, resulting in group selection.[22] The selection process propagates culture (the rules) as well as genes, with researchers concluding that:

> If culturally transmitted systems of rules (institutions) that limit individual deviance organize cooperation in human societies, then it is not clear that any extant alternative to cultural group selection can be a complete explanation.[23]

In the end, the criticisms of group selection are far from compelling. Accordingly, one should be very cautious about people who, nevertheless, do not accept the concept's veracity. The most charitable explanation is that they do not want group selection to be a reality for some personal or ideological reason.

21—See Brian Kiernan, *Blood and Soil: A World History of Genocide and Extermination from Sparta to Darfur* (New Haven: Yale University Press, 2007).

22—Robert Boyd and Peter Richerson, *Culture and the Evolutionary Process* (Chicago: University of Chicago Press, 1985).

23—Peter Richerson, Ryan Baldini, Adrian Bell, *et al.*, "Cultural Group Selection Plays an Essential Role in Explaining Human Cooperation: A Sketch of the Evidence," *Brain and Behavioral Sciences,* 39 (2016): e30.

LIFE HISTORY STRATEGY

Another model upon which we will draw in our exploration is "Life History Strategy" (LHS). When applied to humans, this is the theory that all humans sit on a spectrum from *fast* Life History strategy, known as r-selected, to *slow* Life History Strategy, termed *K*-selected. To understand LHS, imagine two different ecologies. The first is tropical and bounteous—a place of low-hanging fruit and abundance, but also of dangers, as it undergoes random flooding and droughts. The other ecology is cruel and seasonal, with icy winters and short periods of fecundity. There, you must plan, sacrifice, and struggle just to survive. In essence, fast Life History Strategists invest most of their energy in copulation and very little in their offspring. An r-strategy is prevalent in an unstable yet relatively easy ecology, one in which basic needs are met. In such an ecology, you can be wiped out at any minute, so you evolve to "live fast, die young." The optimal strategy is to have sex with as many fertile, genetically fit people as you can as quickly as you can in the hope that some of your abundant offspring will survive. Slow Life History Strategists, in turn, invest relatively little energy in sex and direct most of their energy into nurturing their young and planning for the future. The "r" and "*K*" designators are borrowed from the logistic equation for population growth within a confined space: "r" stands for biotic potential or the maximum reproduction "rate" of an organism, and *K*, for the carrying capacity—in German "*Kapazitätsgrenze*"—of the environment, that is, how many individuals an ecology can sustain.[24]

24—For a discussion of "Life History Strategy," see Edward Dutton, *Making Sense of Race* (Whitefish: Washington Summit Publishers, 2020), Chapter 6.

As the ecology becomes harsher and more stable, then the carrying capacity of the environment for the species is reached and members need to start competing with each other for resources. In such an ecology, if you have lots of offspring, they will all simply die of starvation or cold. Consequently, a *K*-strategy develops where you invest less energy in copulation and more energy in nurture. You have a smaller number of offspring with a smaller number of partners but you nurture your offspring in order to ensure that they survive and that they are prepared to compete in the highly competitive environment in which they live. In order to achieve this, life slows down. There is a longer and longer childhood, in which offspring can learn the rules of survival independently. In such an ecology, cooperative groups are more likely to survive than individuals. In that the ecology is predictable, it is worth helping others, because they, too, will likely survive and return the favor.

Intelligence is also prized in a *K*-selected ecology. You are more likely to be able to compete if you can successfully solve problems, this being the essence of intelligence. Intelligence in general can be conceived rather like a pyramid. At the base are numerous specialized abilities that are weakly associated with intelligence, such as pattern spotting or operating machinery. These can be reduced to the next level up; verbal, mathematical, and spatial intelligence. These all inter-correlate—though some people have a more verbal and others a more mathematical tilt—meaning we can conceive of a general factor of intelligence, known as *g*. This factor is measured, however imperfectly, by IQ tests.[25]

25—See Dutton, *Making Sense of Race, op cit.*, Chapter 7.

Intelligence is strongly genetic, being about 0.8 heritable in adulthood according to twin studies. It is valued in all cultures, even if they don't articulate it the same as we do, because it is positively associated with pro-social behavior, planning, impulse control, empathy, health, social status, memory, and even being trusting; on the other hand, intelligence is negatively associated with criminality. You will be better at nurture—and cooperating with others—if you are higher in the personality traits Agreeableness (altruism and empathy) and Conscientiousness (rule-following and impulse control), so these start to increase. These are also highly heritable, being at least 0.5 genetic.[26] The other "Big 5" personality traits, accepted by psychologists, are Extraversion (feeling positive feelings strongly and thus taking risks in pursuit of the positive pay off), Neuroticism (feeling negative feelings strongly; mental instability), and Openness (being intellectually curious, artistic, and open to novelty).[27]

Mental stability, with the exception of social anxiety, also tends to be higher in more *K*-evolved environments, as people who feel negative feelings strongly will tend to be less cooperative, less under control, and more likely to be cast out by the band. These all inter-correlate, meaning that we can conceive of a "General Factor of Personality" (GFP) in which people are high in aspects of Agreeableness, Conscientiousness, Extraversion, and Openness, and are low in Neuroticism. As a result,

---

26—Edward Dutton. *J. Philippe Rushton: A Life History Perspective* (Oulu: Thomas Edward Press, 2018).

27—See Daniel Nettle, *Personality: What Makes You Who You Are* (Oxford: Oxford University Press, 2007).

they are socially effective, with GFP predicting high socioeconomic status.[28]

That said, we all have a limited level of bio-energetic resources. Thus, groups with higher levels of GFP, fascinatingly, tend to have smaller and less pronounced secondary sexual characteristics. This is because these are a means of advertising, quickly and conspicuously, your high genetic quality in an unstable environment. They are genetic "honesty signals" that proclaim: "My immune system is so good that, having fought off disease, I still have bio-energetic resources left over to grow this large and symmetrical sexual ornament." An example would be a peacock's tail, already noted. Another example would be women's breasts. It should be no surprise that, on average, White women with larger breasts are lower in Agreeableness and Conscientiousness and are more sexually promiscuous than are White women with smaller breasts. White males who are attracted to large breasts share the psychological characteristics of the women that have them. This is because they are both relative r-strategists.[29]

K-strategists invest in their offspring and in their partners. Consequently, they need to ensure that their investments pay off. For men, the greatest concern is being "cuckolded," that is, raising another man's child due to choosing a promiscuous wife. This fear leads men to be

---

28—Caroline Just, "A Review of Literature on the General Factor of Personality," *Personality and Individual Differences,* 50 (2011): 765-771.

29—Jerry Wiggins, Nancy Wiggins, and Judith Conger. "Correlates of Heterosexual Somatic Preference," *Journal of Personality and Social Psychology,* 10 (1968): 82-89. See also, Edward Dutton, *How to Judge People By What They Look Like* (Oulu: Thomas Edward Press, 2018).

far more interested in the personality of prospective mates. *K*-strategist men will be less interested in large secondary sexual characteristics, so there will be less of an arms race to produce them; he will instead put a higher value on Agreeableness and Conscientiousness. Consequently, features like breasts will tend to carry less value. *K*-selected females tend to have small breasts and *K*-selected males find these attractive.[30] Fast Life History Strategy females will be evolved to a dangerous ecology, where they might be abandoned by men and even have to fight each other for the best men. In that sense, they will be physically and mentally masculinized. They will also be in strong competition to conspicuously advertise their genetic quality, leading to larger secondary sexual characteristics that are typically perceived as "feminine."

SELECTION FOR RELIGIOUSNESS

One of the traits we were under selection for was religiousness, and this will become highly relevant as the book progresses, because we will see that mutational load tends to be negatively associated with religious conviction. It also crosses over with many aspects of a slow Life History Strategy, to the extent that some psychologists examine religiosity as an example of this.[31]

In his book *Religion Explained* (2001), French-American evolutionary psychologist Pascal Boyer presents the key psychological traits that appear to be common to

---

30—*Ibid.*

31—See Jordan Moon, Jamie Krems, and Adam Cohen, "Religious People Are Trusted Because They Are Viewed as Slow Life-History Strategists," *Psychological Science,* 29 (2018): 947-960.

accepted religions.[32] Each of these appears to be hardwired into human psychology, meaning they are significantly genetic and were adaptive in our evolutionary past. We are likely to succumb to these cognitive biases when we are subject to acute stress or feelings of exclusion or our own mortality, because that is when we are most in touch with our cognitive biases. Religiousness tends to be elevated at precisely these times.[33] The key adaptations are as follows:

1. Pattern Over-Detection

We tend to see patterns, and even causation, when confronted with images of randomly moving dots. It is adaptive, rather like an over-sensitive smoke alarm, because it means that when there is a genuine pattern then we are certain to detect it. This phenomenon helps explain why religious people see evidence of the divine all around them and have a strong sense of fate. Think "Relax, God is in charge."

2. Agency Over-Detection

In prehistory, if we heard a noise in the forest and assumed it was an animal, when it was in fact the wind, then we lost nothing. If we assumed it was the wind, when it was in fact an animal, we might lose everything—either by being predated or by not killing a quarry, which could save us from starvation. Consequently, we are evolved to

---

32—Pascal Boyer, *Religion Explained: The Evolutionary Origins of Religious Thought* (New York: Basic Books, 2001).

33—See Norenzayan and Shariff, "The Origin and Evolution of Religious Pro-Sociality," *op cit.*

over-detect agency. This is why religious people perceive evidence of the divine in the world itself, and it is why we are prone to believing in "conspiracy theories," rather than coincidences or mistakes, even if the theory is wildly improbable. This also, in part, helps to explain the certainty with which religious people are often imbued. Their worldview is uniquely true. They *know* that God is there. They can *feel* His presence and perceive signs of Him all around them. Taken to an extreme, this tendency manifests as schizophrenia, whereby sufferers have paranoid delusions of sinister agents controlling their minds. For this reason, schizophrenia not only predicts accepting conspiracy theories but, often, having intense religious belief.[34]

3. Follow the Leader

Being pack animals, we are evolved to obey authority. In general, the most intelligent people rise to the top of the human pack, something demonstrated, using general knowledge as a proxy for intelligence, even among primitive tribes.[35] So, all else being equal, it makes sense to follow the leader.

This cognitive bias is most obvious in the infamous "Milgram Experiment." Under laboratory conditions, it was demonstrated by American psychologist Stanley

---

34—See Edward Dutton, Guy Madison, and Curtis Dunkel: "The Mutant Says in His Heart, 'There Is No God': The Rejection of Collective Religiosity Centred Around the Worship of Moral Gods is Associated with High Mutational Load," *Evolutionary Psychological Science,* 4 (2018): 233-244.

35—Edward Dutton and Michael A. Woodley of Menie, *At Our Wits' End: Why We're Becoming Less Intelligent and What It Means for the Future* (Exeter: Imprint Academic, 2018), 37.

Milgram (1933-1984) that the majority of people (more than 50 percent) would be prepared to knowingly administer a lethal electric shock to an innocent person in another room simply to comply with the instructions of an authority, in the form of a white-coated scientist.[36] Subjects, known as "teachers," were told that they were taking part in an experiment to see whether electric shocks increased learning ability. They watched as their "student" (really an actor) was strapped into the electric device. Then, in another room, they had to ask the student questions over a speaker system, observed by a scientist, with teachers increasing the electric shock level each time the student gave a wrong answer. Eventually, students were audibly screaming in pain and teachers questioning whether they should continue. Told that "the experiment must go on," over half continued past the point where the machine said "Danger: Severe Shock" and even after the students had fallen silent, presumably fainted or worse, simply because they were instructed to do so by an authority. This phenomenon can be seen, in religious terms, in the strongly hierarchical nature of many religions and the willingness of adherents to obey religious authorities.

4. Consensus Effect

We have evolved a strong capacity to conform to the group, and this extends to the tendency to alter one's beliefs, even if a dissenter knows he is correct, in order to conform to the group. Indeed, the phenomenon of *cognitive dissonance* shows that people will alter even

---

36—Stanley Milgram, *Obedience to Authority* (New York: Harper & Row, 1974).

their memories in order to ensure that their worldview is congruous with that of the group.[37] This cognitive bias can be seen in religious conformity and, especially, in the way that people adopt obviously empirically inaccurate beliefs if the group of which they are a part, or of which they want to be a part, advocates such beliefs and regards them as essential to group membership. This cognitive bias is adaptive because it allows the individual to remain part of the group and to appear to genuinely believe its dogmas. Having irrational dogmas is adaptive because it drives out the non-conformers, and it is crucial, as we will now see, that groups are internally highly cooperative.

5. In-Group Cooperation

We are evolved to be highly cooperative with our in-group. This is the broader cognitive bias of which the consensus effect is a part. And it is adaptive. This explains phenomena such as religious martyrdom. Adherents are prepared to make incredible personal sacrifices for the good of the group. This cognitive bias has been found in experiments. In Game Theory, there is a game called the "Prisoner's Dilemma." In this experiment, two players play a game on networked computers; they will neither meet each other nor know anything about each other. Each player can decide to "cooperate" with the other player or "defect" on him. "Cooperation" benefits the other player, while "defection" hurts the other player but benefits the defector. In a "two shot" game, it may be rational to "cooperate" because, if you don't, then the

37—Leon Festinger, *A Theory of Cognitive Dissonance* (Stanford: Stanford University Press, 1957).

other player can "defect" on you in the future. In a "one-shot" game, however, it is always rational to defect, as you will always get a higher pay-off by doing so. Despite this, numerous experiments have shown that around 50 percent of people cooperate in a "one shot" game.[38]

6. Out-group Hostility

Groups are more likely to win battles with other groups if they are high in negative ethnocentrism, that is, if they are hostile to outsiders. In addition, outsiders are likely to bring with them contagious diseases, to which your own group is not adapted. And, if they incur onto your territory, they will generally reduce the genetic fitness of your group by reducing the extent to which it controls resources.[39] Accordingly, we are evolved to be hostile to outsiders, and religious groups will tend to regard outsiders as, in effect, "evil." Similarly, we tend to be extremely hostile to "defectors" (those that have used our group for their own benefit and then abandoned it), "free-riders" (who take the benefits of group membership without making the attendant sacrifices), and generally uncooperative members of our own group. In many ways, these types are more dangerous than outsiders, because they threaten the internal cohesion of the group, and thus people react to them very strongly.

Boyer's summary crosses over with American psychologist Jonathan Haidt's Moral Foundations

---

38—Satoshi Kanazawa, *The Intelligence Paradox: Why the Intelligent Choice Isn't Always the Smart One* (Hoboken: John Wiley & Sons, 2012), 32.

39—Salter, *On Genetic Interests, op cit.*

Theory, which was referenced in the last chapter. This model highlights five fundamental human concerns: Care vs. Harm, Fairness vs. Cheating, Loyalty vs. Betrayal, Authority vs. Subversion, and Sanctity vs. Disgust.[40] The fifth foundation manifests, negatively, as a strong sense of disgust towards the out-group or towards deviant members of the in-group. One study has even shown that religious people feel a sense of physical nausea when exposed to the beliefs of other religious groups.[41] Religious people also feel a stronger generalized disgust response to common stimuli like foul smells and rotting foods.[42] We will return to Haidt's model later, because it is also highly relevant to understanding the differences between "liberals" and "conservatives," as also briefly explored in the last chapter.

RELIGION AND EVOLUTION

Pascal Boyer argues that religion is a manifestation of the different cognitive biases and instincts outlined above. There is, however, every reason to argue that religiousness, once manifested, became selected for in itself. Religion displays all of the dimensions of an adaptation. Religiousness, in the specific sense of collectively

40—Jonathan Haidt, "Moral Psychology for the Twenty-first Century," *Journal of Moral Education*, 42 (2013):, 281-297. See also Moral Foundations Theory, https://moralfoundations.org.

41—Ryan Ritter and Jesse Preston, "Gross Gods and Icky Atheism: Disgust Responses to Rejected Religious Beliefs," *Journal of Experimental and Social Psychology*, 47 (2011): 1225-1230.

42—Ruile Wang, Qi Yang, Peng Huang, *et al.*, "The Association Between Disgust Sensitivity and Negative Attitudes Toward Homosexuality: The Mediating Role of Moral Foundations," *Frontiers in Psychology*, 10 (2019): 1229.

worshiping a god or gods, is a human universal; it correlates with mental and physical health, as well as with longevity; it correlates with fertility; it is around 0.4 genetic and in the case of being "born again," approximately 0.7 genetic; and specific parts of the brain associated with religiosity have been identified. The correlation between religiosity and overall health is 0.3. This relatively weak correlation reflects the fact that extreme religiosity is associated with schizophrenia, periods of depression, and bipolar disorder, for reasons we will explore later.[43]

We can also understand how religiousness would have been selected for. At the individual level, it has been shown that religiousness tends to become more pronounced at times of stress and, in turn, reduces stress by persuading the devotee that God or the gods are looking after them. It has been shown that the belief that one is being watched, such as by a moral god, makes one behave in a more pro-social manner, so those that had this belief would have been less likely to have been ostracized by the band for breaking its rules.[44] Religion is also sexually selected for because it can be regarded as a marker of pro-social personality. Across cultures, religiousness predicts being altruistic and rule-following.[45] This means that a religious person is less likely to be unfaithful: a religious woman is less inclined cuckold her husband; a husband,

---

43—Dutton, Madison, and Dunkel, "The Mutant Says in His Heart 'There is No God,'" *op cit.*

44—See Norenzayan and Shariff, "The Origin and Evolution of Religious Pro-Sociality," *op cit.*

45—Jochen Gebauer, Wiebke Bleidorn, Samuel Gosling, *et al.*, "Cross-Cultural Variations in Big Five Relationships with Religiosity: A Sociocultural Motives Perspective," *Journal of Personality and Social Psychology*, 107 (2014): 1064-1091.

abandon his wife while pregnant. Consequently, it would make sense for people to sexually select for religiousness in partners.[46]

Religiosity is group-selected for because religious groups tend to be higher in ethnocentrism, meaning that they ultimately triumph in battles of group selection, as shown by the computer models cited above.[47] Indeed, there is neurological evidence of the relationship between religiousness and ethnocentrism. In one study, an area of the brain called the posterior medial frontal cortex was rendered less active by trans-cranial magnetic stimulation. As a consequence, the subjects became both less negatively ethnocentric and less likely to believe in God.[48] Again, religion essentially takes adaptive behavior, in terms of Darwinian selection, and turns it into the "will of God," thus making such behavior more likely to be followed. It promotes positive and negative ethnocentrism, as well as more mundane goods like eating healthy food.[49]

46—Curtis Dunkel, Charlie Reeve, Michael Woodley of Menie, *et al.*, "A Comparative Study of the General Factor of Personality in Jewish and Non-Jewish Populations," *Personality and Individual Differences*, 78: 63-67; Michael Blume, "The Reproductive Benefits of Religious Affiliation," in *The Biological Evolution of Religious Mind and Behavior*, eds. Eckart Voland and Wulf Schiefenhövel (New York: Springer, 2009), 117-126.

47—Hammond and Axelrod, "The Evolution of Ethnocentric Behavior," *op cit.*

48—Colin Holbrook, Keise Izuma, Choi Deblieck, *et al.*, "Neuromodulation of Group Prejudice and Religious Belief," *Social Cognitive and Affective Neuroscience*, 11 (2016): 387-394.

49—Yael Sela, Todd K. Shackelford, and James R. Liddle, "When Religion Makes It Worse: Religiously Motivated Violence as a Sexual Selection Weapon," in *The Attraction of Religion: A New Evolutionary Psychology of Religion*, ed. D. Jason Sloane and James A. Van Slyke (London: Bloomsbury, 2015); Victor Meyer-Rochow, "Food Taboos: Their Origins and Purposes," *Journal of Ethnobiology and Ethnomedicine*, 5 (2009): 18.

Group-selection would also neatly explain the way in which patriarchy tends to become interlinked with religion and is presented as God's will. Females sexually select mates on the basis of status because a high-status male is better able to invest in them and their offspring, meaning that both are more likely to survive.[50] Until the Industrial Revolution, wealth and status strongly predicted completed fertility, and this is the case among preindustrial peoples today.[51] If a male is to dedicate resources to a female in order to obtain sexual intercourse, then he wants to be certain that the offspring, in which he is also investing so much, are actually his own. The result is a system of patriarchy in which females are controlled by males such that male paternity anxiety can be reduced. This system tends to be promoted by the society's religion as divinely ordained, possibly because patriarchal societies reduce paternity anxiety, meaning that they, in turn, reduce inter-male conflict, thus causing males to be more internally cooperative.

Patriarchy, however, means that females are strongly selected to be accepting of the practice, as well as the religion that undergirds it.[52] Consequently, there would be a religious "arms race" among females in order to obtain the highest-status males, especially in the kind of polygamous

---

50—Edward Dutton and Guy Madison, "Why Do Finnish Men Marry Thai Women But Finnish Women Marry British Men? Cross-National Marriages in a Modern Industrialized Society Exhibit Sex-Dimorphic Sexual Selection According to Primordial Selection Pressures," *Evolutionary Psychological Science*, 3 (2017): 1-9.

51—Dutton and Woodley of Menie, *At Our Wits' End, op cit.*, Chapter 3.

52—Rachel A. Grant and V. Tamara Montrose, "It's A Man's World: Mate Guarding and the Evolution of Patriarchy," *Mankind Quarterly* 58 (2018): 384-418.

societies in which humans have lived for most of history, in which the highest-status males monopolize the most desirable females. As such, we would expect females to be strongly prone to wishing to signal their virtue and, if religiosity were regarded as virtuous, to signal this. And they would be more convincingly able to signal it if they genuinely believed it. This would be one of the reasons why females tend to be more religious than males.[53]

Another would be their higher Agreeableness and high Conscientiousness, traits that would make them better nurturers.[54] These personality traits have been found to be associated with religiousness, while Neuroticism, which women are also higher in, is associated with extrinsic religiousness—external religious conformity— and periods of intense fervor.[55] High female empathy— which involves being attuned to external signals of internal states—could be carried over into the world itself, as those who are high in empathy are more likely to perceive evidence of a "mind" behind the world and thus intuitively feel that there is a god, something that those who are low in empathy do not feel.[56]

The consequence of this is that under conditions of harsh Darwinian selection—in which there was intense

---

53—Darren Sherkat, "Sexuality and Religious Commitment in the United States: An Empirical Examination," *Journal for the Scientific Study of Religion*, 41 (2002): 313-323.

54—See Nettle, *Personality, op cit.*

55—Peter Hills, Leslie Francis, Michael Argyle, *et al.*, "Primary Personality Trait Correlates of Religious Practice and Orientation, *Personality and Individual Differences*, 36 (2004): 61-73.

56—Anthony Jack, Jared Friedman, Richard Boyatzis, *et al.*, "Why Do You Believe in God? Relationships Between Religious Belief, Analytic Thinking, Mentalizing and Moral Concern," *PLOS One,* 11(2016): e0155283.

individual, sexual, and group selection—religiousness was selected for. Indeed, it has been demonstrated, using the proxy of the population percentage who were religious devotees, that the English people became more religious across the Medieval period. In part, this occurred because all felonies carried the death sentence, and those who were executed—amounting to two percent of the male population each generation—would have been high in personality traits that predict criminality, these being the same traits that negatively predict religiousness. Specifically, criminals would have had low Conscientiousness and low Agreeableness, whereas religiousness is associated with being high in these traits.[57] Furthermore, as societies became more complex, morphing into cities in which one had to constantly interact with strangers who one might never see again, gods became far more concerned with generalized morality. This, it seems, helped to persuade people to cooperate with strangers with their belief in the same moral god acting as an insurance policy that they could be trusted.[58]

The result of this selection is that religiousness became genetically correlated with other traits that were being selected for. Religiousness, for example, is negatively correlated with carrying forms of genes that predict depression; it is associated with genetic physical health; and it correlates with other evidence of a low number of (almost always harmful) mutations.[59]

57—See Dutton, Madison, and Dunkel: "The Mutant Says in His Heart, 'There Is No God,'" *op. cit.*

58—Norenzayan and Shariff, "The Origin and Evolution of Religious Pro-sociality," *op cit.*

59—Dutton, Madison, and Dunkel, "The Mutant Says in His Heart, 'There

In other words, religiousness is the "genetic norm" under Darwinian conditions. But the intensity of these conditions changes across time due to climate and other factors.

THE COLLAPSE OF DARWINIAN SELECTION AND ITS CONSEQUENCES

In 1800, the child mortality rate was about 50 percent; it has now fallen to 1 percent,[60] as we noted earlier. Industrialization heralded better medicine, inoculations against formerly killer childhood diseases, cheaper food, and, eventually, much healthier living conditions. As a consequence, the intensity of Darwinian selection was heavily weakened. Until around 1800, the high child mortality meant that mutations that caused, for example, a poor immune system were purged from the population every generation. This resulted in the population being strongly adapted to the ecology and having a very low mutational load.

With the Industrial Revolution, more and more people with more and more mutations—that would have caused them to die in childhood and thus not reproduce under harsher conditions—began to survive and pass on their genes. They walk among us. This is leading to an increasingly genetically sick population. This process is known as "dysgenics."[61] The result has been a rise across

---

Is No God,'" *op cit.*

60—Tony Volk and Jeremy Atkinson, "Is Child Death the Crucible of Human Evolution?" *Journal of Social, Evolutionary, and Cultural Psychology,* 2 (2008): 103-116.

61—Richard Lynn, *Dysgenics: Genetic Deterioration in Modern Populations*

time in the prevalence of numerous partly heritable physical conditions and similar mental conditions. These include: autism, schizophrenia, psychopathology, Narcissistic Personality Disorder, paranoia, hysteria, manic depression, suicide,[62] obesity, diabetes,[63] and many more serious conditions, such as haemophilia and cystic fibrosis.[64]

Consistent with a rise in mutation, it has been shown, from analyses of skulls, that the average British face has become less symmetrical across time.[65] We are supposed to be symmetrical, so the failure to develop a proper phenotype implies "developmental instability." "Developmental instability" is a product of a sub-optimal environment, such as a mother who is ill while you are in the womb or being born prematurely, high mutational load, or a combination of the two. It means that you must invest proportionately more of your bio-energetic resources in fighting off disease, leading to the inability to develop a symmetrically. Another manifestation of developmental instability is left-handedness, as it implies a highly asymmetrical brain. Left-handedness levels are increasing across time, consistent with increasing mutational load.[66]

(London: Ulster Institute for Social Research, 2011).

62—Matthew Sarraf, Michael Woodley of Menie, and Colin Feltham, *Modernity and Cultural Decline: A Biobehavioral Perspective* (Basingstoke: Palgrave Macmillan, 2019), 152.

63—*Ibid.*, 141.

64—Lynn, *Dysgenics, op cit.*, 183.

65—Michael Woodley, "The Cognitive Differentiation-Integration Effort Hypothesis: A Synthesis Between the Fitness Indicator and Life History Models of Human Intelligence," *Review of General Psychology,* 15 (2011): 228-245.

66—Michael Woodley of Menie, Heitor Fernandes, Satoshi Kanazawa, *et al.*, "Sinistrality is Associated with (Slightly) Lower General Intelligence: A Data Synthesis and Consideration of Secular Trend Data in Handedness,"

SPITEFUL MUTANTS

British evolutionary psychologist Michael Woodley of Menie, in a theory known as the Social Epistasis Amplification Model (SEAM), argues that cooperation is so central to humans, and bees, that, in many crucial respects, their societies can be conceived as kinds of organisms, with each individual playing a small but important role in the optimum functioning, and thus survival, of that organism. Every individual is part of a profoundly interconnected network, wherein he relies on those with whom he interacts to behave in an adaptive fashion such that his own genes are expressed, phenotypically, in the same way. It follows that if a feeder bee (in charge of feeding the larvae) has a mutation that causes her to feed the larvae at random, rather than according to an instinctively "normal" pattern, then she will damage the fitness of the entire hive, because there will be, in this case, far too many queens and not enough workers.[67]

Similarly, if a human carries a spiteful mutation that makes him believe, and strongly propagate the view, that life has no meaning, his mutation impacts those who associate with him by causing (as with the bees) their environment to be different from that to which their genes are optimally adapted. Woodley of Menie and his colleagues have, indeed, presented a large amount of evidence that nihilism is maladaptive and a product of deleterious mutations that would have been selected out

---

HOMO: *Journal of Comparative Human Biology,* 69 (2018): 118-126.

67—Quoted in Edward Dutton, *The Silent Rape Epidemic: How the Finns Were Groomed to Love Their Abusers* (Oulu: Thomas Edward Press, 2019), 55.

under harsh conditions. Believing in nothing, or that nothing really matters, is associated with psychopathology, with such people tending to be killed by the band under conditions of intense selection.[68] It is also associated with depression and schizophrenia, both of which are strongly genetic and lead to very bad life outcomes and reduced fertility. Thus, people who have nihilistic worldviews tend not to pass on their genes.[69]

Nihilists, however, also spread their way of thinking to those with whom they associate and on whom they exert influence. This means that their friends' and acquaintances' genes will be expressed differently—sub-optimally—and this will also begin to impact how children are socialized. These non-carriers of spiteful mutations may be somewhat genetically predisposed to be nihilists and abandon reproduction because "life's pointless" due to certain environmental conditions or simply because a society with a lot of mutants creates an "evolutionary mismatch" and thus a general sense of dysphoria, something we will expand on shortly. If these conditions never occur, because the spiteful mutation carriers are not present in their society, they will not develop those destructive behaviors. But once the Spiteful Mutant manifests, he can undermine the broader culture (such as its religious rituals) and stop his genetically normal co-ethnics from being religious, meaning that his evolutionarily damaging worldview can spread like a virus, even to those who lack the spiteful mutation or lack its most virulent form. And, so, this single mutant (even more

---

68—Matthew Sarraf, Michael Woodley of Menie, and Colin Feltham, *Modernity and Cultural Decline: A Biobehavioral Perspective* (Basingstoke: Palgrave Macmillan, 2019), 15.

69—*Ibid.*, 16.

so if there are many of them) can undermine the extent to which the group is optimally group-selected. In particular, as noted above, they can subvert the adaptive way in which children are socialized, such that children develop in a fashion that is optimal to achieving evolutionary success.

The term "evolutionary mismatch" refers to an organism being in conditions to which it is not evolved.[70] This can seriously compromise its fitness, because it will pursue in-built behaviors that suddenly become maladaptive. As discussed earlier, humans have numerous instincts or cognitive biases, with varying degrees of strength. They wish to have children; they seek higher socioeconomic status (as this was formerly strongly associated with your children surviving or having access to females); and they have the inclination to conform to the group and even be "brainwashed" to a certain extent, aiding group-selection. Under purifying Darwinian conditions, these are all useful, but they can become a problem when these conditions are heavily weakened. People can be brainwashed into killing themselves by schizophrenic cult leaders—themselves a product of high mutational load. With the breakdown of patriarchy, to which we are adapted, women will have status-ambition and a desire for children, but they will no longer experience the two being directed towards a high-status match. Thus, they may end up trading a desire for status for the ability to have children, putting off having children until it's too late, or until all the higher-status males are spoken-for. It is a clear "mismatch" that women are more educated than men, and thus on a crucial marker

---

70—Jack Riggs, "Stone-age Genes and Modern Lifestyle: Evolutionary Mismatch or Differential Survival Bias," *Journal of Clinical Epidemiology*, 46 (1993): 1289–1291.

have higher status than them. If we are evolved to live in a traditional religious environment, and this collapses, there is no social or divine pressure to have children, so those with very high socioeconomic ambition may simply go barren.

As we will see below, the breakdown of harsh group selection will mean a move towards individualistic values, as those who deviate from the Darwinian norm of being highly group-selected will be more individualistic, more selfish, and more concerned with the individual over the group. This can lead to runaway individualism, where you signal your focus on the good of individuals over the good of the group—the importance of individuals being content and feeling valued. This signaling can continue until, for status reasons, you don't have children at all, in order to signal your adherence to a group that believes, for example, that we must put other races or classes above ourselves. In line with this, younger people, raised in this individualistic regime, have higher self-esteem and are thus more narcissistic and selfish ("snowflakes" who can't deal with criticism or discipline).[71]

Runaway individualism, as we will see below, also leads to a mismatch in itself, because it suppresses our group instincts, resulting in depression, anhedonia, giving up, and not breeding. It will thus create a society that raises its offspring sub-optimally, meaning that many will develop sub-optimally as well. As we will see later, intelligent people will be more likely to be sucked into this, because intelligence predicts better absorbing the dominant ideology and convincing yourself of its veracity, being

---

71—Jennifer Twenge, *Generation Me: Why Today's Young Americans Are More Confident, Assertive, Entitled—And More Miserable than Ever Before* (New York: Simon and Schuster, 2014).

easier to inculcate, being less fervent in religious belief, and being less instinctive, with passing on your genes being the ultimate "basic instinct." In this sense, intelligent people are more environmentally sensitive. This negative association between intelligence and fertility always seems to occur when civilizations reach a certain level of luxury and development, something which reduces harsh Darwinian pressures. It was observed in Athens; it was observed in Rome; and we will return to its significance below.[72]

"Intelligence" is an adaptation to an environment that is harsh and stable. When that environment becomes easy, intelligent people are in an evolutionary mismatch. They are evolved to think about the future and plan for it, possibly limiting their fertility accordingly. Those who don't plan at all will simply have lots of children and, with the ecology now being both easy and stable, they'll all survive. Moreover, intelligence develops in an environment of extreme competition in which a long childhood is necessary such that you can learn how to negotiate a highly complex difficult environment. Thus, as noted above, intelligent people are more environmentally sensitive, less instinctive, and more reliant on being placed on an optimum road map by the group. If the group genetically changes, due to weaker selection pressures, they will be less likely to be pushed along the precisely correct path.

72—For further discussion, see Edward Dutton and Michael Woodley of Menie, *At Our Wits' End: Why We're Becoming Less Intelligent and What It Means for the Future* (Exeter: Imprint Academic, 2018).

THE GREAT AWOKENING

The term "Woke" arose around 2014 and was initially a kind of call sign for the Black Lives Matter protests.[73] The title was embraced by activists, referencing their critical awareness of structural racism and inequality. They had "awakened," as it were, and were protesting something much bigger than a single incident of police brutality.[74] "Wokeness" became a general grievance in the minds of African-Americans and a "bad conscience" or "poison pill" in the minds of Whites: you can't, for instance, just honor the Founding Fathers without acknowledging that they were cruel slave-masters; you can't donate to your local police union without admonishing them for systemic racism; if you root for the Washington Redskins or Cleveland Indians, you're really cheering for genocide; etc. Wokeness means that things that were once valued or taken for granted in a functioning society are now problematized or deemed morally reprehensible.

All of the ideologies associated with Wokeness can be regard as "spiteful." They promote fitness-reducing behavior and evolutionary mismatch. Advocates of multiculturalism imply that Europeans should feel guilty

---

73—It's worth pointing out that at the time of writing, "Woke" has become overused and hackneyed and is now mostly employed by conservatives as a catch-all nickname for the Left. In this way, it is largely synonymous with "liberal" or "socialist." I use "Woke," "Wokeness," and "Wokeism" in this volume to highlight a particularly spiteful variation of the Left, which should be distinguished from, for example, democratic socialism or social and religious tolerance. The term "SJW" has gone through a similar trajectory.

74—See Aja Romano, "A History of 'Wokeness,'" *Vox*, October 9, 2020, https://www.vox.com/culture/21437879/stay-woke-wokeness-history-origin-evolution-controversy.

for being European and should accept mass immigration of non-Europeans into their countries. This clearly damages the genetic interests of Europeans, because it causes them to become a smaller and smaller group, controlling less and less land. It undermines social trust, because people tend to trust those who are genetically similar to themselves,[75] resulting in people becoming increasingly isolated, friendless, and unhappy. This is worsened by the ethnic conflict that has been shown to almost inevitably occur in multiracial societies.[76] It creates an evolutionary mismatch, as we are evolved to be with people who are genetically similar to ourselves, as evidenced in numerous studies that have shown that we cooperate more, prefer to be around, and are more trusting with people who are genetically similar to ourselves, including members of our own ethnic group and race.[77] This desire is so intense that, as American biologist E.O. Wilson (1929-2021) has put it:

> When in experiments black and white Americans were flashed pictures of the other race their amygdalas, the brain's center of fear and anger, were activated so quickly and subtly that the conscious centers of the brain were unaware of the response. The subject, in effect, could not help himself.[78]

75—J. Philippe Rushton, "Ethnic Nationalism, Evolutionary Psychology and Genetic Similarity Theory," *Nations and Nationalism,* 11 (2005): 489-507.

76—Tatu Vanhanen, *Ethnic Conflicts: Their Biological Roots in Ethnic Nepotism* (London: Ulster Institute for Social Research, 2012).

77—Rushton, "Ethnic Nationalism, Evolutionary Psychology and Genetic Similarity Theory," *op cit.*

78—Edward O. Wilson, *The Social Conquest of Earth* (New York: W.W. Norton, 2012), 100.

In other words, living in a racially diverse society makes people, no matter how hard they might try to suppress their feelings, constantly unhappy, frightened, and angry. It creates dysphoria through perpetual stress as a consequence of a pronounced evolutionary mismatch. People can, of course, become friends with those of a different race, but they will react in this way to strangers of a different race, in a way that they will not to strangers of their own race. Worse still, multiculturalism acts to humiliate and depress White people, especially White males, even as children. Mixed-race relationships, where the female is White, are now constantly presented in the media, conveying the message to White males that they are losers and foreigners have taken their women, whom they have failed to defend. Research by Congolese physician Denis Mukwege argues that the rape of the enemy group's females is a way of asserting dominance, not just over the females, but, by extension, over their fathers, brothers, male cousins and, in many ways, all males on the opposing side. It destroys their morale and undermines their confidence, because the conquerors assert dominance and control over the central resource for future existence, namely the wombs of the women of those whom they are conquering.

Based on an analysis of the Democratic Republic of Congo, Mukwege and colleagues aver that rape can be a quite deliberate war strategy, as it creates deep trauma and insecurity among the victims and their networks, helping to undermine their ability to defend themselves.[79] In some ways, the portrayal of consensual relationships is

79—Denis Mukwege, Olaa Mohamed-Ahmad, and Joseph Fitchett, "Rape as a Strategy of War in the Democratic Republic of the Congo," *International Health,* 2 (2010): 163-164.

psychologically worse. Females sexually select for status, meaning that they will "horizontally collaborate"[80] with the invader only if they are confident that the invasion is successful and these are the new "dominant males." In other words, they will sexually select hypergamously in terms of ethnicity or race, something known as "Dutton's Rule." This is one of the reasons why people tend to be descended from the older population of a country in the female line; on the male line they will descend from the more recent invader. Thus, most Hispanics (in the sense of the racial cline of that name) are White in the male line but Native American in the female line.[81]

Constantly over-representing ethnic foreigners in the media is a means of sapping male morale, as is using Black actors in British historical dramas, which is effectively rewriting history. It is more than a reflection of an obsession with "equality" and not hurting the feelings of ethnic minorities. It is a trampling on the sacred—for example the sanctity of truth or the group's history—and of authority, in the sense of order and thus of truth. It is "gas lighting," and thus sowing dysphoria, among the population and it is a means of humiliation: "Look what we can do. We can rewrite your history. You are invaded to such an extent that your history is lost and there's nothing you can do." Naturally, this creates dysphoria,

---

80—This term was originally coined to refer to French women who had relationships with German soldiers in Nazi-occupied France. See Fabrice Virgili, *Shorn Women: Gender and Punishment in Liberation France* (Oxford: Berg Publishers, 2002).

81—Tomás Cabeza de Baca, Aurelio José Figueredo, Heitor Fernandes, *et al.*, "Exchanging Fluids: The Sociocultural Implications of Microbial, Cultural, and Ethnic Admixture in Latin America," *Politics and the Life Sciences,* 39 (2020): 56-86.

only furthered by the fact that to even discuss this means you are weak; you suffer from "White Fragility," as one female, American sociologist has titled her book on this subject. The book's Foreword was penned by an African-American male.[82]

Neuroticism, which is strongly correlated with depression and anxiety, is negatively associated with fertility,[83] and being depressed has been shown to be a factor in males being unable to successfully impregnate females, while female use of anti-depressants elevates the risk of miscarriage.[84] Male use of anti-depressants also appears to reduce fertility.[85] Multiculturalism is, thus, maladaptive in the extreme. Atheism creates an evolutionary mismatch, as we are evolved to live in a religious environment. Thus, it potentially fosters nihilism and despair. It also undermines an institution that promotes adaptive ideas—such as pro-natalism and group-oriented behaviour—as God's will. Thinking about God and concepts like "Karma" make people less selfish, so atheism helps to foster an unpleasant, friendless, uncooperative mismatch.[86]

82—Robin DiAngelo, *White Fragility: Why It's So Hard for White People to Talk About Racism* (New York: Beacon Press, 2018).

83—Markus Jokela, "Birth-cohort Effects in the Association Between Personality and Fertility," *Psychological Science,* 23 (2012): 835-841.

84—Emily Evans-Hoeker, Esther Eisenberg, Michael Diamond, *et al.*, "Major Depression, Antidepressant Use, and Male and Female Fertility," *Fertility and Sterility,* 109 (2018): 879-887.

85—Lauren Breeder and Mary Samplaski, "Effect of Antidepressant Medications on Semen Parameters and Male Fertility," *International Journal of Urology,* (2019): doi.org/10.1111/iju.14111.

86—Cindel White, John Kelly, Azim Shariff, *et al.*, "Supernatural Norm Enforcement: Thinking About Karma and God Reduces Selfishness Among Believers," *Journal of Experimental Social Psychology,* 84 (2019): 103797.

At its most extreme, environmentalism puts the interests of other species above that of humanity and calls for the death of humanity. The promotion of homosexuality—which tends to become more acceptable when civilizations become luxurious, be they Greece, Rome, or the West[87]—is likely to fill many people with a constant sense of disgust, and thus dysphoria, and also encourage people who would otherwise breed to embrace homosexuality as a lifestyle, especially environmentally plastic younger people. Many other strands of Woke thought—questioning the nature of gender, promoting transsexuality, and so on—all contribute to evolutionary mismatch, dysphoria, and a constant state of disgust and nihilism that makes people act maladaptively and thus not breed. In this sense, the Woke can be regarded as a kind of "death cult." Unsurprisingly, as we will explore below, espousing it is strongly associated with evidence of high mutational load: with being a Spiteful Mutant, as, indeed, is atheism, which correlates with left-handedness and autism, both of which are markers of developmental instability and thus mutational load.[88]

ALTERNATIVES TO THE MUTANT MODEL

It might be argued that the Spiteful Mutant model is unnecessary as a means of making sense of the way in which developed countries have been pushed towards fitness-reducing ideas. A potential alternative is simply "runaway individualism." Broadly, humans have two sets of instincts. We are pack animals, meaning we must defeat

---

87—See Chapter 6.

88—Dutton, Madison and Dunkel, "'The Mutant Says in His Heart, "There Is No God,"'" *op cit.*

other packs. This leads to instincts to act for the good of the pack: obedience to hierarchy, self-sacrifice for the group, and a sense of group sanctity—three of Haidt's Moral Foundations. But all animals also want to protect their own interests and have at least as much as everyone else: they desire harm avoidance and equality—the two other foundations. So, these are "individualist" concerns, which we touched on above. "Individualizing" strongly correlates with being "liberal" or "left-wing," while the group-oriented foundations, known as ""binding"" values, are strongly associated with being "conservative." Congruous with this, "psychoticism"—a broad personality trait composed of low altruism, low empathy, low rule-following, and low impulse control, and thus a trait which makes you individualistic rather than group-oriented—strongly predicts being "liberal" rather than "conservative."[89]

As already discussed, conservatives are about the same in all five Foundations, but liberals are high in "individualizing" and low in the others. This means that conservatives can sympathize with liberals in a way that is not reciprocated, which, in turn, means that liberals can hijack the culture and push it in an ever more individualistic direction. This will continue until there is an evolutionary mismatch for a sufficient portion of

---

89—Infamously, a widely reported study was published in 2010, which incorrectly proclaimed that psychoticism was strongly associated with conservatism. It turned out that the authors had made a "coding error" and that the real results were thus "exactly reversed." See Brad Verhulst, Peter Hatemi, and Nicholas Martin, "The Nature of the Relationship Between Personality Traits and Political Attitudes," *Personality and Individual Differences,* 49 (2010): 306-316; Brad Verhulst, Peter Hatemi, and Nicholas Martin, "Corrigendum," *Personality and Individual Differences,* 99 (2016): 378-379. For discussion of the affair see, Jesse Singal, "Why It Took Social Science Years to Correct a Simple Error About 'Psychoticism,'" *The Cut,* July 14, 2016.

the population: insufficient sanctity and group-loyalty and too much equality and disgust. The result will be a "right-wing backlash," which may continue until there is another evolutionary mismatch for many people; too little concern with harm and equality. This may be regarded as central to political mood swings.

These are general relationships. For example, though "liberals" are lower in "disgust," they are higher in "moral disgust," which would explain why they tend to be less tolerant of those who disagree with them than are "conservatives."[90] In terms of Life History Strategy, it is noticeable that "binding" values are more K-oriented, whereas individualist values, where you are out for yourself, are more r-oriented. Congruous with this, it has been found that "binding" foundations correlate more strongly with a slow Life History factor than do "individualizing" foundations. Conservatives tend to form secure attachments to a greater extent and have experienced lives that are more secure and predictable.[91]

Humans want to be part of the pack, but, as individuals, also seek to work their way up the hierarchy. Moreover, their own individual survival—as against that of their group—is clearly an individualist concern. They seek status because those at the top of the pack have more access to resources (and females, with women sexually selecting for status), meaning they are more likely to pass

90—Jesse Graham, Brian Nosek, and Jonathan Haidt "The Moral Stereotypes of Liberals and Conservatives: Exaggeration of Differences across the Political Spectrum," *PLOS One* (2012), https://doi.org/10.1371/journal.pone.0050092.

91—Paul Gladden and Anthony Cleator, "Slow Life History Strategy Predicts Six Moral Foundations," *EvoS Journal*, 2 (2018): 44-63.

on their genes. In a pack, they cannot afford to appear selfish, so subalterns play for status by signaling what cooperative people they are; how concerned they are about harm and fairness, appealing to foundations also held by those at the top and so encouraging them to cede ground to them, with "binding" foundations inherently being in the interests of whoever are the current elite. In fact, it has been shown that when people are physically uncomfortable, which they are more likely to be if they are poorer, then they become more morally judgemental; in other words, being physically uncomfortable elevates a left-wing trait.[92]

There will be individual variance in the group with regard to the extent of these moral foundation concerns, leading to an approximate divide between "collectivists" and "individualists," with individualists having a strong incentive to indicate, to an exaggerated degree, that they are actually extraordinarily collectivist. This means that, ironically, the most individualistic people will likely be those who make it known the loudest just how much more "collectivist" they are than the next man, with extreme exaggeration being the obvious mark of the faker.

We would expect societies to oscillate between periods of group and individualist values. As noted, the groups that tend to win in the battle of group-selection are those that are highest in these collectivist, group-oriented values, so in conditions of intense inter-group conflict (harsh Darwinian conditions, in other words), individualists are suppressed as the entire group is under

---

92—Bunmi Olatunj, Bike David Puncochar, and Rebecca Cox, "Effects of Experienced Disgust on Morally Relevant Judgments," *PLoS ONE*, 11(2016): e0160357.

threat. In periods of relative peace, however, it is quite understandable that those who are not at the top of the hierarchy—those in the middle—will themselves play for status for their social class; this is ultimately acting on behalf of people who are genetically similar to them, with socio-economic differences having been shown to be about 0.7 heritable,[93] and with even average blood type differing along social class lines.[94]

Accordingly, traits that are highly adaptive in evolutionary terms—such as religiousness or a desire for large families—are associated, during these periods, with the "individualist" values of harm avoidance and equality, as subalterns signal their virtue with these values and concern themselves with them as a means of increasing their relative place in the social hierarchy. Such people will, to some extent, move up into the ruling class, followed by a period of equilibrium and further concern about group values. Due to the way in which such group-oriented societies tend to survive, there is evidence that we have been under selection for conservative values—group-orientation—for thousands of years, with these being very intense during cold periods, in which there is elevated inter-group conflict due to scarcity.

This situation is different now because being "leftist" is negatively associated with evolutionarily adaptive traits and thus negatively associated with fertility. This

---

93—Gregory Clark, *The Son Also Rises: Surnames and the History of Social Mobility* (Princeton: Princeton University Press, 2014).

94—J.A. Beardmore and F. Karimi-Booshehri, "ABO Genes are Differentially Distributed in Socio-economic Groups in England," *Nature,* 303 (1983): 522-524.

change has taken place due to the breakdown in the intensity of Darwinian selection. This has created a very easy and predictable environment, in which basic needs are almost always met and there is little need to worry about the future. The postindustrial world thus maintains characteristics of both r- and K-selected environments. It is a place of abundance, with food and medical care as "low hanging fruit;" the world has also become more predictable. With some obvious exceptions, flooding, famine, and war have been relegated to history; in fact, economic cycles ("boom and bust") have more of a "life or death" quality than natural disasters. This new environment has resulted in a huge build-up of individualists, there no longer being strong selection pressure against them. The result is runaway individualism, where individualism—in its desire to attain status, often through signaling virtue and other desirable traits—veers into evolutionarily damaging ideas, with no real selection pressures to stop it doing this. The next step from signaling that you should help non-Whites is to argue that Whites are bad and next step from that, in the arms race of virtue-signaling, is to argue that Whites should not breed, and so on.

As a consequence, we have a group—generally in the middle of society—that combines adaptive traits, such as a desire for power, with desires to be destructive not only to their group but also to themselves. Being genetically relatively similar, these people find each other and work together to attain status via advocating "liberal values," which they also combine with assorted maladaptive ideas, most obviously anti-natalism and being irreligious. They even spread these ideas to others. The "conservatives" are the only ones who are resistant to them. Thus, perhaps for the first time in history, the usual system has been turned on its head. In a time of weak inter-group conflict, it is now conservatism and traditional religiosity that is associated with fertility, and which has been relegated to the lower- or lower-middle-class.[95] These remnant conservatives can be conceived of as, in some respects, the remnant preindustrial population, who are genetically evolved to be resistant to anything fitness-reducing.

In this sense, then, it can be averred that the Spiteful Mutant hypothesis is simply unnecessary. The counter-argument to this perspective is the evidence that, at least at the extreme, "traditional" perspectives, such as the collective worship of a moral god, are associated with genetic physical and mental health.[96] Other markers of low mutation are associated with "conservatives," who have been found to be more attractive (having more symmetrical faces) than liberals, when socioeconomic status is controlled for.[97] Liberals are also far more prone to mental illness and especially to depression. In addition, the more extreme a liberal is, the higher in mental illness he or she tends to be.[98] This would be congruous with

95—Martin Fieder and Susanne Huber, "Political Attitude and Fertility: Is There a Selection for the Political Extreme?" *Frontiers in Psychology* (2018), https://doi.org/10.3389/fpsyg.2018.02343.

96—Dutton, Madison, and Dunkel, "The Mutant Says in His Heart, 'There Is No God,'" *op cit.*

97—Niclas Berggren, Henrik Jordahl, and Panu Poutvaara, "The Right Look: Conservative Politicians Look Better and Voters Reward It," *Journal of Public Economics*, 146 (2017): 79-86; Rolfe Peterson and Carl Palmer, "Effects of Physical Attractiveness on Political Beliefs," *Politics and Life Sciences*, 36 (2017): 3-16.

98—Emil Kirkegaard, "Mental Illness and the Left," *Mankind Quarterly*, 60 (2020): 487-510.

a model whereby, even though there may be many genetically healthy individualists who are liberal, we were so group-selected in 1800 that deviations from this tend to be in an individualist direction and, thus, associated with mutational load and those who espouse the most extreme, and maladaptive, deviations will be very high in mutational load, indeed.

This is consistent with analyses of the physiognomy and mental health of Second Wave feminists such as Andrea Dworkin (1946-2005).[99] Such people do not tend to have children, but more importantly, they are operating at the group level in such a way as to reduce the fitness—in terms of group-selectedness and even overall fertility. In other words, they are spiteful. Similarly, those who induce a state of dysphoria and disgust, via their high mutational load, will be indirectly reducing group fitness by indirectly suppressing fitness in less mutated people. Those who, due to mutation, promote wild conspiracies which make the group less unified in the face of a rival group are rendering it less group selected, though, unlike with the Left, this fitness-damage is done in a more passive way. Thus, there is no reason why runaway individualism and spiteful mutation should be mutually exclusive models. Spiteful mutation seems to parsimoniously explain an important element of runaway individualism, and it also makes sense of why it is those who would have been the "norm" under conditions of harsh Darwinian selection, who remain resistant to these destructive ideas.

This process has led to a gradual reversal of what was normal, because once roughly 20 percent of a population

99—See Edward Dutton, *Witches, Feminism and the Fall of the West* (Whitefish: Radix, 2021), Chapter 8.

question a system of thinking, a "tipping point" is reached: people start to lose faith in the system and begin to defect to the new way of thinking.[100] The "norm" has become the destruction of the family, the promotion of deviant sexuality, the favoring of foreigners over your own, the ridicule and even persecution of (native) religious people, and the destruction of patriarchy and persecution of those who promote it. As stated, this is the new crucible of evolution, because you will only survive if you can resist this environmental onslaught, and that is only likely to occur if, for genetic reasons, you are resistant to this extreme evolutionary mismatch, and to these zombies who are out to get you.

MUTATION AND WORLDVIEW

Throughout this book, we will explore in depth a number of people who spread runaway individualism, paranoid chaos, and spiteful ideas. In terms of personality, their minds strongly deviate from the preindustrial norm, and these individuals often evince common personality and mental disorders: autism, Narcissism, depression, and schizophrenia.

A person suffering from autism commonly has difficulty understanding social cues, resulting in his feeling that the world is chaotic and makes no sense. This can lead to anxiety and a weak sense of identity, as the autistic person feels out of control and out of place. Such anxiety may inspire a fast Life History Strategy, and the

---

100—Damon Centola, Joshua Becker, Devon Brackbill, *et al.*, "Experimental Evidence for Tipping Points in Social Convention," *Science*, 360 (2018): 1116-1119.

concomitant focus on individualist foundations. Autism can also be associated with extremely pronounced negative feelings, such as depression, anger, and insecurity.[101] One manifestation of this, whether autism is a factor or not, can be Borderline Personality Disorder, whereby a person deals with chronic insecurity by presenting a very strong identity, though this is unstable and subject to dramatic change, such as between political or religious extremes. Sufferers see the world in a black-and-white way, something known as "splitting." Narcissism, which crosses over with psychopathology, can also be an example of this. This disorder is characterized by many of the same traits, such as grandiosity, selfishness, and a belief that one is special. These areas are also associated with transsexuality, due to an unstable sense of self, and because, as we will see, there is an extent to which transsexuality involves being in love with yourself and regarding yourself as so special that you can redefine yourself and others just must accept the new "you."

This cross-over also exists because autism is associated with masculinization, becoming easily sexually aroused, and easily developing sexual associations with objects and thus with developing sexual fetishes, of which, as we will see, transsexuality is an example. For the same reason, autism is associated with pedophilia. Homosexuality, which correlates with depression, appears to be, in part, an expression of high mutational load, while being an "Incel"

101—Jessica Greenlee, Angela Mosley, Amy Shui, *et al.*, "Medical and Behavioral Correlates of Depression History in Children and Adolescents with Autism Spectrum Disorder," *Pediatrics,* 137 (2016): s0105-114; Barbara van Heijst, Marie Deserno, Didi Rhebergen, *et al.*, "Autism and Depression are Connected: A Report of Two Complimentary Network Studies Show," *Autism*, 24 (2020): 680–692.

(involuntary celibate), which we will also explore, means that you are sufficiently distinct from the preindustrial "norm" that you are not resistant to fitness-reducing ideas and forms of behavior. So, all of these deviations are inter-related, due to their association with autism, high mutational load, or both.

Being staunchly left-wing is associated with mental illness, though this should be put into its proper context. We in the West live in a society that is broadly left-wing and based on values of individualization. Thus, signaling your leftism is also associated with Narcissism, desiring approval, and Machiavellianism, desiring power.[102] Anxious people might want to strongly conform, feeling isolated and fearing social ostracism. It may well be that when society was broadly "conservative" and group-oriented, these traits were associated with signaling group-oriented, right-wing values. Regardless, leftism is essentially about individualism, and individualism is an expression of a chaotic and fast Life History; this is, itself, associated with Neuroticism, whereby the world is regarded as dangerous and unstable. Accordingly, an extreme left-wing, individualist outlook is an expression of mental instability. The world is a dangerous, unpredictable, and maybe evil place, so you need to focus on pure survival, including on attaining power. It could thus be argued that there is an inherent relationship between leftism and Neuroticism.

If you feel negative feelings strongly, you have low self-esteem, perceive yourself as and identify with others whom you perceive as weak, such as women or ethnic

---

102—Ekin Ok, Yi Qian, Brendan Strejcek, *et al.*, "Signaling Virtuous Victimhood as Indicators of Dark Triad Personalities," *Journal of Personality and Social Psychology* (2020), https://doi.org/10.1037/pspp0000329.

minorities, meaning you promote their interests. You perceive the world as "unfair" and yourself as in danger from the powerful, so you become Machiavellian, such that you can gain control in this dangerous world. The negative feelings, however, never go away, and you can never have enough power. You have a strong need to socially conform on the one hand, as you fear the consequences of not doing so, but you also have a strong need to make the world more "fair" and under control—creating an unresolvable tension. This is expressed, for example, in the way in which left-wing Europeans tended to support "lockdowns" during the Covid-19 pandemic of 2020, but then took to the street *en masse* to participate in Black Lives Matter demonstrations (regardless of how many Africans might actually live in their countries). Some might have later become involved in protests against "lockdowns," as these, too, were understood as protests against those in power, whom individualists regarded as wicked by virtue of having power.

This model is consistent with the evidence that conservatives feel more in control of their world, feel that the world is fair, and generally feel more content with their lives than liberals. They also feel that life has "meaning," while liberals tend not to.[103] Conservatives are also happier to debate with liberals than *vice versa*, presumably because liberals feel intensely negative feelings—to the point of feeling "unsafe"—when challenged, in a way that

---

103—Barry Schenkler, John Chambers, and Bonnie Le Bon, "Conservatives Are Happier Than Liberals, But Why? Political Ideology, Personality, and Life Satisfaction," *Journal of Research in Personality,* 46: 127-146.

conservatives do not.[104] It could be argued that hating your opponents would make you more power hungry.

Autism may be associated with leftism indirectly, due to the association between autism and depression, and, more directly, because autistic people are, on average, atheistic and individualistic. They are plagued with negative feelings; they strongly desire to make sense of the world; and they do not experience the world as a secure place, perhaps with a loving god behind it. This Neuroticism can lead to Borderline Personality Disorder and the "splitting" associated with it. Convincing themselves that they are morally superior to others, absolutely correct, and part of a crusade to purge the world of "evil," could help to assuage their profound feelings of inadequacy, self-doubt, and fear of abandonment, these being key components to BPD. Indeed, it has been found that virtue-signaling and being morally judgmental actually strongly elevate mood, so they can be highly addictive for mentally unstable people, like a drug.[105]

At his best, you could say, an autistic person is someone who can "think outside the box;" he applies logic and imagination to a subject or problem and does not care if his innovation offends vested interests; he might even enjoy "rocking the boat."[106] It is thus not surprising that evidence of autism is found in recognized "geniuses"—

104—Siqi Wu and Paul Resnick, "Cross-Partisan Discussions on YouTube: Conservatives Talk to Liberals but Liberals Don't Talk to Conservatives," *arXiv*: 2104.05365 (2021).

105—See Geoffrey Miller, *Virtue Signaling: Essays on Darwinian Politics and Free Speech* (Cambrian Moon, 2019).

106—Edward Dutton and Bruce Charlton, *The Genius Famine* (Buckingham: University of Buckingham Press, 2015).

those who make major breakthroughs—combined with outlier high intelligence and moderately low Agreeableness and moderately low Conscientiousness, and, indeed, with psychopathic traits.[107] Psychopathology is also currently associated with being "Alt-Right," that is, having radical conservative views.[108] In a traditional society, it would be dangerous to be left-wing, so this would have been attractive to psychopaths in a way that is no longer the case.

It may seem odd that psychoticism is associated with being liberal, while psychopathology correlates with being Alt-Right. But it should be stressed that conservatism, which negatively correlates with psychoticism, is psychologically distinct from the kind of radical conservatism that would characterize the Alt-Right.[109] Moreover, "psychopathology" involves specific aspects of psychoticism; it cannot simply be reduced to it. In particular, psychopaths are strongly non-conformist; they quite enjoy upsetting people. Clearly, in a liberal society, you can better achieve this by being Alt-Right than by being far Left. The latter may be non-conformist as well, but its adherents are limited by their anxiety, for example, about being socially excluded. They are subject to competing psychological pressures in this regard in a way that the psychopath is not.[110]

107—See Felix Post, "Creativity and Psychopathology," *British Journal of Psychiatry*, 165 (1994): 22-34.

108—Jordan Moss and Peter O'Connor, "The Dark Triad Traits Predict Authoritarian Political Correctness and Alt-Right Attitudes," *Heliyon,* 6 (2020): e04453.

109—See Patrick Forscher and Nour Kteily, "A Psychological Profile of the Alt-Right," *Perspectives on Psychological Science*, 15 (2020): 90-116.

110—Raymond Novaco, "Anger and Psychopathology" in *International Handbook of Anger*, edited by Michael Potegal, Gerhard Stemmler, and

Although it is possible to be diagnosed with both "autism" and "schizophrenia"—as some of the symptoms cross over—in a key respect, they are diametrically opposed. Autism involves being very high in systematizing but being low in "empathy." A schizophrenic's personality profile is the reverse: he is low in systematizing but suffers from hyper-empathy. He is obsessed with and hyper-sensitive to external signals of internal states. This means that he will interpret a slight frown as a sign of malevolent intent, rendering him paranoid. This also means that he sees evidence of a "mind" everywhere, even in the world itself. Completely lacking this, autistic people tend to be atheists, something which may fuel their nihilism. By contrast, schizophrenics tend to be hyper-religious and prone to believing in bizarre and paranoid "conspiracy theories." Schizophrenia is at the extreme end of the schizotypy spectrum. The least severe schizotpy disorder is "schizoid personality." This is characterized by being antisocial, withdrawn, emotionally cold, secretive, apathetic, socially anxious, and detached. More severe is "schizotypal personality." This combines schizoid traits with easily taking offence, unusual thinking, paranoid thoughts, belief in special powers or superstitions, and unusual speech patterns. In schizophrenia, this is taken even further and involves firm paranoid delusions and psychoses, such as hearing voices.[111] Those who are reasonably high on the schizotypy spectrum will be very high in empathy and thus the associated focus on equality and harm avoidance. Thus, they will tend towards "individualist" and "left-wing" values.

Charles Spielberger (New York: Springer, 2010).

111—See Gordon Claridge (ed.), *Schizotypy: Implications for Illness and Health* (Oxford: Oxford University Press, 1997).

We would expect rising mutation to correlate with autism, which is associated with masculinization, on the one hand, and schizophrenia, which is associated with feminization, on the other. Both conditions are higher in males, due to greater male genetic variability, but autism is very considerably higher and has been termed the "extreme male brain," with hyper-empathy being, in turn, the "extreme female brain."[112] This would help to explain the illogical and emotional arguments that are presented by many left-wing people: they are high in empathy but low in systematizing.

So, with our key theoretical questions explored, let us now turn to looking in detail at some of the zombies that are out to infect us.

112—Simon Baron-Cohen, "The Extreme Male Brain Theory of Autism," *Trends in Cognitive Sciences* 6 (2002): 248-254.

CHAPTER 3

THE RETURN OF HERESY

The Faith of the Social Justice Warrior

So many of us believe that we live in a "secular age," and one that's becoming more secular by the day. Religious communities still exist, of course; however, these will be "secularized" in the coming years—neutered and brought up to date, if not ended entirely. Witch hunts, heretics burned at the stake, or the dogmatic denunciations of dissidents are, we tell ourselves, safely confined to the benighted past. This premise seems to hold for quite a large portion of the population, and in Western Europe more so than in the United States. Assuming that weekly church attendance is a measure of how religiously committed a society is then the United Kingdom, for example, has become a quite irreligious place. In 1900, 27 percent of the British population attended church on Sundays. By the year 2000, this was down to just 10 percent.[1] The collapse of religiousness is particularly pronounced among young people. A European Social Survey conducted in Britain between 2014 and 2016 found that 70 percent of those aged between 16 and 29 claimed that they were "not religious."[2]

1—Steve Bruce, *God is Dead: Secularization in the West* (Oxford: Blackwell, 2002), 67.

2—Shiona McCallum, "70% of Young Brits are 'Not Religious,'" *BBC News*, March 21, 2018, https://www.bbc.com/news/newsbeat-43485581.

In these kinds of surveys, "religiousness" is defined in the way the term is commonly understood. A religion involves believing in and worshiping a god or gods and some sort of community of shared practice. In general, these gods are what we might call "moral gods"—gods that direct their worshipers to behave in pro-social ways, at least in relation to fellow religious adherents.[3] Nevertheless, the assumption that people are no longer religious seems to obscure more than it reveals. There are behaviors that are typically associated with religiousness—intolerance of disagreement, fervent belief, or casting dissenters as "evil"—which are alive and well and, if anything, seem to be increasing in frequency rather than decreasing.

THE RISE OF SJWs AND CANCEL CULTURE

Over the past decade, popular discourse on the left in the United States and Europe has changed key, and sounded different tones and themes. Talk of "civil rights," "welfare," and clichés such as "helping working families" have gradually given way to highly moralized language surrounding being "Woke," getting "triggered," and finding mundane and previously unremarkable matters "problematic." These range from men disagreeing with women ("mansplaining") to sitting aggressively on public transport ("manspreading"). Throughout the last century, the Left was defined, on the one hand, by "liberals,"[4] who

---

3—Ara Norenzayan and Azim Shariff, "The Origin and Evolution of Religious Pro-Sociality," *Science*, 322 (2008): 58-62.

4—In Europe, "liberal" has a different resonance than in the United States, and can refer to someone in favor of free-market capitalism and dismantling the welfare state—that is, someone who would be called a "libertarian" or even a "conservative" in the United States. These semantic variations aside,

were socially permissive but supported welfare socialism and economic intervention as a national purpose, and, on the other, by "Communists," who thought that the state should plan (if not outright own) the economy. Today, the most vocal and intense segment of the Left bears the moniker "Social Justice Warrior," and it is a new breed altogether. Much like liberals and leftists, SJWs fight for "equality," but what they mean by that word seems to differ markedly from the 20th-century Left. "Equality" has less to do with, for example, job security, healthcare, or a social safety net, and more with the rights of transsexuals to use the bathrooms (as Americans euphemistically term them) of their choosing, removing statues and paintings of Dead White Males at universities, and discussing the "shameful flirting with blackface" in *Mary Poppins*.[5]

Wokeism might be most prevalent among young adults at university; however, its popularity is broad, and it is informing electoral outcomes.[6] And SJWs are shaking up what were previously consensus political issues. Erstwhile sacred cows like "free speech" are, for the SJWs, no longer sacred. Indeed, monitoring, censoring, denunciation, iconoclasm—ultimately erasing or canceling—is one of their chief *modus operandi*. In 2018, SJWs at an Oregon law school issued the following statement with regard to a speaker they found highly "problematic":

there is clearly a "social democratic" or "center Left" in Europe that, more or less, tracks with the American term "liberal."

5—Daniel Pollack-Pelzner, "'Mary Poppins,' and a Nanny's Shameful Flirting With Blackface," *New York Times*, January 28. 2019, https://www.nytimes.com/2019/01/28/movies/mary-poppins-returns-blackface.html.

6—Matthew Yglesias, "The Great Awokening," *Vox*, https://www.vox.com/2019/3/22/18259865/great-awokening-white-liberals-race-polling-trump-2020.

> Freedom of speech is certainly an important tenet to a free, healthy society, but that freedom stops when it has a negative and violent impact on other individuals.[7]

This missive was not directed at, say, a perceived radical such as Richard Spencer, who sparked controversy on campuses in 2017, but at Bari Weiss, a female journalist for the *New York Times*, who could fairly be described as a liberal feminist, though one who is decidedly "not Woke." Putting aside the ethical and legal questions of whether speech can ever be violence—or whether speech should be curtailed by those who feel offended— what's important for our purposes is that SJWs have reintroduced the concept of *heresy* into public discourse. Language can be designed as having "violent impact" even if the speaker is discussing quotidian, cultural, political, or scientific matters and not actually calling for violence by any reasonable definition. In other words, language can "anger the gods," with horrific consequences for us all. This is precisely where the issue of "hate speech," "deplatforming," and "canceling" become most relevant. In recent times, countless people have been kicked off social-media platforms, banks, and payment processors; fired from their employment; expelled from universities; or publicly humiliated for, essentially, *talking*. The examples are now too numerous to recount.

So what is going on? What is the origin of this new "heresy" designation, as well as the particular emotional vehemence with which SJWs denounce "heretics"? Moreover, how is it that we are becoming, as a whole,

7—See Bari Weiss, "We're All Fascists Now," *New York Times*, March 7, 2018, https://www.nytimes.com/2018/03/07/opinion/were-all-fascists-now.html.

less religiously observant and yet religiosity seems to be reasserting itself in surprising ways? We have already explored the way in which traditional religiousness— the collective worship of a moral god—was selected for under harsh Darwinian conditions, and, also, the way in which religiousness is composed of a variety of adaptive traits, which, being adaptive, become bundled together and selected for as one. With the collapse of harsh Darwinian selection, we would, therefore, expect deviation from this "norm" and the break-up of the "sacred bundle." We would also expect deviation from the specific form of religiousness that has been selected for in Western countries.

EVOLUTION AND RELIGIOUS DIVERSITY

Even though religion in general can be regarded as a "genetic norm," the nature of religion varies in subtle ways between human ecologies. This is because each of these ecologies are slightly different, meaning that there is likely to be variation in what kind of religion is adaptive at any given point. In other words, there are significant differences in the details when comparing different religious groups, differences that we would expect, mindful of the diverse ecologies to which humans are adapted. As societies become more complex, the nature of the gods appears to change. In essence, those groups that triumph in the battle of group selection are more ethnocentric, but also more intelligent, because the more intelligent society will be strategically superior and will be able to produce better weapons, for example. This results in the size of the polity expanding and, therefore, its members no longer being as closely related as they once were. This is potentially problematic because there is a large body of evidence that we are more prepared to cooperate with people who are genetically similar to ourselves.[8] Thus, as societies became larger, something had to happen to persuade distantly related strangers to be ethnocentric. It appears that this was a change in the nature of the gods.

It has been proposed that intelligence has co-evolved with more universalistic religions.[9] Universalist religions are very different from ethnic ones. They are characterized by membership via religious belief and practice rather than simply through being a member of a particular ethnic group. Intelligence predicts the ability and desire to cooperate, the ability to trust others, and the ability to innovate new ideas. These factors would mean that the more intelligent populations would develop into larger groups with greater and greater levels of internal genetic diversity: they would be the groups who would develop cities where constant fraternization with non-kin would become a fact of life. Thus, it would make sense that these kinds of societies would increasingly develop a belief in a moral god. This moral god would compel people to be altruistic even to strangers. It would also follow that such a society would develop a universalist form of religion, because its members would increasingly be from diverse kinship and ethnic groups, and the society would be continuously expanding.

8—See Frank Salter, *On Genetic Interests: Family, Ethnicity and Humanity in an Age of Mass Migration* (New Brunswick: Transaction Publishers, 2007).

9—Nathan Cofnas, *Reptiles with a Conscience* (London: Ulster Institute for Social Research, 2012).

Adherence to a universalist religion would become the key marker that you were "one of us"—that you could be trusted because you believed in the same (moral) god who was watching over you and influencing your actions. The society that adopted this kind of religiosity would be better able to spread, becoming larger and larger. In other words, the city-based society that evolved from believing merely in gods who were placated by ritual to believing in a moral god or gods would be at an advantage in terms of promoting positive ethnocentrism (and negative ethnocentrism towards non-believers) among an ever-larger group. It would, therefore, ultimately triumph. As such, we would expect that highly successful groups might even be at an advantage were they to be intolerant of those who questioned components of the religion—this being so central to holding the group together.

A number of scholars have developed similar theories to this. Most prominently, Lebanese psychologist Ara Norenzayan has proposed that the rise of city-states and large polities is paralleled by the rise of moralistic monotheism, as this helps to create a bonded society of people who are not kin.[10] A slight nuance to this can be found in the way that monotheism first prominently developed among certain specific groups of pastoralists, the Hebrews and, later, the followers of the Prophet Mohammed. It begins as monolatry: the idea that there are many Gods but that you must only worship one of these, Yahweh, and "He" is a god who demands not only ritual adherence but highly moral behavior. Indeed, if the Old Testament is correct, it would appear that it is

10—See Norenzayan and Shariff, "On the Origins and Evolution of Pro-Sociality," *op cit.*

the bonding mechanism presented by this belief in one moral god that allows His followers to triumph. Once the Hebrews have developed cities and high levels of comfort, they turn away from monolatry and start worshiping other gods, such as Baal. This, inevitably, leads to them losing ground to other groups, possibly because the Hebrews have become less internally similar and thus less ethnocentric. But as long as the different tribes of Israel are united under the watchful and judgmental eye of Yahweh, they are successful in terms of group selection.

In addition, monolatry, or, at least, intolerant monolatry, that regards worshipers of other gods as evil, seems to first develop among groups that are excluded and on the borders of wealthier societies. Exclusion, along with stress, is one of the factors that is associated with elevated levels of religiousness.[11] It is unclear how this intolerant monolatry developed into a similarly intolerant form of monotheism. It may have been via the influence on Judaism of the Neo-Platonic belief in a single divine presence, the Demiurge, a belief that became increasingly significant in Greek paganism from the time of Plato (c. 424-348 BC) onwards.[12] However Jewish monotheism developed, Jewish-style intolerant monotheism not only helped hold together an increasingly diverse society, but provided it with a sense of moral superiority that incentivized further expansion, as can be seen among the followers of Yahweh. Accordingly, we would expect

11—Edward Dutton and Guy Madison, "Even Bigger Gods Developed Amongst the Pastoralist Followers of Moses and Mohammed: Consistent with Uncertainty and Disadvantage Not Pro-Sociality," *Behavioral and Brain Sciences*, 39 (2016).

12—Colin Wells, "How Did God Get Started? *Arion* 18 (2010): 2, https://www.bu.edu/arion/archive/volume-18/colin_wells_how_did_god_get-started/.

that, all else being equal, groups that adopted intolerant monotheism would triumph in the battle of group selection, because they would be fanatically high in negative ethnocentrism, perceiving outsiders—and even insiders who questioned minor aspects of the religion—as in league with Satan.

This intolerant dimension to monotheism may be of central importance to understanding its success. French philosopher Alain de Benoist has observed that there tend to be consistent differences between monotheism and polytheism, beyond merely the number of gods that are worshiped or that are believed to exist.[13] We can conceive of a spectrum, with extreme monotheism at one end and extreme polytheism at the other. Monotheistic religions, such as Judaism in its purest form, are characterized by a number of other beliefs. God is regarded as perfect and held in contrast to humanity, which is regarded as sinful. In polytheistic religions, on the other hand, gods have human-like personalities, including human-like failings.[14] Christianity and Islam have a clear understanding of good and evil, with the latter being embodied in Satan. In polytheistic religions, this sense of duality is much less pronounced. The difference is most obvious in terms of the relationship between humanity and the gods. In Greek myth, for example, characters negotiate with the gods or even defy them, though there may be dire consequences for this. The relationship with God in Christianity, by contrast,

13—Alain de Benoist, *On Being a Pagan* (Atlanta: Ultra, 2004).

14—In the Pentateuch, Yahweh appears to humans in various scenes and possesses a robust personality and human qualities. As Judaism and Christianity developed, however, God became increasingly invisible, abstract, unapproachable, and even "Platonic" (*Theos*). It was Jesus—the Son of God and a god-man—whose personality was most prominent.

is far more black and white. God is to be obeyed without question. Those who do not obey God will be punished, and in the Old Testament this is often through being immolated. The New Testament would seem to portray God rather differently. It rejects the harsh punishments of the Old Testament. But it is still clear that you must either accept Jesus as your Lord or you are condemned to Hell. Even the understanding of history tends to be different when comparing these two religious extremes. Monotheistic religions have a clear sense of what has happened in the past and what is true. Thus, many conservative Christians claim to believe in the Biblical account of Creation and in the "inerrancy" of the Bible in general. By contrast, in polytheistic religions, there are different accounts of history and of the creation of the world, and this tension is not generally regarded as a problem.

Additionally, the concept of "heresy" is inherent to any form of intolerant monotheism. As this kind of religion was selected for over time, we might expect people to become increasingly intolerant of heretics. Historian Joseph Klaits' analysis of Medieval Europe finds precisely this to be the case.[15] As the Middle Ages progress, heretical Christian sects—as well as adherents to other religions, such as the Jews—are increasingly persecuted and persecuted with ever greater ruthlessness. In 1401, in England, heresy was finally made a capital offense. There followed a period in Europe, up until the early 19th century (in Spain), were heretics could be subject to execution. Under the conditions of harsh Darwinian selection prevalent prior to the Industrial Revolution,

15—Joseph Klaits, *Servants of Satan: The Age of Witch-Hunts* (Bloomington: Indiana University Press, 1985).

the persecution of heretics would have ensured that the optimum form of religiosity was maintained. Those who questioned it, either by being insufficiently religious or even by being fanatically religious, would have been subject to persecution.[16]

Indeed, it could be argued that the sects that were persecuted—broadly termed Gnostics—were insufficiently ethnocentric and they made evolutionarily damaging ideas the will of God. As American philosopher Paul Gottfried has noted, these sects tended to be very strongly focused on creating a community of "equality" to the neglect of fostering order or hierarchy, a problem under conditions of harsh group-selection. Many regarded the world as an evil place created by Satan and preached that nobody should have children. In other words, they took maladaptive ideas and promoted them as divine edicts. As such, these individualistic heretics were purged by those who aimed to foster a successful group.[17] As environmental conditions became harsher, as they did as we moved from the Roman and Medieval warm periods to the Maunder Minimum of the late 17th and early 18th centuries, group and individual-level selection intensity would have increased, heightening selection for adaptive, group-selected religiosity, and selecting out those inclined to individualism and thus heretical,

---

16—See Edward Dutton and Guy Madison, "Execution, Violent Punishment and Selection for Religiousness in Medieval England," *Evolutionary Psychological Science*, 4 (2018): 83-89.

17—Paul Gottfried, *Multiculturalism and the Politics of Guilt: Towards a Secular Theocracy* (Columbia: University of Missouri Press, 2004); T. Rasimus, *Paradise Reconsidered in Gnostic Mythmaking: Rethinking Sethianism in Light of the Ophite Evidence* (Leiden: BRILL, 2009).

Gnostic ideas.[18] The Industrial Revolution has put us firmly back in a *de facto* warm period, and, in fact, we are literally in a warm period. The result is an even more pronounced version of the decline of Rome in terms of rising mutation and increasingly individualistic and fitness-damaging ways of thinking.

THE RISE OF ATHEISM

By the beginning of the 18th century, Darwinian selection had become particularly intense in Europe. This was the time of the Maunder Minimum, meaning it was particularly cold due to a very low level of sunspot activity. This meant that insufficient food could be grown to feed the population and there was mass starvation and disease as a result. This struggle to survive meant that group selection—battles for resources waged by different ethnic groups against each other—was also ferocious, their being many bloody wars. By the year 1800, up to approximately 90 percent of people born in European countries did not pass on their genes. Child mortality stood at around 50 percent and another 40 percent of people, those that survived childhood, either didn't marry or witnessed all their children die young.[19] The Industrial Revolution, which began around 1800, radically changed this situation, as we have discussed.

18—See, Michael Woodley and Aurelio J. Figueredo, *Historical Variability in Heritable General Intelligence: It's Evolutionary Origins and Sociocultural Consequences* (Buckingham: University of Buckingham Press, 2013).

19—Tony Volk and Jeremy Atkinson, "Is Child Death the Crucible of Human Evolution?" *Journal of Social, Evolutionary, and Cultural Psychology*, 2 (2008): 103-116.

Three consequences to the breakdown in selection have been highlighted, as we discussed earlier. Firstly, you would expect to find more and more people with instincts and desires that would have been fitness-reducing under Darwinian conditions, and these instincts and desires would be comorbid with other fitness-reducing traits. One such example is atheism. As we have discussed, the collective worship of a moral god is adaptive and is, therefore, associated with other adaptive traits and general evidence of low mutational load. Atheism is maladaptive and is, therefore, correlated with evidence of high mutational load, such as autism and non-right-handedness. The latter is because people with symmetrical brains are generally right-handed. Non-right-handedness correlates with assorted mental and psychosexual pathologies.[20]

Matthew Sarraf and colleagues have observed that being an advocate of liberalism—which is fitness-reducing because it puts the interests of other ethnicities ahead of your own—is associated with physical and mental illness and with low fertility.[21] By contrast, conservatism, even when controlling for religiousness, is associated with mental and physical health and with fertility. Interestingly, it has been shown that right-wing people, on average, have faces that are more symmetrical than those of left-wing people. This implies that right-wing people in our industrial world are lower in mutational load.[22]

20—Dutton, Madison, and Dunkel: "The Mutant Says in His Heart, 'There Is No God,'" *op. cit.*

21—Sarraf, Woodley of Menie, and Feltham, *Modernity and Cultural Decline: A Biobehavioral Perspective* (Basingstoke: Palgrave Macmillan, 2019). See also Frank Salter, *On Genetic Interests, op cit.*

22—Niklaas Berggren, Henrik Jordahl, and Panu Poutvaara, "The Right Look: Conservative Politicians Look Better and Voters Reward It," *Journal of*

It should be emphasized that this was not necessarily always the case, as we discussed in Chapter 2. It has become the case, however, in a situation of runaway individualism. This is the second consequence. Group-selection collapses, so there is nothing to hold individualism in check. So people virtue-signal individualistic values in an arms-race, until they start to become fitness-reducing and self-destructive. The third consequence of this breakdown is the Spiteful Mutant, who will, in some ways, inspire the individualists with especially destructive ideas.[23] When people carry mutations that make them inclined towards evolutionarily damaging behavior, they will damage the genetic interests even of non-mutants. They will do this, firstly by espousing maladaptive ways of thinking—such as that women should heavily limit their fertility or even have no children at all—influencing many non-mutants to damage their own genetic interests.

Secondly, they will critique and otherwise undermine societal structures that act to optimize adaptive behavior, such as religion. Indeed, they may even take control of such structures and gradually change them such that they advocate fitness-reducing behavior. This can be seen in the Church of England and its leaders, such as the current Archbishop of Canterbury Justin Welby, now being little more than "multiculturalists in mitres."[24] They do not even have to ascend to positions of great influence to do

Public Economics, 146 (2017): 79-86.

23—Michael Woodley of Menie, Matthew Sarraf, Robert Pestow, *et al.*, "Social Epistasis Amplifies the Fitness Costs of Deleterious Mutations, Engendering Rapid Fitness Decline Among Modernized Populations," *Evolutionary Psychological Science,* 3 (2017): 181-191.

24—Justin Welby, *Reimagining Britain: Foundations for Hope* (London: Bloomsbury, 2018).

this. Spiteful mutants will simply influence everyone they know to behave in a maladaptive way, consistent with evidence that if a healthy person associates with a person who suffers from depression, the healthy person is more likely to become depressed himself.[25]

It might be argued that increasing scientific knowledge causes people to increasingly understand that there is no God. It can, however, be countered that religiousness is significantly genetic in origin and becomes stronger at times of stress, mortality salience, and exclusion. It is hard-wired into us. Modernity may create conditions that reduce our religiosity, and even make us better able to calmly reason, but it does not follow that this is why we don't believe in God. Intelligence—the ability to reason through problems—weakly predicts atheism even in relatively religious populations. But a likely explanation is that intelligence involves, in effect, being low in instinct, with this better permitting you to solve problems.[26] Congruous with this, it has been shown that very high intelligence is more environmentally-mediated than lower intelligence, implying that more intelligent people are less governed by instinct, meaning they are more environmentally plastic.[27]

25—T.E. Joiner, "Contagious Depression: Existence, Specificity to Depressed Symptoms, and the Role of Reassurance Seeking," *Journal of Personal and Social Psychology* 67 (1994): 287-296.

26—Edward Dutton and Dimitri Van der Linden, "Why is Intelligence Negatively Associated with Religiousness?" *Evolutionary Psychological Science*, 3 (2017): 392-403.

27—Angela Brant, Yuko Munakata, Dorret Boomsma, *et al.*, "The Nature and Nurture of High IQ: An Extended Sensitive Period for Intellectual Development," *Psychological Science*, 24 (2013): 1487-1495.

THE MUTATION OF RELIGION

With the collapse of harsh Darwinian selection, we would, therefore, expect fitness-reducing inclinations to become increasingly prominent in society, and even to become a new "normal." Religiousness would no longer be, in effect, fundamental to survival and passing on your genes, though it might still be associated with fertility (which, indeed, it is). As we have seen, religiousness hits in at times of stress, so with the collapse of mortality salience, we would also expect religiousness to collapse for environmental reasons, even if the remnants of traditional religious populations were still steadily outbreeding the non-religious one. Accordingly, due to a combination of low stress and the increasing influence of Spiteful Mutants, we would expect a long, if temporary, period of relatively low religiosity in the traditional sense of the word.

We would also expect religion to start to mutate in the *mimetic* realm. Under harsh conditions, religion was very strongly selected for and thus the "bundle" that constitutes religiousness was itself strongly selected for. With the weakening of these pressures, we would expect to see all kinds of deviations from the preindustrial norm of collectively worshiping a moral god as part of a religion that promoted group-selected behavior as God's will. And we would expect these to be associated with elevated mutational load. These mutant religions would likely involve some aspects of religiosity, sometimes taken to extremes—but not all of them. For example, the type of monkish loner, who fervently believes in religious doctrines and yet does not communally worship a god, is associated with schizophrenia and bipolar disorder.

Such people are religious in their way, but they do not tend to be regular participants in a religious community. Fervent belief in conspiracy theories is also associated with schizophrenia. Conspiracy theorists display some of the dimensions associated with religiousness—such as agency over-detection, pattern over-detection, out-group hostility, and intense certainty—but they do not display all of them, because they don't necessarily believe in God.[28]

Following this line of thinking, we would expect Christianity itself to mutate. The Romanian anthropologist Mircea Eliade (1907-1986) highlighted two key "replacement religions" that appear to have evolved from Christianity in Industrial Europe: Romantic Nationalism and Marxism.[29] It can be argued that both of these "replacement religions" involve many of the key dimensions to religiousness with the exception of belief in a moral God, although some forms of romantic nationalism, and occasionally even Marxism, syncretize Christianity with their ideology, much like Medieval Catholicism syncretized itself with European paganism.[30] They are theologically comparable to Christianity, in the sense that Christianity stresses identifying with the poor and Marxism, with the international worker. Multiculturalism and political correctness have extended this to the "Wretched of the Earth"[31] (that is, the non-

28—Dutton, Madison, and Dunkel: "The Mutant Says in His Heart, 'There Is No God,'" *op. cit.*

29—Mircea Eliade, *The Sacred and the Profane: The Nature of Religion* (Oxford: Oxford University Press, 1957).

30—Eric Maroney, *Religious Syncretism* (London: SCM Press, 2006).

31—See Dennis Forsythe, "Frantz Fanon: The Marx of the Third World," *Phylon* (1973): 34: 160-170.

White living under colonialism), to the sexual minority, and many others.

Evidently, nationalism is the more adaptive of these two mutations, because it is explicitly group-selected. The identification with the peasant was actually a way of purifying the group of foreign influence, the attitude being that only in peasant culture were the foreign and otherwise materialistic influences of the city absent. Indeed, it could be argued that with the decline of Christianity—which by the mid-19th century had been subjected to withering critique—Romantic Nationalism provided a revitalized, alternative group-selected religion. In general, it syncretized with Christianity, but Eliade points out that, where it did not, it attempted to revive pagan gods and notions of fate. Accordingly, we would expect this kind of replacement religion to be associated with fertility, and this, indeed, was the case. Of all those on the political spectrum, independent of religion, extremist conservatives (in other words far-right nationalists) have the highest fertility.[32]

Accordingly, it is Marxism—which is explicitly anti-nationalistic—that can be understood to be maladaptive, and this is evidenced by the fact that those who hold to ideologies that are related to Marxism—such as postmodernism, nihilism, and atheism—have limited fertility.[33] Certainly, it creates an evolutionary mismatch by stressing individualist values far too strongly, something

32—Martin Fieder and Susanne Huber, "Political Attitude and Fertility: Is There a Selection for the Political Extreme?" *Frontiers in Psychology* (2018), https://doi.org/10.3389/fpsyg.2018.02343.

33—Sarraf, Woodley of Menie, and Feltham, *Modernity and Cultural Decline, op cit.*

which will create a sense of dysphoria. It can also be argued, in terms of group-selection, that the group that is more intelligent tends to dominate the less intelligent group, due to superior technology, while the group that is more conscientious and altruistic internally will be more ethnocentric and, thus, dominate other groups.

All of these traits are positively associated with socioeconomic status, meaning that the promotion of "equality" will decrease the dominance of these traits. Moreover, traditional religiousness seems to elevate ethnocentrism, yet Marxism suppresses it.[34] It can also be argued that all modern leftist ideas reflect the runaway individualism that is possible when group-selection collapses. As individualists compete in an arms race in order to signal their belief in equality and harm avoidance, we eventually move to maladaptive ideas. You signal your guilt for the sins of humanity by not having children or by advocating for the interests of other ethnic groups and encouraging others to do the same. This provides individualists with individual-level power, which is what they crave, so they continue, even to the point of reducing fitness.

We would, therefore, expect the growing Spiteful Mutant population, and those whom they successfully influence, to adopt a fitness-reducing "replacement religion," which would be materialistic and maladaptive at the level of group selection. Such a religion would, potentially, share many aspects with preindustrial Christianity—but with two important exceptions. It would eschew the (adaptive) belief in and collective worship

34—See Richard Lynn, *Dysgenics: Genetic Deterioration in Modern Populations* (London: Ulster Institute for Social Research, 2011).

of a moral god, and its members would be focused on destroying, rather than promoting, their genetic interests, whether of themselves, their ethnic group, their race, or even (in the case of the most extreme animal rights or climate activists) humanity itself. In other words, whereas Christianity and nationalism would believe in eternity and their members' genetic interests as an unquestioned metaphysical good, the Marxism-descended groups could properly be described as "death cults," much like the anti-natalist Gnostic cults were when Classical Civilization became luxurious and went into decline.

With high mutational load and Spiteful Mutants undermining adaptive societal institutions, we would expect this death cult to become increasingly influential. This is why it is possible for Western societies to be, concomitantly, increasingly "secular" but also, in a sense, increasingly less rational and more religious and fanatical. In this sense, multiculturalism can be regarded, as Paul Gottfried has argued, as a literal Christian heresy: a new form of Gnosticism, able to spread, once again, due to weakened selection against individualism.[35] (We will return to the religious dimensions of multiculturalism in more depth in the next chapter; we return to the topic of Gnosticism in Chapter 5.)

This irrationalism would also be congruous with what we know about the personality of the SJW. Accepting traditional religiosity is associated with high Agreeableness (altruism), high Conscientiousness (rule-following, impulse control), low Neuroticism (low mental

---

35—Gottfried, *Multiculturalism and the Politics of Guilt: Towards a Secular Theocracy* (Columbia: University of Missouri Press, 2004).

instability), and high Openness (novelty-seeking).[36] We would, therefore, expect the modal SJW personality to be exactly the opposite of this. They would be low in Agreeableness (that is, selfish people). This would explain their double standards—preaching multiculturalism, while cloistering themselves in well-off, academic campuses. It would also explain the glee they seem to take in attacking those who dare to disagree with them.

This would be in line with the evidence, explored earlier, that they are high in individualism, Narcissism, and Machiavellianism. They would be low in Conscientiousness, which would make sense of the emotional breakdowns they display when things don't go their way, such as the young SJW who collapsed to the ground and screamed like a wounded animal during Trump's inauguration. They would be highly mentally unstable, experiencing negative feelings very strongly. Indeed, this correlation has been specifically demonstrated. Leftists are high in mental instability.[37] Indeed, vulnerable Narcissism is characterized by creating a fake and supposedly perfect self as a means of dealing with a fundamental sense of worthlessness and shame. When the vulnerable Narcissist SJW is shown the reality of race differences in intelligence, for example, then the SJW knows that his or her critic is right and the SJW is confronted with his or her own fakeness. In turn, this confronts the SJW with the fundamental feelings of worthlesness. The result is, in extreme cases, "Narcissistic

36—Gebauer, Bleidorn, Gosling, *et al.*, "Cross-Cultural Variations in Big Five Relationships with Religiosity," *op cit.*

37—Emil Kirkegaard, "Mental Illness and the Left," *Mankind Quarterly*, 60 (2020): 487-510.

Rage," or otherwise attacking the messenger, in order to end the horrific feelings and reassert the fake identity.[38]

As such, we can better understand why these people are so easily "triggered," and why they require "safe spaces" to protect them from opinions that might induce negative feelings. Finally, their high Openness explains their constant desire for change and novelty, as well as their potent "herd instinct." People who are high in Openness are susceptible to hypnotism and thus to being indoctrinated.[39] This is consistent with Alexander Neduva and colleagues' summary of the modal personality of those who are extreme advocates of political correctness:

> usually artistic, theatrical, vain and narcissistic, poseurs who need attention at any cost. Their views on life in general, as well as on questions of PC, are characterized by colorfulness, picturesqueness and emotional satiety.[40]

ATTACKING THE MESSENGER

This brings us back to the issues of "canceling," shrill denunciations, and deplatforming. We would expect the New Religion, in its race to destroy humanity, to take

---

38—See Stephanie Freis, Ashley Brown, Patrick Carroll, *et al.*, "Shame, Rage and Unsuccessful Motivated Reasoning in Vulnerable Narcissism," *Journal of Social and Clinical Psychology*, 34 (2015): 877-895.

39—Martha Glisky, Douglas Tataryn, Betsy Tobias, *et al.*, "Absorption, Openness to Experience, and Hypnotizability," *Journal of Personality and Social Psychology*, 60 (1991): 263–72.

40—Alexander Neduva, Michael Kanevsky, and Vladimir Lerner, "Perverse Political Correctness and Personality Traits," *Medical Hypothesis,* 78 (2012): 146-150.

control of every organ of power that it could, in order to be maximally "spiteful" and exert as much negative influence on its group's genetic interests as possible. In a sense, everything of importance would need to be controlled by the Church. Heretics—those who disagree with the Church—would, therefore, have to be purged from these institutions. This would not even necessarily be because the Church feared that the heretics' message undermined their own, though this would be part of it. More prosaically, as we have seen, religious people feel a keen sense of disgust towards those who disagree with their doctrines. This "disgust" makes them feel, at best, uncomfortable and, at worst, physically unsafe. For this reason alone, heretics cannot be allowed to use the platforms that members of the Church use. Heretics' use of them besmirches them; it renders them "unclean." Interestingly, being high in individualism—that is left-wing—correlates with being high not just in mental instability but also in moral disgust.[41] And liberals regard conservatives as far more reprehensible than conservatives regard their liberal opponents.[42] High in anxiety and paranoia as well,[43] we can understand why the simple presence of people who disagree with them on the same social-media platform makes them literally feel "unsafe."

41—Jesse Graham, Jonathan Haidt, and Brian Nosek, "Liberals and Conservatives Rely on Different Sets of Moral Foundations," *Personality Processes and Individual Differences*, 96 (2009): 1029-1046.

42—Jesse Graham, Jonathan Haidt, and Brian Nosek, "The Moral Stereotypes of Liberals and Conservatives: Exaggeration of Differences across the Political Spectrum," *PLOS One* (2012), https://doi.org/10.1371/journal.pone.0050092.

43—Kirkegaard, "Mental Illness and the Left," *op cit.*

One of the great ironies of contemporary censorship is that, since the Church is obsessed with topics such as "racism," "homophobia," "the patriarchy," and so forth, SJWs spend a great deal of time and effort discussing these matters and publishing their knowledge of various "racists," "homophobes," and "chauvinists"—ultimately drawing attention to these ideologies and their adherents. If the Church were concerned solely with the heretic's message, it would seek to suppress that message—to ban explicitly all speech about certain topics, ideas, or facts in order that nobody should learn about them. This is not what the Church does. The heretic's message should, in fact, *be heard*, in order to prove the charge of heresy and set the heretic up for being cancelled. In other words, the Church seeks to *damn the messenger* much more than it seeks to damn the message itself. That damnable message must be made known, at least to a certain extent, so that the messenger can be suitably demeaned and destroyed.

The heretic must be deplatformed from any public space in which he could gain a following, whether that be the ivory towers of academia, a city council, or even Twitter. In this way, cancelling and deplatforming resembles the death sentences dealt out to the heretics of the 16th century. After being once cancelled for "racism" or similar offenses, there is little chance of coming back. Even someone convicted of the crimes of manslaughter, rape, or armed robbery is allowed to re-enter society after serving their time. A "racist," on the other hand, must be permanently ostracized.

THE FUTURE OF THE DEATH CULT

On the face of it, it seems implausible that a maladaptive religion—a death cult—could have become so powerful in Western countries, and done so with such relative speed. But it actually makes a great deal of sense. Humans are a highly collective species, one might even say that we are "eusocial"—a "hive mind"—and, in that sense, more comparable to social insects than chimpanzees. Consequently, we are strongly evolved to be part of an intensely bonded group. We have also co-evolved, in a sense, with religiosity, which has always been there to ensure that adaptive behavior is perceived as the will of the gods. Put simply, most of us behave adaptively, or are forced to do so. This means that we are particularly sensitive to our environment and to those around us. And if the nature of that environment changes, then we can expect to become maladaptive rather quickly. This is exactly what has happened.

Once Darwinian selection is overcome, and a society's delicate equilibrium is undermined, it starts to become less religious and the percentage of potential Spiteful Mutants, and mutated people who might be easily indoctrinated by them, begins to rise. At first, these mutants' influence is minuscule, and they are suppressed by society's religiousness. Eventually, a "tipping point" is reached where a sufficient percentage of people reject the ways of the old gods. Experiments have shown that once this ratio is reached—somewhere around 20 percent—the society loses confidence in the dominant way of thinking and increasingly migrates towards the new one, which, in this case, is fitness-damaging.[44] As this maladaptive way of thinking becomes the norm, it will not only spread but force Spiteful Mutants and their most fervent followers to fight for status and power, by pushing the new way of thinking leftwards and thus in an ever more fitness-reducing direction. In other words, their religious fervor will increase, causing them to question more and more "sacred cows" from the previous dispensation, including, as we've seen, free speech. Those of us who stand against this trend must be aware that we are not dealing simply with those who oppose free speech; the problem goes much deeper. We are dealing with a religion, with all the attractions to human psychology inherent in it.

Humans are simply not adapted to be in this situation of relative luxury and low mortality salience. To make things worse, Darwinian conditions quickly collapsed once this situation was reached, meaning that a large percentage of Western populations are likely, to varying degrees, to be prone to fitness-damaging ways of thinking for genetic reasons as well. We are in an evolutionary mismatch. This creates a sense of dysphoria and despair and causes us to do maladaptive things, as discussed in detail earlier. Until around the 1960s, these feelings were held back by the not-yet-breached dam of traditional religion, which gave life eternal meaning and forced us to behave adaptively. But that dam has burst, allowing a tsunami of mutation to overwhelm us. As a result, we are in a very different world—one in which the new religion is the death cult and the SJWs are its

44—Damon Centola, Joshua Becker, Devon Brackbill, *et al.*, "Experimental Evidence for Tipping Points in Social Convention," *Science*, 360 (2018): 1116-1119.

fanatical warrior-nuns. By earlier standards, right is wrong; good is evil; or as Friedrich Nietzsche (1844-1900) so eloquently put it:

> Whither are we moving? Away from all suns? Are we not plunging continually? Backward, sideward, forward, in all directions? Is there still any up or down? Are we not straying, as through an infinite nothing? Do we not feel the breath of empty space? Has it not become colder? Is not night continually closing in on us? Do we not need to light lanterns in the morning? Do we hear nothing as yet of the noise of the gravediggers who are burying God? Do we smell nothing as yet of the divine decomposition? Gods, too, decompose. God is dead. God remains dead. And we have killed him.[45]

45—Friedrich Nietzsche, *The Gay Science*, Translated by Walter Kaufmann (New York: Vintage, 1974 [1882]).

CHAPTER 4

THE NEXT GREAT AWAKENING

The Black Lives Matter Movement

n May 2020, the death of an obscure African-American criminal, George Floyd (1973-2020), at the hands of a White police officer in Minneapolis, Minnesota, sparked one of the largest series of protests in American history. These quickly spread, like a virus, throughout Europe and the Western World. Floyd's death, which garnered media attention and outrage, initially resulted in spontaneous riots and looting by African-Americans in Minneapolis. But the whole thing morphed into an ideological and highly coordinated movement—under the already extant slogan Black Lives Matter[1]—in which localized anarchy and widespread moral panic swept across America, encouraged by Social Justice Warriors and, to a great extent, the leftist media and political establishment. This moment in time was best summarized by a CNN report on August 26, in which national correspondent Omar Jimenez stood before a dangerous scene in Kenosha, Wisconsin—cars and buildings in flames— with the caption, "Fiery But Mostly Peaceful Protests After Police Shooting."[2] The image spoke for itself, but

---

1—Black Lives Matter, "Herstory," Black Lives Matter, https://blacklivesmatter.com/herstory/.

2—Joe Concha, "CNN Ridiculed for 'Fiery But Mostly Peaceful' Caption

the mainstream media would not dare condemn mayhem and violence. This was about something greater.

Flagrantly breaking the "lockdowns," which had been in action for two months due to the Covid-19 pandemic, Whites gathered in the streets and knelt in the name of George Floyd. Many police officers publicly engaged in this deferential behavior, often holding out their open hands to signify their willingness to make themselves defenseless. White Americans were filmed not just kneeling before Blacks but symbolically washing Blacks' feet.[3] The riots were stated, by the media, to be "largely peaceful" even as buildings were aflame behind them or as White news reporters or police officers were physically attacked by rampaging mobs.[4] There were calls to abolish the police and even for complete anarchy, under the slogan "No Justice, No Peace."[5]

The hysteria spread to other Western countries. There were Black riots—assisted by White SJWs—on the streets of central London. White news reporters were attacked

with Video of Burning Building in Kenosha," *The Hill*, August 27, 2020, https://thehill.com/homenews/media/513902-cnn-ridiculed-for-fiery-but-mostly-peaceful-caption-with-video-of-burning.

3—Associated Press, "Police Officers Wash Feet of Black Pastors in North Carolina, June 8, 2020, https://apnews.com/article/race-and-ethnicity-north-carolina-prayer-raleigh-american-protests-ab636068d57de116e1c2685306646518.

4—James Robinson, "BBC Blasted for Headline Saying Black Lives Matter Protests in London Were 'Largely Peaceful' After 27 Police Officers Were Injured," *Mail Online*, June 8, 2020, https://www.dailymail.co.uk/news/article-8398095/BBC-blasted-Black-Lives-Matter-protests-largely-peaceful-headline-despite-27-officers-injured.html.

5—Brian Mahoney, "'No Justice, No Peace': Protests Resume in NYC for 4th Day," *ABC News*, June 1, 2020, https://abcnews.go.com/US/wireStory/nyc-reels-days-unrest-amid-nationwide-protests-70980270.

live on air. British police, in front of the gates of Downing Street, knelt before Black protestors rather than arrest them for breaking the lockdown and for rioting, as English Law demanded.[6] Companies began to signal their support for "Black Lives Matter," with those who were slow to do so being criticized as "racist;" according to one slogan, "Silence is Violence."[7] In a BLM protest in Lahti in Finland, the overwhelmingly White and female "protestors" didn't merely kneel but lay prostrate on the ground in order to signal total submission and deference.[8] Young females posted videos of themselves online renouncing their Whiteness, showing their "solidarity" with BLM.

Then came the attacks on statues and other public monuments. A statue of Winston Churchill (1874-1965) in central London was graffitied with the term "Was a Racist" next to the inscription of his name on the plinth.[9] Britain's Cenotaph war memorial was desecrated, and a young Black woman, apparently a "transman," attempted to burn the Union Jack that hung from it.[10] The statue of

---

6—Rebecca Speare-Cole, "London Police Officer Takes the Knee with Black Lives Matter Protesters in Downing Street," *Evening Standard,* June 3, 2020, https://www.standard.co.uk/news/london/london-police-office-take-knee-downing-street-a4459081.html.

7—Ellie Abraham, "I Quit My Job Over My Company's Weak Black Lives Matter Response," *Vice,* June 29, 2020, https://www.vice.com/en/article/z3e3w8/i-quit-my-job-over-my-companys-weak-black-lives-matter-response.

8—*Etelä Suomen Sanomat,* "Iskulauseet Kaikuivat Lahden Torilla—Yli Sata Ihmistä Osallistui Black Lives Matter—Miele—nosoitukseen, Katso Kuvakooste," June 5, 2020, https://www.ess.fi/paikalliset/1986535.

9—Ewan Somerville, "Winston Churchill Memorial Defaced with 'Was a Racist' During London Black Lives Matter Protest," *Evening Standard,* June 7, 2020, https://www.standard.co.uk/news/london/black-lives-matter-protest-london-winston-churchill-statue-a4462086.html.

10—Faith Ridler, "Black Lives Matter Protestor, 19, Faces Jail After Admitting

an 18th-century philanthropist and slave trader, Edward Colston (1636-1721), which had stood in Bristol since 1895, was dragged down by a mob and thrown in the dock.[11] Other statues that "offended" the sensitivities of the mob were preemptively removed, likely never to be re-erected, to prevent their destruction, including some of Belgium's King Leopold II (1835-1909), which stood in various Belgian cities.[12]

The streaming service *HBO Max* removed the American civil war epic *Gone With The Wind* (1939)—a film preserved by the Library of Congress as "culturally, historically, and aesthetically significant"[13]—after its Romanticization of the South and depiction of African slaves was deemed unwatchable in the current climate. The chairman of Warner Media called the ban a "no brainer," a curious choice of words.[14] The BBC even removed from its streaming sites relatively recent comedies, made by liberal comedians only a decade ago, such as the light-hearted *Little Britain*, because "times have changed."[15]

Trying to Set Fire to Union Flag on Whitehall Cenotaph," *Mail Online,* November 5, 2020, https://www.dailymail.co.uk/news/article-8917341/Black-Lives-Matter-protestor-19-faces-jail-admitting-trying-set-fire-Union-Flag.html.

11—Dan Whitehead, "Edward Colston: Bristol statue vandalised and toppled during Black Lives Matter protest goes on display," *Sky News,* (5th June 2020), https://news.sky.com/story/edward-colston-bristol-statue-vandalised-and-toppled-during-black-lives-matter-protest-goes-on-display-12324146

12—Richard Allen Greene, "King Leopold II statues are being removed in Belgium. Who was he?" *CNN,* (11th June 2020). https://edition.cnn.com/2020/06/10/europe/belgium-king-leopold-ii-statue-intl/index.html

13—Complete National Film Registry.

14—Ryan Parker, "Bob Greenblatt Calls Temporary Removal of 'Gone with the Wind' From HBO Max a 'No-Brainer,'" *The Hollywood Reporter,* June 20, 2020.

15—*BBC News,* "Little Britain Pulled From iPlayer and Netflix Because

BLM AS A RELIGIOUS REVIVAL

The Black Lives Matter protests of 2020 are best understood as a religious revival, emerging from the United States but global in scale. This new religion is "multiculturalism," with a heavy dose of White guilt, and it is based on institutions and ideals outside traditional churches; however, its structure and sacraments strikingly resemble those of Christianity. It could even be considered a kind of heresy. Religious revivals take place in the wake of wars and disasters, periods of elevated stress and widespread angst. They are spearheaded by and attractive to people who are relatively high in neurotic traits such as anxiety. Their disturbed mental states are, temporarily, alleviated by the religious experiences that take place through these revivals—with religion, more generally, being an adaptation that allows us to cope with an unpredictable and traumatic world.

Leftists and atheists, of course, proudly reject traditional religion and sexual morality, and we should appreciate the irony of a "religious revival" capturing their hearts and minds. However, as a group, leftists and atheists are high in mental instability—especially those who are young and female—and thus they are highly susceptible to religious *experience*, if not religion as it has been historically understood. As noted above, the collapse in Darwinian selection pressures has resulted in the rise of the Multiculturalist heresy as a new, and fitness-reducing, "religion." The result, in 2020, was a Multiculturalist revival, where 70 years ago there would have been a Christian one.

'Times Have Changed,'" June 9, 2020, https://www.bbc.com/news/entertainment-arts-52983319.

WHAT CAUSES THIS KIND OF RELIGIOUSNESS?

This wasn't just mob rule and anarchy. On display was a religious intensity. And people were sucked into it. If the mob declared that you were not a "true believer," you could lose your job, or perhaps even be subject to a police investigation. So, as more people exhibited their adherence to the Cult of George Floyd, an arms-race developed to indicate ever-greater fervor. This eventuated in some White protestors "going Medieval" and actually engaging in self-flagellation—a grotesque spectacle but a seemingly inevitable culmination of the White guilt narrative.

This was all so predictable. In April 2020, experts in the study of religion cautiously suggested that there might be some kind of religious revival in the wake of the Covid-19 crisis, though they focused on what might happen in traditional churches.[16] There are always religious revivals after or during wars, famines, and pandemics. Why would Covid-19 be any different? When police officer Derek Chauvin was found guilty of murdering George Floyd, Nancy Pelosi anointed Floyd a martyr to "Justice"—in a sense to the New Religion where "Equality" or even "Non-Whiteness" is reified as god-like, while "Whiteness" is Satanic. Pelosi thanked George Floyd for "sacrificing his life for justice."[17] It was as though this drug-addict and violent criminal was the New Christ. Jesus, after

16—Baylor Institute for the Studies of Religion, "Religious Revival or Reversal Emerging From the Pandemic?" *Religion Watch*, 35: 6 (2020).

17—Schweta Sharma, "Pelosi Faces Backlash for Thanking George Floyd for 'Sacrificing' Himself," *Independent,* April 21, 2021, https://www.independent.co.uk/news/world/americas/us-politics/pelosi-george-floyd-tweet-sacrifice-b1834911.html.

all, operated among the lowly and dispossessed and told us that we would not recognize Him when He came.[18] And, as He held a gun to a pregnant woman's stomach while demanding money for drugs,[19] we did, indeed, fail to recognize Him. Through attaining justice for Him, we could be cleansed, at least for a time, of the guilt we feel for our "Original Racism." Through His sacrifice, we recognize our sin and atone for it by jailing his Judas Iscariot-like killer. Only in a period of religious fervor, brought about by mortality salience and sudden change, could such thoughts be entertained.

We witnessed another "Great Awakening," one of the many throughout American history. This religion of a significant portion of Western populations, and especially the young, is not Christian, though aesthetically and structurally, it could be viewed as Christianity's latest mutation. In order to understand what has taken place, we need to make sense of what religion is; why "mortality salience" is relevant to it; and how, precisely, religious revivals occur. Once this is clear, we will see that multiculturalism is not just an ideology, partisan politics, or passing fad. It must properly be understood as a religion itself.

18—"Then the righteous will answer him, 'Lord, when did we see you hungry and feed you, or thirsty and give you something to drink? When did we see you a stranger and invite you in, or needing clothes and clothe you? When did we see you sick or in prison and go to visit you?' "The King will reply, 'Truly I tell you, whatever you did for one of the least of these brothers and sisters of mine, you did for me'" (Matthew, 35: 37-40).

19—*Daily Mail.com*, "EXCLUSIVE: A New Start Turns to a Tragic End for George Floyd, Who Moved to Minneapolis Determined to turn his life around after being released from prison in Texas," *Mail Online*, (28th May 2020). https://www.dailymail.co.uk/news/article-8366533/George-Floyd-moved-Minneapolis-start-new-life-released-prison-Texas.html.

One of the key predictors of becoming religious is being confronted with your own mortality or that of your loved ones. No matter what an inveterate skeptic might say or write throughout his life, when told that his mother is in intensive care or his daughter has been in a car accident, there is a very strong possibility that, in private, he will beg God for help. "There are no atheists in foxholes," as the saying goes. So-called "mortality salience" is an extreme example of the kind of psychological stress that appears to elevate religiousness. "Feelings of exclusion" seem to cause people to become more religious, too, as do periods of dramatic change, such as the rise and fall of governments.[20] People who are high in neurotic personality traits are prone to depression and anxiety, these being manifestations of "mental instability." Neuroticism seems to decrease considerably after one has undergone conversion and other religious experiences.[21]

Intrinsic religiousness—genuinely believing in a god or gods—is negatively correlated with Neuroticism.[22] We can see this in the average churchgoer of the past century, a man who conforms to the belief system of his community, intellectually believes in a higher power, but likely doesn't take his religion overly seriously, nor does he worship with particular emotional affect. On the other hand, extrinsic religiousness—outward conformity to religion—

20—Ara Norenzayan and Azim Shariff, "The Origin and Evolution of Religious Pro-Sociality," *Science*, 322 (2008): 58-62.

21—Peter Halama and Mária Lačná, "Personality Change Following Religious Conversion: Perceptions of Converts and their Close Acquaintances," *Mental Health, Religion and Culture*, 8 (2011): 757-768.

22—Peter Hills, Leslie Francis, Michael Argyle, *et al.*, "Primary Personality Trait Correlates of Religious Practice and Orientation, *Personality and Individual Differences*, 36 (2004): 61-73.

is positively associated with Neuroticism. We can think of the fanatic or obnoxious scold, someone who wears his faith on his sleeve, perhaps even so devoted that religion negatively affects his welfare. Being a "religious seeker" is also associated with Neuroticism. This involves going through phases of mental instability that are alleviated by an unusual and often very extreme form of religiosity, which is duly abandoned during periods of sound mental health.[23] Overall, it's reasonable to argue that religiousness would have been selected for, because it promoted mental health, with the result that mental health and religiosity have become genetically related, due to both being simultaneously selected over a lengthy period of time.[24]

WHY ARE WOMEN SO SUSCEPTIBLE?

The high female presence both in BLM protests and in churches is obvious to anyone who has ever attended either. And this shouldn't be surprising. Women are more religious than men, across cultures, in terms of how likely they are to believe in a god or gods and engage in collective worship.[25] In the United States, Catholics, Evangelical Protestants, Mainline Protestants, and Mormons are each 55 percent female. Some 70 percent of American women report an "absolute certainty" in their belief in God, compared to 57 percent of men. American women are

---

23—*Ibid.*

24—See Dutton, Madison, and Dunkel, "The Mutant Says in His Heart, 'There Is No God,'" *op cit.*

25—Darren Sherkat, "Sexuality and Religious Commitment in the United States: An Empirical Examination," *Journal for the Scientific Study of Religion*, 41 (2002): 313-323.

also much more likely to report that religion is important in their lives, and atheism is found twice as often among men than women (12 percent vs. 6 percent).[26]

This occurs because religion has been *sexually selected* for, too, as it is associated with being pro-social, rule-following (and thus not cuckolding your husband or abandoning your family and child), and with being part of a supportive group of co-religionists. These clear sex differences in the strength of religiousness will become significant later when we analyze the BLM protests. There are a number of probable reasons for higher female religiousness, one of which is empathy and another of which is adaptation to patriarchy, both explored above. It is also clear to anyone that has ever attended a BLM protest that many of those involved—with their stereotypical unnatural colored hair and screams of righteous fury—are not mentally well. By contrast, most females in churches appear sober and under control. We have already looked at why religiousness in general—though not necessarily religious conversion experiences, as we will see shortly—is associated with mental health. Periods of religious fervor, on the other hand, are associated with Neuroticism, so these would be more noticeable among females.

WHAT CAUSES RELIGIOUS REVIVALS?

Religious revivals appear to occur when the kind of situation that would lead to a period of religiousness in an individual—such as stress and mortality salience—are experienced relatively suddenly by a substantial portion of

---

26—*Pew Research*, "Religious Landscape: Gender Composition," 2020, https://www.pewforum.org/religious-landscape-study/gender-composition/.

a society. There will be variation in the nature of the revival, depending on the kind of people who are impacted. But, in general, dramatic change and a period of difficulty can be expected to lead to a religious revival of some kind. These can be charted throughout history and, interestingly, there is often a time lag separating the period of stress from the revival itself. Christian evangelists are constantly attempting to create revivals, traveling to different communities and preaching their message of conversion and redemption. However, they only seem to be able to achieve major expansion during, or just after, periods of significant distress.

An examination of British revivals during the 20th century is consistent with this pattern. The first major revival of the 20th century took place in Wales between 1904 and 1905. At the time, South Wales was ravaged by industrial unrest and unemployment in a society in which there was no welfare state. Accordingly, Welsh workers, many of whom were already heavily influenced by Methodism and were facing serious hardship and the realistic possibility of destitution, began to become extremely religious.[27] Interestingly, there was no religious revival during World War I in the UK, nor during the Spanish Flu pandemic that immediately followed it.[28] There were, however, various revivals during the 1920s. The lack of communications at the time meant that it was more difficult than in the 1950s for these to become national phenomena. A major revival in East Anglia

27—Pippa Catterall, *Labour and the Free Churches, 1918-1939: Radicalism, Righteousness and Religion* (London: Bloomsbury, 2006), 94.

28—Callum G. Brown, *Religion and Society in Twentieth Century Britain* (London: Routledge, 2006), 92.

in 1921 focused around socioeconomically deprived fishing communities, which were under considerable distress even compared to ordinary people recovering from the Great War. The following year, there were revivals in other parts of the country, most notably in fishing communities in northeast Scotland.[29] There was no major revival in Britain in the 1930s, other than in the deeply conservative Hebridean islands off the north west of Scotland in 1939. This year was a time of elevated distress due to the very real possibility that Britain might go to war again.[30]

There was no major revival in the UK during World War II itself. The next Christian revival, and a concomitant reassertion of conservative attitudes, came after the War, and especially in the 1950s. There was a revival in the Hebrides in 1949, in which large numbers of people, who had not previously been especially devout, underwent religious experiences and became more involved in their church; those who were already religious became more fervent. According to revival leader the Rev. Duncan Campbell (1898-1972), in late 1949, in the village of Barvas on the Island of Lewis, he conducted a nighttime meeting at which:

> Three o' clock in the morning came and God swept
> in. About a dozen men and women lay prostrate on
> the floor, speechless . . . We left our cottage at 3am
> to discover men and women seeking God. I walked
> along a country road and found three men on their

29—Stanley C. Griffin, *A Forgotten Revival: East Anglia and Northeast Scotland, 1921* (Bromley: Day One Publications, 1992).

30—Matthew Backholer, *Revival Fires and Awakenings: Thirty-Six Visitations of the Holy Spirit* (ByFaith Media, 2009).

faces, crying to God for mercy. There was a light in every home; no-one seemed to think of sleep.

At 5 o'clock that morning, 14 buses full of people arrived from all parts of the island and even from the island of Harris. People at these meetings fell into trances, fainted, swayed, and collapsed to the floor.[31] Campbell felt that he had been inspired by the Holy Spirit to go and revive the Outer Hebrides and, given the stressful conditions of the time, people were extremely receptive to the fervor in a way that they otherwise wouldn't have been.[32]

Wartime rationing did not cease until 1954, so it could be argued that it was only at this point that "normal life" finally reasserted itself.[33] In an era of mass-communication, a spark was needed to set off a nationwide revival, and this came in the form of American pastor Billy Graham (1918-2018), as witnessed in his British rallies, which took place between 1954 and 1955. The postwar religious fervor was such that it has been estimated that roughly 21 percent of the London population attended a Billy Graham rally, while up to 73 percent of the Glasgow population did so.[34] In 1955, 100,000 people packed a Glasgow stadium to attend a single service conducted by Graham.[35] I am not aware that the relationship has been quantitatively

31—Quoted in Colin Whittaker, *Great Revivals: When God Moves in Power* (Eastbourne: Kingsway Publications, 2006), 114.

32—Andrew Woolsey, *Duncan Campbell: A Biography: The Sound of Battle* (London: Hodder and Stoughton, 1974).

33—Ina Zweiniger-Bargielowska, *Austerity in Britain: Rationing, Controls, and Consumption, 1939-1955* (Oxford: Oxford University Press, 2000), 237.

34—Callum G. Brown, *The Death of Christian Britain: Understanding Secularisation, 1800-2000* (London: Routledge, 2009), 173.

35—*Ibid.*, 6.

tested, but, as a rule of British Modern History, religious revivals seem to manifest in areas of elevated mortality salience as a consequence of impoverishment or, directly, famine and other highly stressful phenomena.

WHAT KIND OF PEOPLE HAVE RELIGIOUS EXPERIENCES?

What was happening, in terms of individual and mass-psychology, during these revivals? As we have discussed, quotidian, stable religiousness—in which you are religious all the time—is correlated with sound mental health. But even religious people who are mentally healthy go through periods of stress and mortality salience in which they may become fanatical. They may even undergo forms of what is known as a "religious experience."

Religious experiences are profound psychological experiences in which a person may be overwhelmed by a feeling of "God's love" and even hear "God's voice" or believe themselves to have seen God in some manifestation. In making sense of these kinds of experiences, American neuroscientist Andrew Newberg and colleagues argue that the mind has two effective systems, calming and arousal. When either of these systems is pushed to the extreme, through meditation or hyper-arousal—both of which can be achieved via religious services—they argue that it is dangerous for the body. Accordingly, the other system hits in, leading to alternative states of consciousness and intense psychological experiences.[36]

36—Andrew Newberg, Eugene D'Aquili, and Vince Rause, *Why God Won't Go Away: Brain Science and the Biology of Belief* (New York: Ballantine Books, 2002).

English biologist Richard Dawkins has suggested that they may be provoked by the way in which stress makes us highly instinctive, and thus prone to religious belief anyway. Dawkins further argues that we are also evolved to over-detect agency: as mentioned above, if we mistake a distant rock for a wolf, we have lost nothing, but if we make the opposite mistake, we may be killed. Accordingly, at times of very intense stress, we are much more likely to mistake some unidentified sound as the "voice of God" and, at the same time, find that our calming system would hit in. This would lead to an intense religious experience combined with feelings of relief and joy.[37] Undergoing mild religious experiences—known as "spiritual" experiences—is about 0.3 heritable. Undergoing intense religious experiences is approximately 0.66 heritable.[38] This high heritability might imply that the ability to undergo a religious experience is extremely beneficial, in evolutionary terms, because it combats stress and, due to its profound nature, keeps you low in negative feelings for a substantial period of time afterwards.

That said, we must distinguish between the "religious experience" and the "conversion experience"—and also between being "religious," being "hyper-religious," and going through a phase of being intensely religious. American psychologist William James (1842-1910) distinguished between the religion of the "sick soul" and that of "healthy mindedness." The religion of healthy mindedness is characterized by relatively mild religious

37—Richard Dawkins, *The God Delusion* (London: Bantam Books, 2006), 116.

38—Matt Bradshaw and Christopher Ellison, "Do Genetic Factors Influence Religious Life? Findings from a Behavior Genetic Analysis of Twin Siblings, *Journal for the Scientific Study of Religion*, 47 (2008): 529-544.

experiences. The religion of the "sick soul," on the other hand, is marked by dramatic conversion experiences, which occur at times of intense stress.[39] Those who lead religious revivals—people such as Billy Graham—can be regarded as constantly "hyper-religious." As already noted, this is associated with either schizophrenia or with being a severely depressive personality.

Psychological studies of those who lead religious revivals have found that most of them display evidence of these pathological traits. They require, for example, the absolute structure and order which fanatical religiousness provides in order to allay their anxiety and frequently undergo intense religious experiences.[40] Such is the nature of revival "leaders." It may be beneficial for a healthy society to be able to maintain a very small percentage of such people, precisely because they are able to inspire fervent religiosity in other people and religiosity is traditionally a means of promoting ethnocentrism. In this regard, it has been noted that tribal shamans tend towards the same kinds of psychological characteristics as modern-day charismatics.[41]

What about the followers, and those who become followers during a revival? What is their psychology? Religious revivals are characterized by the "conversion" type of religious experience, in which a person undergoes a kind of psychological breakdown and, to some extent, adopts a new identity—as a "Christian" or as a "*real* Christian," for

---

39—William James, *The Varieties of Religious Experience: A Study in Human Nature* (New York: Longmans, Green, and Co., 1902).

40—William Sargent. *Battle for the Mind: A Physiology of Conversion and Brainwashing* (Cambridge: International Society for Human Knowledge, 1997).

41—See John Ingham and Denis Feeney, *Psychological Anthropology Reconsidered* (Cambridge: Cambridge University Press, 1996).

example, in a way that they somehow were not prior to the revival.[42] They, consequently, go through a transient phrase of hyper-religiosity. Transient hyper-religiosity is associated with high Neuroticism,[43] while bipolar disorder and bouts of depression also predict periods of extreme religious fervor, as does schizophrenia.[44] Schizophrenia, and its milder forms, is also elevated at times of stress, just as is anxiety.[45] Having undergone a conversion experience has been found to be associated with having been, prior to that experience, high in anxiety and other Neuroticism traits.[46]

When people suffer from Post-Traumatic Stress Disorder, which is associated with high Neuroticism, they can develop a very specific kind of religiosity known as "spiritual struggle" or "negative religious coping." Those who undergo this believe that God is punishing them for their sins, plead for God to intervene in the world, and project hostility towards out-group members. "Positive religious coping" can cross over with this, insomuch as it involves conversion, but this also involves the belief that God has forgiven you and that you are purified of your sins.[47]

42—Thomas Hywel Hughes, *Revival: The New Psychology of Religious Experience* (London: Routledge, 1933).

43—Hills, Francis, Argyle, *et al.*, "Primary Personality Trait Correlates of Religious Practice and Orientation," *op cit.*

44—Harold Koenig, "Religion, Spirituality, and Health: The Research and Clinical Implications," *ISRN Psychiatry* (2012).

45—Cheryl Corcoran, Lilianne Mujica-Parodi, Scott Yale, *et al.*, "Could Stress Cause Psychosis in Individuals Vulnerable to Schizophrenia?" *CNS Spectrum*, 7 (2002): 33-42.

46—Benjamin Beit-Hallahmi and Michael Argyle, *The Social Psychology of Religion* (London: Routledge, 1975).

47—Crystal L. Park, Philip H Smith, Sharon Lee, *et al.*, "Positive and

In other words, mentally stable religious people believe in a loving god; mentally unstable religious people perceive the world as a hostile place, or strongly believe in an evil god, or that Satan is tormenting them. In a secular society, we can see how this might morph into "devious and evil people control the world." This is a view, which we will explore below, that seems to unite both SJWs—*The world is controlled by racists!*—and right-wing conspiracy theorists—*The world is controlled by blood-drinking Satanists!* In a sense, the "conspiracy theory"—agency behind events—is a key aspect of religiousness, so it may be taken to extremes by people who are in an evolutionary mismatch or who are high in mutational load.

That aside, people who are high in Neuroticism— and even in the pre-industrial age, there would have been population variance in this trait—are more likely to become part of religious revivals. They feel stress more acutely and, accordingly, are more likely to become extremely religious in the aftermath of periods of intense societal distress. Females score higher than males in Neuroticism. For this reason alone, we would predict that females would play a noticeable part in religious revivals.[48] Consistent with this, studies of religious revivals in the U.S. have found that "white and black women were among the most visible participants at religious revivals,

Negative Religious/Spiritual Coping and Combat Exposure as Predictors of Posttraumatic Stress and Perceived Growth in Iraq and Afghanistan Veterans, *Psychology of Religion and Spirituality*, 9 (2017): 13-20.

48—Christopher Soto, Oliver John, Samuel Gosling, *et al.*, "Age Differences in Personality Traits From 10 to 65: Big Five Domains and Facets in a Large Cross-Sectional Sample," *Journal of Personality and Social Psychology*, 100 (2011): 330-348.

where converts wept, wailed, writhed, and fainted as they received God's grace."[49]

Neuroticism tends to decrease with age in males. In females, Neuroticism decreases with age until adolescence and, at that point, it increases, possibly due to the adaptive need to worry about one's children. This can be seen most obviously among university students, where females in particular tend to suffer mental health problems of various kinds that they often have recovered from by the time they are in their mid-20s.[50] Neuroticism, in women, begins to decline in early adulthood.[51] For this reason, as well as due to their higher general religiousness, we would expect females in their mid-teens to mid-20s to be attracted to religious revivals. In line with this prediction, there is detailed data on those who "came forward" to receive God's forgiveness during Billy Graham's British rallies. In London, 65 percent were female and 50 percent, under the age of 19. In Glasgow, 71 percent were women and 73 percent, under the age of 30.[52]

Even those who are not sufficiently Neurotic to undergo religious experiences can be expected to be influenced by a religious revival if it appears to be sufficiently popular. Neuroticism predicts extrinsic religiousness, that is,

49—Kathleen Brown, "The History of Women in the United States to 1865," in *Women's History in Global Perspective*, ed. Bonnie G. Smith (Chicago: University of Illinois Press, 2004), 264.

50—Paul E. Jenkins, Imogen Ducker, Rebecca Gooding, *et al.*, "Anxiety and Depression in a Sample of UK College Students: A Study of Prevalence, Comorbidity, and Quality of Life," *Journal of American College Health* (2020) DOI:10.1080/07448481.2019.1709474.

51—Soto, John, Gosling, *et al.*, "Age Differences in Personality Traits from 10 to 65," *op cit.*

52—Brown, *The Death of Christian Britain, op cit.*, 173.

religious outward conformity.[53] People who are high in Neuroticism will fear being judged negatively or even being ostracized for failure to conform, meaning they may fake religious fervor even if they don't actually feel it. This means that religious revivals that become particularly prominent can envelop people who are far lower in Neuroticism than those who are, as they see it, "slain by the Holy Spirit." Accordingly, popular revivals can generate a kind of group hysteria and thus appear far more popular than they really are. This is obvious when we consider how so many celebrities felt compelled to jump on the bandwagon of Black Lives Matter.

A NEW AWAKENING

So, with the nature of "religion" and "religious revivals" clear in our minds, we can now explore the "religious" nature of the Black Lives Matter protests. There are obvious parallels between 20th-century religious revivals—such as that spear-headed by Billy Graham—and the Black Lives Matter revival. The leaders of the movement are extreme "liberals"—with this being clearly associated with mental instability, where conservatism and traditional religiosity are correlated with mental stability.[54] The "revival" has taken place in the wake of a period of elevated mortality salience; in other words, it is a response to stress. Those who are drawn into it are politically left-wing themselves, with

---

53—Hills, Francis, Argyle, *et al.*, "Primary Personality Trait Correlates of Religious Practice and Orientation," *op cit.*

54—Emil Kirkegaard, "Mental Illness and the Left," *Mankind Quarterly*, 60 (2020): 487-510.

this being associated with mental instability.[55] It should be stressed again, that in the context of a generally liberal society, many mentally stable people adopt some left-wing views as a way of conforming, getting on with people, and securing status. But in many respects, multiculturalism can be argued to be a secular "replacement religion" for Christianity—and perhaps even a kind of Christian sect. The same argument has been made with regard to Marxism, as we saw in the last chapter.

The key difference between the Church of Multiculturalism and Christianity is that there is no god—no non-physical existence. Moreover, Black Lives Matter represents an extremely "spiteful" form of religiosity, in the sense that there doesn't appear to be any "forgiveness." In Billy Graham rallies, you could "step forward" and be forgiven for your sins. In Black Lives Matter rallies, it doesn't matter how many times you "take the knee," there can be no forgiveness for your sin of being White. You must simply learn to live with the guilt, slightly assuaging it every so often by campaigning to empower non-Whites.

As previously discussed, we can conceive of two distinct kinds of religion: those that are selected for under centuries of Darwinian conditions—that tend to involve the collective worship of a moral god—and those that deviate from this norm, having arisen in post-industrial conditions. Due to the way in which mental health and religiousness were co-selected under Darwinian conditions, as we have explored, this "traditional religiosity" is now positively associated with mental health, while deviations

---

55—Sarraf, Woodley of Menie, and Feltham, *Modernity and Cultural Decline, op cit.*

from it—such as New Age affectations or belief in the paranormal—are associated with anxiety and depression, either on-going or periodic. People who are high in mental instability can be expected to become highly religious in the wake of a crisis and being low in traditional religiosity as well as fervently left-wing correlates with being high in mental instability.

Accordingly, we would expect such people—self-identified "liberals"—to become extremely religious (in terms of their religious deviation) in the wake of the Covid-19 pandemic, and this is what we saw. In previous situations of gravity, the overwhelming majority of the British population was Christian and believed, to varying degrees, in its doctrines. This would have meant that the relationship between being a traditional Christian and mental stability would have been much weaker than is now the case. It also meant that the revivals were Christian in nature, because this was the religious belief even of the kind of mentally unstable people who tend to undergo intense religious experiences. As already noted, a specific form of religiosity has been found to manifest among mentally unstable people suffering from high levels of stress— "spiritual struggle." Those who felt the Holy Spirit during this revival would be, in general, relatively high in Neuroticism, something that would be soothed, temporarily, by their religious experience. Usually, their Christian zeal would be temporary. It would no longer be psychologically required once the period of stress was over and recovered from, by which time the factor that was elevating their anxiety to intolerable levels would have dissipated.

In 2020, especially for younger people, their religion is multiculturalism and *not* Christianity. Christianity is now the religion of a shrinking minority. Consequently, we would expect some variant on the kind of revival outlined above to occur in the wake of Covid-19, especially among such people. Its leaders, as with Christian revivals, would be mentally unstable people. However, many of the "followers," caught up in the revival, would be prone to mental instability and would be going through a particularly acute phase of anxiety. As with a Christian revival, these feelings would be alleviated by the collective experience—in this instance of "Black Lives Matter"—in which they would feel a sense of certainty that they were morally superior; that they were better than most ("racist") people; and maybe even that they were part of creating a paradise on Earth. Once the anxiety-reducing feelings this induced wore off, such people would no longer be subject to acute mortality salience and they would return to being much less fervent believers in the Church of Multiculturalism.

We would expect any such revival to be more pronounced among multiculturalists than among Christians. Social Justice Warriors are irreligious and liberal, both of which correlate with mental instability. "Christians" are conservative and religious, both associated with mental stability. Accordingly, in a world in which remnant Christianity is associated with sound mindedness, a multiculturalist revival in the wake of a pandemic becomes far more probable than a Christian one—though there still may be a Christian one of some kind in the near future. We would expect this multiculturalist revival to be elevated among young people—because people go through a period of relatively high mental instability when they are young adults—and, in particular, among young females, because females are more religious than males and they are more prone to depression and anxiety. Multiculturalism is the "new religion"—the "new morality"—and thus females would be evolved to want to signal the extent of their adherence to it, being ultimately psychologically adapted to polygamous societies in which they must compete for the highest status males by strongly signaling their religiosity and sexual faithfulness.[56]

Females are also evolved to a patriarchal society in which decisions tend to be made for them by their fathers and husbands. With the breakdown of patriarchy, it has been argued that we would expect females—especially young females—to make particularly maladaptive decisions.[57] These would include strongly aligning with a religion that seeks to destroy their ethnic group and effectively encourages them to be childless. In the absence of being inculcated with traditional religiosity, they would not only conform to the multiculturalist heresy due to high Neuroticism and fear of ostracism but also due to their Neuroticism-mediated higher levels of guilt and generalized empathy, with multiculturalism focusing on deifying the "marginalized," creating "equality," and preventing "harm."

It should be noted that, in relatively religious societies, females tend to be more politically conservative than males, seemingly because females are more religious and the

---

56—See David Buss. *The Evolution of Desire: Strategies of Human Mating* (New York: Basic Books, 1989).

57—Menelaos Apostolou, *Sexual Selection Under Parental Choice: The Evolution of Human Mating Behavior* (Hove: Psychology Press, 2014).

religion promotes "traditional" values as the will of God. However, when the influence of traditional religiousness breaks down, the female propensity towards higher empathy—and thus leftism and anti-traditionalism— begins to manifest. In 1992, in Britain, women born in the 1920s were more conservative than men of the same age. This flipped over a generation. Women born in the 1960s were *less* conservative than males of the same age.[58] These younger women, no longer as influenced by traditional religious ideas, tend to promote leftist ones—including altruism towards competing ethnic groups—with a kind of religious zeal. One commentator astutely termed them "The New Church Ladies," evoking the subterranean religious quality to so much of contemporary female discourse.[59]

Traditional religiousness took the female propensity to strongly believe in God and engage in religious worship and focused this into an adaptive form of religiosity in which God promoted group-selected values. With the breakdown of this religion, we are left with females tending to be religiously fervent and high in generalized empathy and thus attracted to multiculturalism and leftism. Females are also higher than males in Agreeableness, Conscientiousness, and Neuroticism, and, thus in social conformity.[60] So, for this reason as well, we would expect them to be more heavily involved in the New Church into which younger females have been inculcated.

58—Pippa Norris, "Mobilising the 'Women's Vote': The Gender Generation Gap in Voting Behaviour," *Parliamentary Affairs*, 49 (1996): 333-342.

59—Jim Goad, *The New Church Ladies: The Extremely Uptight World of Social Justice* (Stone Mountain: Obnoxious Books, 2017).

60—Ronald Johnson and Joan MacDonnell, "The Relationship Between Conformity and Male and Female Attitudes Toward Women," *Journal of Social Psychology*, 1 (1974): 155-156.

It has been observed that highly educated young people—those with post-graduate degrees—are significantly over-represented among Black Lives Matter activists.[61] One possible explanation for this—beyond the fact that university Humanities and Social Science departments are increasingly dominated by leftist ideas[62]—is that there is a positive relationship between Neuroticism and academic success at university, especially when this is combined with high Conscientiousness (impulse control and rule-following).[63] This is possibly because anxiety acts as a motivator towards diligence, or because Neuroticism means you desire greater certainty about the nature of the world and believe you can attain this through higher education. In that Neuroticism predicts extrinsic religiousness[64]—that is, outward religious conformity—we would expect non-SJWs, who were relatively high in these traits, to be drawn into this dominant, public revival due to their fear of not conforming.

ANARCHIC RELIGIOUS AWAKENINGS

The other difference between the British religious awakenings in the 20th century and Black Lives Matter

61—Ed West, "Why the Rich are Revolting," *UnHerd*, June 10, 2020, https://unherd.com/2020/06/why-the-rich-are-revolting/.

62—See Noah Carl, "Can Intelligence Explain the Overrepresentation of Liberals and Leftists in American Academia?" *Intelligence*, 58 (2015): 181-193.

63—James McKenzie, Mahdad Taghavi-Khonsary, and Gary Tindell, "Neuroticism and Academic Achievement: The Furneaux Factor as a Measure of Academic Rigor," *Personality and Individual Differences*, 29 (2000): 3-11.

64—Hills, Francis, Argyle, *et al.*, "Primary Personality Trait Correlates of Religious Practice and Orientation," *op cit.*

is the anarchy involved: BLM activists flagrantly breaking the law, engaging in dangerous behavior, rioting, inciting perpetual disorder ("No Justice, No Peace"), and engaging in iconoclasm by toppling statues and desecrating memorials. In this sense, a clearer comparison can be found in the Peasants War that took place in German-speaking states in the 1520s, in the early days of the Reformation. There are multiple reasons why the Reformation began when it did—the development of the movable-type printing press being the most famous—but one of them was a period of elevated mortality salience. There had been severe famine in Germany between 1515 and 1520.[65]

Reports indicate that violent Protestant mobs would strip Catholic Churches of their valuables and destroy their idols. As with Black Lives Matter, educated people were heavily over-represented among early Protestant iconoclasts—they were mainly the so-called "middling sort."[66] The Protestant leaders would oppose iconoclasm, publicly stating that idols should only be removed with permission from the proper authorities. Much as occurred in Britain in 2020, the Swiss authorities preemptively removed icons as a way of halting public disorder and also as a way of appeasing Protestant leaders. In June 1524, all Zurich churches were closed in order to prevent riotous vandalism.[67]

65—Andrew Cunningham and Ole Peter Grell, *The Four Horsemen of the Apocalypse: Religion, War, Famine and Death in Reformation Europe* (Cambridge: Cambridge University Press, 2000), 15.

66—Lee Palmer Wandel. *Voracious Idols and Violent Hands: Iconoclasm in Reformation Zurich, Strasbourg, and Basel* (Cambridge: Cambridge University Press, 1999), 14.

67—Bridget Heal, "Visual and Material Culture," in *The Oxford Handbook of*

In other words, Black Lives Matter is a particularly pronounced religious revival. In the 1520s, this happened, in part, due to particularly difficult conditions, specifically famine. In 2020, it may be that the cause was moderately difficult conditions plus a growing percentage of young people who, partly for genetic reasons underpinned by increasing mutational load, increasingly suffer from depression and anxiety and, therefore, cannot psychologically cope with what would have been historically regarded as quite normal levels of mortality salience. Contemporary young people are increasingly in a situation of "evolutionary mismatch": under the influence of modern, anti-traditional ideologies, over-parenting, and leftist education, they are decreasingly socialized as children in the manner that was the norm under harsh Darwinian conditions.

Furthermore, far superior communications—social media and instantaneous reactions to events around the world—mean that what may otherwise have been isolated patches of revivalism have been globalized, impacting millions of people. And there may also be an extent to which these riots are in the interests of some powerful individuals, who are themselves fervent adherents to multiculturalism or who desire a subservient population that will not challenge them. If the population is depressed and demoralized, this subservience is clearly better accomplished.

Accordingly, the riots—which could be subdued if so desired—are permitted to run their course. It is as if ordinary people are being told: "Look what we can allow to happen to you if you elect the wrong people or vote

the Protestant Reformations, ed. Ulinka Rublack (Oxford: Oxford University Press, 2017), 603.

the wrong way in a referendum." Afraid of offending the righteous mob—and their high-level sympathizers—even leaders who oppose leftist disorder dare not act decisively. Again, comparisons to the iconoclasm of the early English Reformation leap to mind. Iconoclasts were permitted to "get away with it" during the periods when the Protestant faction, most notably led by Thomas Cromwell (c.1485-1540), wielded the most influence at Court.[68]

All of this leads us to a final question. How have we reached a situation where so many people—including many in positions of power—wish to destroy their own extended kinship group?

BLM AND THE SPITEFUL MUTANTS

Christianity, even the zealous kind of the Reformation, was an adaptive form of religiosity. Thus, a key part of it is "forgiveness"—after publicly confessing your sins and wavering of faith. It also did not take individualism too far, though it may have been an individualistic means for the middle class to virtue-signal their way into power when it began. With the breakdown of Darwinian selection, we see an increasing deviation from this religious evolutionary norm, including religions that are fitness-reducing, because they are ultimately Nihilistic and lack doctrines that allow a person's highly negative feelings during times of stress to be fully expunged. This is what we see with Black Lives Matter—the ultimate logic of which is that Whites should simply feel perpetual shame throughout their lives with no hope of it being

---

68—Julie Spraggon, *Puritan Iconoclasm During the English Civil War* (Woodbridge: The Boydell Press, 2003), 4.

alleviated, other than in a very mild and brief way via "taking the knee."

Young people have been inculcated with this fitness-damaging religion due, in part, to the breakdown of traditional Christianity, which, like all religions that survived under harsh Darwinian conditions, tended to take behavior that was adaptive in terms of group selection and turn this into the will of God. As discussed above, as child mortality collapsed, we had more and more people who would not have survived under harsher conditions—due to their high mutational load—who had mutations of the mind that caused them to hold beliefs that would be highly maladaptive if held by even a small percentage of the group—anti-natalism being only the most obvious.

Incidentally, anti-natalism, like extreme liberalism more generally, has been found to be associated with Machiavellianism and also with suffering from depression. Indeed, depression mediates (causes) the relationship between anti-natalism and Machiavellianism.[69] Due to our being a highly pro-social species—that is, interacting in a "hive mind"—we are heavily influenced by those around us. In this way, it has been found that depression can spread like a contagion. If you are around a person who is depressed, you are more likely to become depressed yourself. And depression is a condition which is negatively associated with fertility.[70] As a result, Spiteful Mutants

69—Philipp Schönegger, "What's Up with Anti-natalists? An Observational Study on the Relationship Between Dark Triad Personality Traits and Anti-natalist Views," *Philosophical Psychology*, (2021), doi: 10.1080/09515089.2021.1946026.

70—T.E. Joiner, "Contagious Depression: Existence, Specificity to Depressed Symptoms, and the Role of Reassurance Seeking," *Journal of Personal and Social Psychology* 67 (1994): 287-296.

helped spread their fitness-reducing ways of thinking even to non-mutants, gradually undermining adaptive institutions, such as traditional churches, and replacing them with their Church of Multiculturalism, a body that is now clearly adhered to, even by the leadership of the Church of England.[71] Having taken over the state's organs of power, such as the education system and the media, they could then inculcate young people into the New Church, alter the evolutionarily adaptive methods of socialization traditionally imposed on them, and push them—and with them, the entire super-organism—to think and behave increasingly contrary to their genetic interests.

This became possible when a "tipping point" was reached, whereby about 20 percent of the population advocated anti-traditional ideas. Experiments have shown that when this happens, people perceive the new worldview as the way forward and begin to abandon the old one *en masse*.[72] We evolved to be obedient and "follow the leader" (and even follow the mob); this can sometimes result in a misfiring of our adaptations such that we start to engage in behavior that is not in our interests. This is particularly likely to be the case if we are subject to "evolutionary mismatch," if we are placed in an ecology to which we are not evolved. We are evolved to a preindustrial ecology, so we can expect to find ourselves increasingly maladapted in the postmodern world. We will engage in behaviors that were

71—See Edward Dutton, "Imagination—It's An Illusion," *Quarterly Review*, May 25, 2018.

72—Damon Centola, Joshua Becker, Devon Brackbill, *et al.*, "Experimental Evidence for Tipping Points in Social Convention, *Science*, 360 (2018): 1116-1119.

adaptive under previous conditions—such as following the crowd—but decreasingly adaptive as the crowd is increasingly mismatched, mutated and influenced by Spiteful Mutants.

In 1954, this tipping point had not yet been reached in Britain. People forced themselves, for fear of ostracism, through so-called "effortful control,"[73] to believe in traditional Christianity. By 1970, there are indications that some kind of tipping point had apparently been reached. The mental disorder autism (that rational "extreme male brain"[74]) is a marker of mutational load, as it is associated with paternal age, due to an age-related increase in mutation in semen. In the 1950s, autism did not predict atheism; by the 1970s, it did. In other words, by the 1970s, in the U.S., having an older father predicted atheism in a way that had not previously been the case. This is because Christianity was so strong during the earlier period that autistic people, who tend to be less religious due to their peculiar psychology, as we noted, forced themselves to conform to the dominant creed. After the tipping point had been reached, they no longer felt a pressing need to conform.[75]

73—Kevin MacDonald, "Effortful Control, Explicit Processing, and the Regulation of Human Evolved Predispositions," *Psychological Review*, 11 (2008): 1012-1031.

74— Simon Baron-Cohen, "The Extreme Male Brain Theory of Autism," *Trends in Cognitive Sciences*, 6 (2002): 248-254.

75—Michael Woodley of Menie, Satoshi Kanazawa, Jonatan Pallesen, *et al.*, "Paternal Age Is Negatively Associated With Religious Behavior in a Post-60s But Not a Pre-60s US Birth Cohort: Testing a Prediction From the Social Epistasis Amplification Model," *Journal of Religion and Health*, 59 (2020): 2733-2752.

THE TOPPLING OF EVOLUTIONARY SUCCESS

If multiculturalism is a new religion, with BLM protests as conversion rallies, then the toppling of "racist" statues by the mob can be perceived as the killing of the "old gods," those whom European peoples once venerated but can no longer. From our perspective, statues have traditionally been erected to honor highly group-selected people who have promoted the genetic interests of Europeans by expanding their territory and leading their ethnic group to victory over rivals. In a sense, such statues are sacred, they are idols; objects of worship. To tear them down— to humiliate gods in broad daylight in full view of the public—is a means of asserting that the religion that they represented no longer has any power, is no longer sacred.

In 1520, Spanish explorer Herman Cortes (1485-1547) destroyed every Aztec idol that he could and desecrated the temples. He noticed that such acts left the Aztecs demoralized and less able to put up a fight.[76] The worshipers were in a state of confusion. The previously certain, unique, and real system by which they made sense of the world— and in which they played an integral and positive part— was under assault. They felt anxious and confused because they had gotten used to this system, and the comforting presence that the statues fostered. Any significant change can cause this by virtue of elevating anxiety about the unknown.[77] This, alongside the symbolism of the system that gives their life meaning being attacked, leads them to

---

76—Victor Davis Hanson, *Carnage and Culture: Landmark Battles in the Rise to Western Power* (New York: Knopf Doubleday, 2007), 175.

77—Ara Norenzayan and Azim Shariff, "The Origin and Evolution of Religious Pro-Sociality, *Science*, 322 (2008): 58-62.

feel depressed and looking for new certainties.

And what if these "new certainties" on offer are nihilistic? What if they tell you that you are inherently evil and should debase and even destroy yourself—that you can never really be forgiven for your ancestors' sins? Such a church would be a Death Cult. It is no coincidence that multiculturalism attracts the same psychological types who are attracted to actual suicide cults. And is it beyond the realm of possibilities that BLM or something like it will soon be fully realized—offering fanatics the opportunity to atone for their sins through self-immolation?

CHAPTER 5

TRUSTING THE PLAN

Conspiracy Theories and the American Right

There was another religious revival that swept the United States in the year 2020. It expanded as far afield as Europe, and its devotees numbered in the millions.[1] It was an esoteric and eccentric, and uniquely American, creed and is perhaps best understood as a new stage of Christianity. It revolves around nothing less than a metaphysical battle between Good and Evil, which plays out at the highest levels of government, media, and finance. The future of the country—and the safety of the world's children—is at stake. Wickedness abounds, but devotees have faith that a messiah is rising, one who will "make America great again." This new religion is regarded as so inflammatory—and perhaps threatening to public order—that major social media companies have purged all content related to its doctrines.[2] Such suppression seemed to only harden the resolve of its members, who were ever more convinced that they had uncovered the truth. It was called "QAnon."

1—Katrin Bennhold, "QAnon Is Thriving in Germany. The Extreme Right Is Delighted," *New York Times*, October 11, 2020, https://www.nytimes.com/2020/10/11/world/europe/qanon-is-thriving-in-germany-the-extreme-right-is-delighted.html.

2—Barabara Ortutay, "YouTube Follows Twitter and Facebook with QAnon Crackdown," *AP News*, October 15, 2020, https://apnews.com/article/youtube-qanon-conspiracy-theories-ef03a889e68239de6692ce42666d97d8.

The rise of "Q" startled and flummoxed most mainstream media commentators. They dismissed, ridiculed, and denounced this online "conspiracy theory" as it continued to grow ever more popular, powerful, and influential. According to polling in October 2020, some 15 percent of President Donald Trump's supporters were committed followers. An additional 22 percent were "fellow travelers": they believed some of Q's claims but worried that the movement might "go too far."[3] A full half of Trump supporters believed that the Democrats were engaged in child-trafficking and that Trump is trying to put an end to it—an opinion clearly derived from the Q cult. Even if we take surveys like this with a grain of salt, they reveal the intense popularity—and likely staying power—of the Q narrative within the United States.

AMERICAN RIGHT, AND BEYOND

This Trump-era internet phenomenon makes a great deal of sense if we conceive of it as a religious revival, and not simply as a popular conspiracy theory, like those surrounding the JFK assassination or the Moon landing. Many of the key components of a religion are obvious: Q has its "angels," "demons," "saviors," and promises of "redemption." And for its adherents, QAnon serves many other vital functions of the religions of the past. Furthermore, this re-conception of Q raises some bigger questions. Why do religious revivals—periodic outbursts of intense devotion—occur in the first place? And if we

---

3—Graeme Bruce, "Half of Trump's Supporters Think Top Democrats are Involved in Child Sex-trafficking," *YouGov*, October 20. 2020, https://today.yougov.com/topics/politics/articles-reports/2020/10/20/half-trump-supporters-believe-qanon-theory-child-s.

accept that QAnon is a creed for our time, why has it taken this superficially bizarre guise, and shed the trappings of traditional religion?

To answer these questions, we will turn to modern history and specifically the impact it had on human evolution. The Industrial Revolution weakened Darwinian selection pressures on Western societies, leading to, among other things, a collapse in child mortality and a collapse in selection pressures for intelligence, traditional religiousness, and highly ethnocentric groups, all of which it is clear were being selected for until that point. Due to an inter-related sequence of consequences, this has resulted in an increasingly genetically diverse—and thus culturally and politically polarized—society. The bundle of inclinations that constitute "religion" have broken apart. As a result, where once a global plague might have led to a Christian revival, in 2020 it led to, or brought to prominence, two distinct quasi-religious movements: Black Lives Matter, which we discussed in the last chapter, and QAnon. Furthermore, I proffer that, despite QAnon's ostensible wackiness, it is far more group-fitness promoting than BLM, not least due to its traditionally religious dimensions. And perhaps most shocking of all, there may be some kernels of truth within its most outlandish claims.

THE RISE OF Q

The exact origins of Q—as well as those behind the cult and profiting from it—are murky and disputed, and beyond the scope of this chapter. Recent linguistic analysis, as well as a popular documentary film, suggests that Paul Furber and Ron Watkins, two operators behind the scenes of the message boards where Q appeared, are the likely suspects—giving new meaning to the phrase "the medium is the message"—but we'll probably never know for sure.[4]

Suffice it to say, in the autumn of 2017, someone supposedly working for the National Security Administration—boasting "Q-level" clearance and calling himself "Q"—began posting on the anonymous message and image board "4chan."[5] His first missive, on October 28, 2017, announced the imminent arrest of Hillary Clinton:

> HRC extradition already in motion effective yesterday with several countries in case of cross border run. Passport approved to be flagged effective 10/30 @ 12:01am. Expect massive riots organized in defiance and others fleeing the US to occur.[6]

Years have passed, and Clinton has not been locked up, but inaccurate predictions never affected the growth of Q's prestige. In his second post, later that day, he began to outline his broader message:

> Mockingbird
>
> HRC detained, not arrested (yet). [...]

4—See David Kirkpatrick, "Who Is Behind QAnon? Linguistic Detectives Find Fingerprints," New York Times, February 19, 2022, https://www. nytimes.com/2022/02/19/technology/qanon-messages-authors.html; Cullen Hoback (dir.), *Q: Into the Storm*, HBO, 2021.

5—For an early examination of "Q," see Paris Martineau, "The Storm Is the New Pizzagate — Only Worse," *New York Magazine*, December 2017 https:// nymag.com/intelligencer/2017/12/qanon-4chan-the-storm-conspiracy-explained.html.

6—Anonymous, BQ7V3bcW, 4chan.org/pol, https://archive.4plebs.org/ pol/thread/146981635/#147012719.

> POTUS knew removing criminal rogue elements as a first step was essential to free and pass legislation.
>
> Who has access to everything classified?
>
> Do you believe HRC, Soros, Obama etc. have more power than Trump? Fantasy.
>
> Whoever controls the office of the Presidency controls this great land.
>
> They never believed for a moment they (Democrats and Republicans) would lose control.
>
> This is not a R v D battle.
>
> Why did Soros donate all his money recently?
>
> Why would he place all his funds in a RC?
>
> Mockingbird 10.30.17
>
> God bless fellow Patriots.[7]

At this early stage, Q's unmistakable style was established. Missives were released as a series of aphorisms and provocations, and Q asks more questions than Socrates. The cryptic, oracular suggestions nudge followers into perceiving politics in new ways. Indeed, Q's message is highly counter-intuitive and revisionary, especially for conservatives. Take these assertions, for example: The NSA is not a shadow government engaged in surveillance and invasions of privacy—it's the headquarters of the "good guys." Donald Trump is not a womanizer and jet-setter—he's the enemy of the globalist class. And FBI director Robert Mueller was not investigating Trump for possible impeachment proceedings—he was working alongside

---

7—Anonymous, BQ7V3bcW, 4chan.org/pol, https://archive.4plebs.org/pol/thread/146981635/#147012719.

him to "drain the swamp." Nothing is as it seems. And in this topsy-turvy world, traditional political reporting must be distrusted and dismissed ("fake news"). The evocative call sign "Mockingbird," in fact, seems to reference an alleged CIA program during the Cold War aimed at manipulating the media. Interestingly, Q's unique brand of contrarianism can be translated for audiences outside the U.S. One German Q supporter exclaimed, regarding the American forces stationed in his country, "these are troops that will free the German people from Merkel."[8]

Each day, Q's followers are tasked with exegesis and elaboration of his latest "Q drops" (anonymous posting on 4chan, certified by his handle BQ7V3bcW). Much like Jesus, the religion of Q was formed, not by the man himself—who always spoke elliptically and poetically—but by his devotees, who wrote the Gospels and formed the movement. Q's crypsis re-enforces his central message: Trust the Plan. You can't know, and maybe wouldn't believe, what is happening behind the scenes. But you must hold fast and have faith that "good" will triumph in the end.

The Q drops birthed a Reddit community of 70,000 members at its height, and the movement gained serious attention when it was discussed by Sean Hannity, Roseanne Barr, and Alex Jones—the latter once claiming to have direct contact with the man himself, which might very well have been true. Q memes were re-tweeted by Republican Party activists.[9] And over the

---

8—Bennhold, "QAnon Is Thriving in Germany," *New York Times, op cit.*

9—William March, "Conspiracy Theorist QAnon Promoted, Then Deleted, by Hillsborough County GOP, *Tampa Bay Times*, July 16, 2018, https://www.tampabay.com/florida-politics/buzz/2018/07/16/conspiracy-theorist-

course of 2018-20, there arose what could be called "Q-adjacent" politicians, pundits, and celebrities, who might not address Q directly, and might not have any direct connection with the movement, but who speak in a language that resonated with the scene. In a video titled "We all know the truth," posted on November 20, 2020, legendary actor Jon Voight declared, to his "friends of all colors, races, and religions," that "this is now the greatest fight since the Civil War." He promised that "the ones jumping for joy now," after Biden had been elected, "are jumping toward the horror they will be in for."[10]

We'll never know whether Q desired to launch a crusade when it all first began, or to inspire events like January 6. He (or she or they) might have merely been "shit posting" on 4chan, a website notorious for conspiracy theories, pornography, and outrageous right-wing opinions. But at least by 2018, Q was aware that he was part of something much bigger than himself and was consciously cultivating his movement, with heavy doses of moralistic platitudes. This impulse is apparent in his posting leading up to the 2020 election:

> One party discusses God.
>
> One party discusses Darkness.
>
> One party promotes God.
>
> One party eliminates God.
>
> Symbolism will be their downfall.
>
> The Great Deceiver(s). [...]

---

qanon-promoted-then-deleted-by-hillsborough-county-gop/.

10—Jon Voight, Twitter post, November 10, 2020, 7:40 PM, https://twitter.com/jonvoight/status/1326323889417322497.

Have Faith in Humanity.

Have Faith in Yourself.

UNITED WE STAND.

GOD WINS.

Q.[11]

A CONSPIRACY SO IMMENSE . . .

Throughout the 20th century, sociologists studied the development, in America and most Western countries, of "public opinion." This is a mostly unified understanding of important events ("the news"), as well as communally shared values, habits, and actions: "watch the news at 5," "vote on Tuesday," "church on Sunday," and so on. "Public opinion" must be fostered and managed; it was a critical component of administering a technological society.[12] Over the course of the past 25 years, such unity has been fragmenting: we don't listen to the same music or watch the same movies and shows, nor do we consider ourselves part of a collective political community. The birth of the World Wide Web accelerated this trend; social networks and alternative media shifted it into overdrive.

Republicans, and especially Q followers, consider themselves "real Americans," but in contradistinction to the "liberal elites," who are, at best, hypocritical and selfish and, at worst, downright evil. The liberals, in turn, mirror this view: conservative Trump voters are deluded

11—Anonymous, BQ7V3bcW, 4chan.org/pol, https://archive.4plebs.org/pol/thread/146981635/#147012719.

12—See Walter Lippmann, *Public Opinion* (New York: Simon and Schuster, 1922); Jacques Ellul, *Propaganda* (New York: Alfred A. Knopf, 1967).

or racist reactionaries, out of touch with their country's true national purpose. Political polarization derives from this "culture of suspicion." Q supporters don't merely distrust the mainstream media; they reject it *because* it's the mainstream media. Authenticity and truth are to be found elsewhere. For some time, right-wing outlets such as Fox News and talk radio served this purpose, but these are quickly being replaced by websites such as *Breitbart. com*, Facebook groups, "citizen journalists," and, yes, QAnon. 4Chan itself acts as a kind of chaotic "id" brain of the online Right. The anonymous poster possessing esoteric knowledge is the most *anti-mainstream*—and thus the most credible—source there is.

Q integrates a number of inter-related sets of conspiratorial beliefs. According to its gospel, throughout the 20th century, the world was gradually taken over by "wicked" people, who were prepared to do anything they could to enrich themselves and become ever-more powerful. Those who are not part of this criminal organization are, generally, "good" people, though many are turned "evil" by their masters. This vicious elite constitutes a shadowy "Deep State," which runs the world behind the scenes. A criminal ruling class— which includes the Clintons, every president after Ronald Reagan, Bill Gates, and the leaders of every dimension of Western societies that have any influence—can be blamed for everything: financial collapses, pandemics, and even child-abuse rings. To turn us into cooperative drones to be exploited, they undermine the cornerstones of Western civilization, such as family and national solidarity, and direct external invasions and drug epidemics. Even childhood vaccinations are part of their dastardly scheme.

Some "good" people still hold positions of power, and they are able to use the digital footprint (emails and other communications) left by "The Cabal" to start to challenge it. These "good guys" are working for the NSA and some other branches of government. Not too long ago, they devised a plan to take the world back and eventually arrest The Cabal's leaders and henchmen. These patriots asked Trump to run for president so that they could enact their "counter-conspiracy." The Cabal struck back and did all it could to overthrow Trump—but he just kept on winning.

Part of the success of QAnon is the way in which it, parsimoniously, brings together and provides an overarching rationale for so many "alternative histories" that have been popular in America for decades. For example, The Cabal killed John F. Kennedy (1917-1963) because he tried to undermine it; it had Ronald Regan (1911-2004) shot to dissuade him from even thinking about doing so. The 9/11 attacks were an "inside job," at the hands of The Cabal, in order to grab power and further erode the freedoms enjoyed by good citizens. Similarly, Covid-19 is a hoax deployed by this Deep State to control the populace and render them despondent.

Relatively recent revelations about high-level sexual abusers and pedophiles, such as Harvey Weinstein and Jeffrey Epstein (1953-2019)—who supposedly killed himself on suicide watch before he could face trial—are drawn into the web.[13] Q followers have theorized that John F. Kennedy Jr. (1960-1999), the son and namesake of the president—and thus a man who knew too much—faked his death in 1999 in order to avoid being assassinated

13—See Jasun Horsley, *The Vice of Kings: How Socialism, Occultism, and the Sexual Revolution Engineered a Culture of Abuse* (London: Aeon Books, 2019).

by The Cabal. He lives on as a Trump supporter in Pennsylvania; some think he might be Q himself.[14] Some QAnon supporters accept the 2016 "Pizzagate" conspiracy, where a Washington, DC pizzeria was the headquarters of this diabolical child-abuse ring. Bill Clinton's former chief-of-staff, John Podesta, convicted sex offender and former congressman Anthony Weiner, and Hillary Clinton are all involved.

Yet another strand of QAnon thought focuses on the significance of Jewish financial interests in controlling The Cabal. According to this theory, the Satanic, child-stealing, baby-murdering Khazar Empire from Babylon was defeated by Russian Tsars and driven underground. They gradually infiltrated the world banking sector and even the British monarchy. The Rothschilds are actually Khazars, who control some of the world's most powerful Satanists. As Q "dropped": "Realize Soros, Clintons, Obama, Putin, etc. are all controlled by 3 families."[15] Q lists these three families in some posts: The House of Saud, George Soros himself, and the Rothschilds. In another post, Q asks: "What happened to Diana? What did she find out? Why was she running?" and invoked the idea of a secret British government, propped up by MI6.[16] The rabbit hole runs deep . . .

14—E.J. Dickson, "QAnon Followers Think JFK Jr. Is Coming Back on the 4th of July," *Rolling Stone*, July 3, 2019, https://www.rollingstone.com/culture/culture-features/qanon-jfk-jr-conspiracy-theory-854938/.

15—Anonymous, BQ7V3bcW, 4chan.org/pol, https://archive.4plebs.org/pol/thread/147433975/#147434025.

16—Ling, "QAnon's Creator Made the Ultimate Conspiracy Theory," *op cit.*

THAT NEW TIME RELIGION

What can we make of all this? America is notorious for its love of conspiracy theories, and these often seem to act much like "replacement religions." Groups battle with each other and the victors pass on more of their genes. Groups are more likely to win if they regard themselves as superior and the other group as evil. Religions tend to promote this adaptive way of thinking: *We are the people of God. They worship the Devil!* As a frontier and settler society at its inception, and one that was founded in many cases by intensely religious English people,[17] the American population has been subject to strong group-selection to be an intensely religious people. A central aspect of religion is "over-detecting agency"—perceiving agents behind the world itself. It should thus be little surprise that in our "secular age," America has become a land of believers in the supernatural, alien abductions, Satanic cabals, and bizarre creeds of all sorts. This has become particularly prominent from the 1960s onwards, as traditional religions have lost social power and prestige.[18]

Some Q followers have fully integrated his conspiracy theory into their religious practice; they, in fact, call themselves "Qvangelicals."[19] In this way, their daily news

17—See David Hackett Fischer, *Albion's Seed: Four British Folkways in America* (Oxford: Oxford University Press, 1989).

18—Peter Knight, *Conspiracy Culture: From Kennedy to The X Files* (London: Routledge, 2013); Michael Barkun, *A Culture of Conspiracy: Apocalyptic Visions in Contemporary America* (Los Angeles: University of California Press, 2003).

19—Justin Ling, "QAnon's Creator Made the Ultimate Conspiracy Theory," *Foreign Affairs* October 6, 2020, https://foreignpolicy.com/2020/10/06/qanon-creator-ultimate-conspiracy-theory-q/.

feed takes on religious significance. Q himself states: "We are living in Biblical times. Children of light vs. children of darkness. United against the Invisible Enemy of all humanity."[20] Trump, in his way, is imagined as a fallen Messiah. According to this strand of Q theology, the Satan-worshipping pedophiles don't just abuse children; they drink their blood in order to achieve immortality.

In many ways, Q followers might be compared to the Gnostics in the Early Church. This was a highly diverse movement, theologically speaking, united by core ideas. In particular, Gnostics believed that the universe was dualistic, reflecting an eternal battle between a higher god and the evil god of this world. This evil god was responsible for all of the world's woes (the world was, in effect, run by a giant conspiracy; an diabolical mega-being) and one could be "saved" by attaining direct knowledge of the higher god, knowledge which the evil god attempted to hide from you, via mystical practices.[21]

QAnon possesses not just a fledgling theology but an *eschatology* as well, a vision of the imminent End Times, both apocalyptic and triumphant. We are living through "The Awakening," the point when the good people in government have begun communicating with and enlightening the broader public. Trump's assumed re-election in November was said to herald "The Storm," in which The Cabal was to be overthrown and America, restored.

The 2020 presidential election was tempestuous, indeed: both sides claimed victory; the Republicans cried

20—Anonymous, BQ7V3bcW, 4chan.org/pol, https://qalerts. app/?q=Biblical+times.

21—Gerard van Grongingen, *First Century Gnosticism: Its Origin and Motifs* (Leiden: BRILL, 1967).

"voter fraud;" and the Democrats suspected a potential coup. Q himself went mostly silent. On November 13—more than a week after Joe Biden was deemed President Elect—Q announced: "Nothing can stop what is coming. Nothing!"[22] But Q did not give his millions of followers direct guidance on how to respond to Biden's election, but his influence on what would come about in early 2021 is unmistakable. Take, for instance, this missive:

> Nothing will stop us . . . they can try and try and try but the storm is here and it is descending upon DC in less than 24 hours . . . dark to light![23]

These words were not written by Q, though they could have been. They were posted on Twitter on January 5, 2021, by Ashli Babbitt (1985-2021), a 14-year Air Force veteran and one-time supporter of Barack Obama. The next day, she was shot dead by police as she, along with an angry mob of Trump supporters, invaded the Capitol building in Washington, DC.

Babbitt was, in many ways, typical of the type of person who came out in support of Donald Trump on the day that his rival was certified as president. Babbitt was, in the words of Robert Pape of the Chicago Project on Security and Threats, part of "a new kind of violent mass movement,

> in which more 'normal' Trump supporters—middle-class and, in many cases, middle-aged people without obvious ties to the far right—joined with extremists

22—Anonymous, BQ7V3bcW, 4chan.org/pol, https://qalerts.app/?n=4950.

23—See Ellen Barry, Nicholas Bogel-Burroughs, and Dave Philipps, "Woman Killed in Capitol Embraced Trump and QAnon, *New York Times*, January 7, 2021, https://www.nytimes.com/2021/01/08/us/who-was-ashli-babbitt.html.

in an attempt to overturn a presidential election.[24]

Babbitt's evocation of "the storm" and "dark to light" were the hallmarks of an avid reader of QAnon and the media that arose around him. The Charlottesville protest of 2017, over the removal of a statue of Confederate General E. Lee (1807-1870), was organized by the Alt-Right and White Nationalists. It could be described (perhaps unfairly) as a gathering of non-conformists. Four years later, "J6" attracted mainstream conservatives and thus demonstrated the depth of Q's reach, as well as his role in the radicalizing of a large portion of the general public. This process continues. According to Pape,

> [N]ine percent of Americans believe the 'Use of force is justified to restore Donald J. Trump to the presidency." More than a fourth of adults agree, in varying degrees, that, "The 2020 election was stolen, and Joe Biden is an illegitimate president." . . . 8.1 percent—that equates to 21 million American adults—share both these radical beliefs.[25]

There have been no Q drops since November 2021, and, not surprisingly, interest has declined since Biden took office. Nevertheless, liberals will be disappointed if they expect a quick end to the phenomenon. The Q movement has deeper causes than Trump's mercurial

---

24—Robert Pape and Keven Ruby, "The Capitol Rioters Aren't Like Other Extremists," *The Atlantic*, February 2, 2021, https://www. theatlantic.com/ideas/archive/2021/02/the-capitol-rioters-arent-like-other-extremists/617895/.

25—Robert Pape, "Why We Cannot Afford to Ignore the American Insurrectionist Movement," August 6, 2021, *Chicago Project on Security and Threats*, https://cpost.uchicago.edu/research/domestic_extremism/why_we_cannot_afford_to_ignore_the_american_insurrectionist_movement/.

political career, and right-wing movements like it are here to stay. Remove Trump from the political scene and watch his cult become more powerful than you could possibly imagine.

THE TIMES THEY ARE A CHANGIN'

As discussed in the previous chapter, religious revivals, historically, tend to take place during periods of dramatic change, especially during those that involve an elevated awareness of death: war, famine, plague, political instability, and the seeming end of the world.[26] This makes sense because experimental research has found that individuals become more religious—more prone to strongly believing in God—in precisely these dire contexts.[27]

In the wake of World War I and the Spanish Flu Pandemic, there were notable religious revivals in eastern England and in northeast Scotland.[28] After World War II and the end of post-War restrictions, there was a huge religious revival in the U.S. and in the UK led by pastor Billy Graham, based around emotional rallies each attended by many thousands.[29]

By 2020, Covid-19 burst on the scene and led to millions of deaths around the world, creating a period

26—See Steve Bruce, *God Is Dead: Secularization in the West* (Oxford: Blackwell, 2002).

27—Ara Norenzayan and Azim Shariff, "The Origin and Evolution of Religious Pro-sociality," *Science*, 322 (2008): 58-62.

28—Stanley C. Griffin, *A Forgotten Revival: East Anglia and Northeast Scotland, 1921* (Bromley: Day One Publications, 1992).

29—Callum Brown, *The Death of Christian Britain: Understanding Secularisation, 1800-2000* (London: Routledge, 2009).

of deep anxiety, in which it seemed very possible that the death toll could be enormous. In turn, the "lockdowns," which governments instituted as a means of containing the plague, marked unprecedented disruptions to normal life. We have also had the sudden and heightened trauma of the Black Lives Matter Movement, resurrected in a newer, more intense form after the death of George Floyd. As I have argued, BLM can be considered a religious revival of its own. Regardless, the protests eventuated in a collapse of public order in parts of the U.S. and UK: an orgy of inter-racial strife, violence, and self-righteous displays, which the political and legal Establishment was unable or unwilling to suppress. This was accompanied by the sapping of White morale through the removal of historical statues and other links with the "certainties" of the past.

With this background, we would expect there to be a religious revival in Western countries—and specifically one that might counter BLM. For various reasons, however, it could not be overtly religious, as was Billy Graham's movement, which developed in a context in which traditional Christianity was still dominant. Since then, we have witnessed the collapse of traditional society, a significant fall in the influence of Christianity, and deviations from traditional religious norms in many directions, with many people creating their own ersatz religions from various sources.[30] Put simply, we've lived through the fallout of the "death of God."

For at least the past 100 years, a *secularization thesis* has informed, sometimes unconsciously, the minds of

---

30—See Edward Bailey, *Implicit Religion: An Introduction* (Hendon: Middlesex University Press, 1998).

scholars, public intellectuals, and policy-makers. Briefly, people and institutions are becoming less religious; those religions that do persist are largely relegated to the private sphere: they are "tolerant" and more like lifestyles than ways of life. In reality, the situation is far more complicated. Society is increasingly divided between "individualists" and those who are high in "binding values" (putting the group ahead of the individual). "Individualist" ideas have gradually become dominant across time. And extreme individualists have ascended to the heights of the social ladder and pushed the broader society in their direction. While this has been happening, however, those who are highest in "binding" values—and especially those prone to intense religiosity-have been having the most children. The result is that America—and, in fact, nations around the world—are undergoing radical polarization.[31] Social trust has collapsed, as each side is increasingly alienated from the other, culturally and morally. Moreover, in "meritocratic" societies, education, IQ, and being "Politically Correct" are all inter-related, as we will see in more detail below. This has led to even greater social and economic distance between the two polarized groups.

It is against this background that QAnon's rise must be understood, as the religion provides a means of making sense of a world that its adherents increasingly don't understand. If Americans' moral foundations veer more towards those of a traditional kind, they will be profoundly concerned with a structured and ordered society, with rescuing and promoting their group, and with destroying

---

31—Eric Kaufmann, *Shall the Religious Inherit the Earth? Demography and Politics in the Twenty-First Century* (London: Profile Book, 2010).

that which fills them with disgust—sexual disgust, in particular. QAnon is attractive to such people because it provides order out of chaos; it offers a rescue plan for the group as a whole; and it is partly focused on destroying sexual deviants and those disloyal to the group—those that want to create chaos.

Needless to say, the Q cult has encourage unhealthy obsessions and antisocial behavior among its believers. On December 4, 2016, a North Carolina man, brandishing a rifle, entered the Comet Ping Pong pizzeria in Northern Virginia and threatened employees before being arrested. He claimed to be "investigating" the Pizzagate affair, discussed above.[32] The January 6th riot—perhaps the ultimate culmination of the Q movement—led to hundreds of arrests, a few deaths, and proved to be a shocking embarrassment for everyone involved. It might be only a matter of time before something similar, or worse, takes place involving a deranged or disappointed reader of Q drops.

That said, we would be remiss if we ignored the ways that the Q cult can be "adaptive," in an evolutionary sense, and brings along many of the benefits of older religions. First, Q offers the promise that, once the evil-doers are dispatched, America will experience a revival of traditional values, which used to be central to American life (including ethnocentrism and pro-natalism). Additionally, in that Q presents itself as a moral crusade, it can also inspire self-sacrificing, group-selected, and ultimately pro-social

---

32—Faiz Siddiqui and Susan Svrluga, "N.C. Man Told Police He Went to D.C. Pizzeria With Gun to Investigate Conspiracy Theory," *Washington Post*, December 5, 2016, https://www.washingtonpost.com/news/local/wp/2016/12/04/d-c-police-respond-to-report-of-a-man-with-a-gun-at-comet-ping-pong-restaurant/.

behavior. And it is the more tightly bonded groups that tend to triumph in the end.

THE EVOLUTION OF RELIGION
IN THE 21ST CENTURY

"Religion," in the widely accepted sense of the word, involves all of the key components of an evolutionary adaptation, as already noted. To be religious became associated with other adaptive traits, but it also elevated group-fitness by elevating being group-selected as "divinely ordained." By 1800, we would expect White Americans to be particularly religious, because the cultural core of the country was founded by Puritans, who would have passed on their intense religiosity as a genetic legacy. The heritability of extreme religiosity is around 0.7,[33] and White Americans were subject to intense group selection, especially in fighting Native Americans and due to the demands of establishing themselves in a hostile environment to which they were not adapted. Then again, evolution never stops. So we need to look closer at what happened to that original American stock.

Some 200 years ago, a basic level of religiosity had been established across European peoples. Indeed, it has been shown that Western Europeans became more religious, seemingly for genetic reasons, throughout the Middle Ages, often due to executing and ostracizing criminals, with criminal personality traits being negatively associated with religiosity.[34] In 1800, White America was a small gene pool

33—Matt Bradshaw and Christopher G. Ellison, "Do Genetic Factors Influence Religious Life? Findings from a Behavior Genetic Analysis of Twin Siblings," *Journal for the Scientific Study of Religion*, 47 (2008): 529-544.

34—Edward Dutton and Guy Madison, "Execution, Violent Punishment

in which people were all relatively genetically similar and strongly genetically fit, because those who deviated from the optimum—due to mutant genes—were purged from the population every generation. Being strongly genetically similar, the population would tend to trust each other, cooperate, and think in the same way. We bond with people who are more genetically similar to ourselves because this is a means of indirectly passing on more of our genes. This trend is found even when looking at relationships between siblings, whose genetic similarity level can be subtly different. This is why husbands and wives—and even best friends—are more genetically similar than could ever come about by chance.[35] With the Industrial Revolution, this homogeneity began to break down, because selection pressure was heavily weakened. The result is a many-fold, inter-related sequence of factors, which changed the nature, cohesiveness, and worldview of the population.

HIGH FERTILITY ON THE "FAR RIGHT"

The portion of the society that is utterly resistant to the new fitness-damaging system of individualist values will be predicted to have been growing due to the association between traditional religiosity and fertility. In this line, it has been found that, using Western samples, being "far Right" predicts having the highest fertility, while being "far left" predicts having the lowest.[36]

---

and Selection for Religiousness in Medieval England," *Evolutionary Psychological Science*, 4 (2018): 83-89.

35—J. Philippe Rushton, "Ethic Nationalism: Evolutionary Psychology and Genetic Similarity Theory," *Nations and Nationalism*, 11 (2005): 489-507.

36—Martin Fieder and Susanne Huber, "Political Attitude and Fertility: Is

Our relatively meritocratic and mobile society has created increasing cognitive stratification, whereby intelligent people, who happen to be born into working-class families, for example, are very easily able to leave this environment, become educated, and move to other areas dominated by educated and intelligent people.[37] This was not possible when society was less meritocratic, in part because it was less interested in values such as "fairness." The result is that people of different intelligence levels, and even of different social classes (socioeconomic status being robustly predicted by intelligence), increasingly inhabit different worlds.[38] And, due to the high genetic component of intelligence of around 0.8, as well as the high genetic component of the personality traits associated with high IQ,[39] they will be increasingly different from each other *genetically*, as well. So, we would expect those at the bottom of society to decreasingly trust and decreasingly admire the elite.

Furthermore, intelligence is associated with realizing what the dominant set of values is, and with forcing yourself to adopt them so that you can get on better in life. This is why professional people, currently, tend to

There a Selection for the Political Extreme?" *Frontiers in Psychology* (2018), https://doi.org/10.3389/fpsyg.2018.02343.

37—See Richard Herrnstein and Charles Murray. *The Bell Curve: Intelligence and Class Structure in American Life* (New York: Free Press, 1994).

38—See Arthur Jensen. *The g Factor: The Science of Mental Ability* (Westport: Praeger, 1998).

39—Richard Lynn. *Dysgenics: Genetic Deterioration in Modern Populations* (London: Ulster Institute for Social Research, 2011).

espouse leftist values.[40] Those of lower socioeconomic status will be less able to do this, so, in a society of cognitive stratification, they will be increasingly alienated from the elite.

DECLINING IQ AND SO DECLINING TRUST

One of the correlates of intelligence is trust. People with high IQ are more trusting, possibly because if you have a low IQ, you are more likely to be taken advantage of, meaning that it is adaptive to trust nobody. Another result of the Industrial Revolution has been declining intelligence. Various factors have contributed to this, but the most salient is contraception. While contraception devices of various kinds have been around since the Stone Age, by the mid-19th century, industrialized nations produced at mass scale reliable, inexpensive condoms made of vulcanized rubber. By the mid-20th century, "The Pill" offered women long-term control over fertility. The implications, many of them unintended, were tremendous.

Intelligence predicts the impulse control to use contraception and the cognitive ability to use it correctly. As a result, large families now happen mostly by accident and are associated with low intelligence, there being a correlation of about -0.2 between IQ and how many children you have. We know this is happening for genetic reasons because the population prevalence of alleles associated with high intelligence in a Western sample has decreased across three generations, and numerous other

---

40—Michael Woodley of Menie and Curtis Dunkel, "Beyond the Cultural Mediation Hypothesis: A Reply to Dutton (2013)," *Intelligence*, 49 (2015): 186-191.

correlates of intelligence all show the same pattern, as we will expand upon later.[41] This results in a society that is less trusting overall, and particularly less trusting of its elite. A lower average intelligence, all else being equal, would also predict a population becoming more conservative, more religious, and more dogmatic.

THE MUTATION OF RELIGION

The genetic diversity, and increased mutation, wrought by the Industrial Revolution means that we would expect the traditional "religious bundle" to break up in a growing number of people. Thus, you would have, in many supporters of Black Lives Matter, for example, high levels of dogmatism, intense hatred of the out-group, fervent belief in certain ideas, belief in the morality of the in-group, even collective worship of sorts, but no belief in gods in the traditional sense. This ideology is underpinned by individualistic foundations which, in some respects, it renders sacred: unquestionable dogmas, like "equality" and "social justice." You might get furiously denounced for suggesting "All Lives Matter;" it is "Black Lives" that are sanctified.

We might also expect a similar deviation among those who have "binding" values: they will semi-sanctify these values, meaning they will have some aspects of religiousness, but they might lack the belief in a moral god—or their belief in god will be so extreme as to be obsessive and damaging to their ability to get along with

41—See Edward Dutton and Michael Woodley of Menie, *At Our Wits' End: Why We're Becoming Less Intelligent and What It Means for the Future* (Exeter: Imprint Academic, 2018).

people. They may be high in "binding" values due to personality traits, and related disorders, or because these values are currently dissident and they are attracted to them due to a psychopathic attraction to danger or a low IQ inability to imbibe the dominant values set. We can see QAnon supporters who worship Donald Trump as a Messianic figure as a possible example. Such people would be expected to be high in evidence of mutation, and there is certainly evidence for this. We have seen in an earlier chapter the evidence of the correlation between conspiratorial belief and poor mental health. Consistent with this prediction, it has been found that people who are high in the personality trait Neuroticism (which is associated with depression and anxiety) are generally low in religious belief. However, they go through phases of extremely intense religious belief. Suffering from manic depression or bipolar disorder, and schizophrenia, as well, is also strongly associated with hyper-religiosity. In sum, mental illness is a marker of genetic mutation, and it seems to make one prone to believing in unlikely conspiracy theories.[42]

This makes sense because an aspect of schizophrenia is hyper-mentalizing, whereby schizophrenics are intensely interested in the feelings of others and external cues from them. Accordingly, they perceive evidence of a mind everywhere, including in the world itself, making them paranoid.[43] A study from Switzerland found that

---

42—Harold G. Koenig, "Religion, Spirituality, and Health: The Research and Clinical Implications," *ISRN Psychiatry* (2012), http://dx.doi.org/10.5402/2012/278730.

43—Christopher Badcock, "Mentalism and Mechanism: Twin Modes of Human Cognition," in *Evolutionary Psychology, Public Policy and Personal Decisions*, eds. Charles Crawford and Catherine Salman (Mahwah: Erlbaum, 2003).

one third of schizophrenics are very strongly involved with their local mainstream church and that a further 10 percent are involved in New Religious Movements: small sects that tend to be fervent and extreme.[44] All people sit on a schizotypy scale, with full schizophrenia at one extreme; the higher one is on this scale, the more attracted one is to conspiracy theories and unconventional and paranoid beliefs.[45] So, this implies that some people on the "Right" are also manifestations of high mutational load. The "Right," however, would be less influenced by mutational load than the Left, because the Right would be closer to the ideas that were prominent under harsh Darwinian conditions and, in line with this, being right wing lineally correlates with fertility and mental health, as noted earlier.

In this sense, it is crucial to distinguish between two kinds of right-wing people, both of whom have relatively high fertility. On the one hand, there are those who hold, for mainly genetic reasons, to the adaptive worldview that was prominent prior to the Industrial Revolution; the remnant "normal" population. These people will be strongly group-selected and will engage in the collective worship of a moral god, for example. On the other hand, there are those who are right-wing as a consequence of low IQ, assorted mental disorders or due to a combination

44—Philippe Huguelet, Sylvia Mohr, Laurence Borras, *et al.*, "Spirituality and Religious Practices Among Outpatients With Schizophrenia and Their Clinicians," *Psychiatric Services*, 57 (2006): 366–372.

45—David Barron, Adrian Furnham, Laura Weiss, *et al.*, "The Association Between Schizotypal Components and Conspiricist Beliefs Through Cognitive Mediators," *Schizophrenia Bulletin*, 44 (2018): 368-369; Jo Hodgekins, "Schizotypy and Psychopathology," in *Schizoptypy: New Dimensions*, eds. Oliver Mason and Gordan Claridge (London: Routledge, 2015).

of these. We would expect these people to pursue an idiosyncratic form of religiosity and we would expect them to be high in mutational load. Congruous with this it has been found that low IQ correlates with genes that predict poor physical health.[46] Whether these people are "Spiteful Mutants" is more moot than is the case with regard to the extreme Left. It could be argued that they are fighting the extreme Left and, thus, reducing their influence. But they also tend to bring about the collapse of whatever cause they are involved in due to their psychopathology and low IQ. In this sense, such people aid the atomization of society into warring groups and tend to ultimately bring about war and chaos, allowing their group to be displaced by a more group-selected group. So, in this far more nuanced sense, they are also Spiteful Mutants.

It might also be noted that extreme Left activists have been shown to score very high in Narcissism (entitlement and desire for adulation) and Machiavellianism (desire for power), which makes sense as, in the current climate, being left-wing is a means of achieving these aims. Those who are "White Identitarian" (Alt-Right or White Nationalist) score high in psychopathology (low empathy), which makes sense because, currently, they are profound non-conformists.[47] If combined with a period of high mental instability, then this could predict attraction to the far Right, at least when that is highly counter-cultural. These

---

46—Ian Deary, Sarah Harris, and W. David Hill, "What Genome-wide Association Studies Reveal About the Association Between Intelligence and Physical Health, Illness, and Mortality," *Current Opinion in Psychology*, 27 (2019): 6-12.

47—Jordan Moss and Peter O'Connor, "The Dark Triad Traits Predict Authoritarian Political Correctness and Alt-Right Attitudes," *Heliyon*, 6 (2020): e04453.

traits are expressions of developmental instability and thus, in some cases, mutational load.[48]

THE INTERNET ECHO CHAMBER

Finally, an important factor, which indirectly emanates from the Industrial Revolution, is the Technological Revolution and rise of the internet. We've all become aware of the power of social media to influence politics. "Hashtag activism" (derided as "Slacktivism") has brought about something new: previously, writing on the internet ("blogging") would come about in reaction to major events and the news of the day; by the 2010s, social media began to drive the news cycle, and even events. Donald Trump's 2015-16 campaign was largely one in which he spoke directly to supporters on Facebook and Twitter and didn't rely on endorsements or the patronage system. All of this has contributed to the process of polarization. There is increasingly no longer a "mainstream media;" instead, there are "media hives," where like-minded people connect with each other and establish communities; these start out online, but eventually spill over into real life. The Alt-Right phenomenon was an example of this, as was QAnon and January 6.

All of this must be taken together with people becoming genetically more individualist. An individualist society does not encourage humility; more people are above the bread line and thus able to be ambitious; more people are educated and thus feel entitled to power; and high levels of mental instability make people crave power

---

48—Martin Lalumiere, Grant Harris, and Marnie Rice, "Psychopathy and Developmental Instability," *Evolution and Human Behavior*, 22 (2001): 75-92.

as a means of controlling an environment they fear, especially in a context of decreasing social trust.

Taken together with the internet, such people can attain influence more easily, can find out more information and thus challenge those in power more easily, and they can create like-minded groups more easily. This will stabilize "power," reduce the power of formally powerful positions, and bring about more competing power-groups as is seen in a society like Somalia or even Medieval England. In such societies, there were numerous competing knightly warlords and retinues (in effect, protection rackets loyal to a warlord) vying for control and numerous loci of identity beyond merely "English." The result is polarization, constant competition, instability and political paralysis.[49] Thus, ironically, the fruits of high civilization—the internet especially—help to return us to a more primitive kind of society.

We have progressively moved from being a "mass society," in which public opinion is managed by an elite, to a "network society" of ever fragmenting, often hermetic groups, each with its own inner-directed propaganda.[50] This has permitted the proliferation of "non-mainstream" opinions, and the managing elite has, to a large extent, lost control of people's minds. This happened previously

---

49—See, Moisés Naím, *The End of Power: From Boardrooms to Battlefields and Churches to States, Why Being in Charge Isn't What It Used to Be* (New York: Basic Books, 2013); Edward Dutton, *The Ruler of Cheshire: Sir Piers Dutton, Tudor Gangland and the Violent Politics of the Palatine* (Northwich, Léonie Press, 2015); Ken Menkhaus, "The Crisis in Somalia: A Tragedy in Five Acts," *African Affairs*, 106 (2007): 357-390.

50—See Yochai Benkler, Robert Faris, and Hal Roberts, *Network Propaganda: Manipulations, Disinformation, and Radicalization in American Politics* (Oxford: Oxford University Press, 2018).

in history, with the birth of printing, but not to this pronounced degree. Elites have attempted to deal with this reality by increasingly censoring social-media platforms, but the train has left the station. The rise of the internet—and social-media echo chambers like Q—are simply amplifying a polarizing tendency that was already underway.

The year 2020 catalyzed two distinct religious revivals for our divided age: BLM and QAnon. They are godless faiths; however, they contain many of the core elements of the Christian revivals of yesteryear. Both are birthed from the evolutionary dynamics of post-Industrial society. And both, in their own ways, are hysterical, schizophrenic expressions of how religiosity manifests itself in our "secular age."

CODA: IS Q GETTING AT SOMETHING?

The mainstream media dismisses QAnon's beliefs as fraudulent—ridiculous at best, dangerous at worst. We should remember that a cult like Q is unlikely to be persuasive if it did not tap into some aspects of reality or contain a few kernels of truth. Indeed, it could be argued that it is just as dogmatic to dismiss the very possibility of conspiracy theories as it is to believe in them without scrutiny. A good liberal who dismisses conspiracy theories out of hand—because they undermine his feeling that the world is certain and safe—is just as dogmatic as a wingnut who fervently believes that Stanley Kubrick (1928-1999) faked the Moon landing, due to the fact that he is high in psychopathology and, perhaps, low in intelligence.

Take, for instance, the belief that causes the most controversy—that Satanic pedophiles are in positions of power around the world. If we break this down, it could be argued that, in the minds of evangelicals, what "Satan" essentially preaches is individualism: wealth, power, and pleasure in the here and now, rather than sacrificing power in this world for glory in the next.[51] There is a substantial body of evidence that people who tend to reach the very top of their professions, especially in business and politics, seem to combine outlier high intelligence with moderately psychopathic traits, such as moderately low altruism and moderately low impulse control. This means, for example, that not being bound by rules and conventions, they have the intelligence and personality traits to conceive of original ideas, and they don't care that their original ideas may offend vested interests.[52] In the world of business, such people will come up with brilliant ideas, as they will in the arts. In the world of politics, such men will be superb at presenting themselves and persuading and manipulating their peers.

In an increasingly individualistic society, in which religious condemnation of individualistic behavior such as adultery has collapsed, such people would be more easily able to attain positions of political leadership. Sexual promiscuity is one of a number of accepted markers of psychopathic personality, alongside grandiosity and superficial charm.[53] A few generations ago, revelations

---

51—See Jesper Peterson, "Carnal, Chthonic, and Complicated: The Matter of Modern Satanism," in *Controversial New Religions*, eds. James Lewis and Jesper Peterson (Oxford: Oxford University Press, 2014).

52—See Edward Dutton and Bruce G. Charlton, *The Genius Famine* (Buckingham: University of Buckingham Press, 2015).

53—See Edward Dutton and Richard Lynn, "Cheating in Sport and Race Differences in Psychopathic Personality," *Mankind Quarterly*, 55 (2015): 325-334.

that a politician had had an affair, let alone fathered an illegitimate child, would mean the end of his career. No longer. A key correlate of originality is testosterone, because it makes one driven, ambitious, competitive, low in impulse control, and low in altruism. It also gives you a high sex drive.[54] Indeed, an analysis of a sample of extremely eminent people found them to have been high both in sexual deviance and sexual promiscuity, as well as being high in sub-clinical psychopathology.

This analysis, by psychiatrist Felix Post (1913-2001), found that six percent of the male population in Western countries could be regarded as archetypal psychopaths. In a sample of "eminent men," whom Post biographically analyzed, none could be described as such. Post estimated that 10 percent of the male population were "subclinical psychopaths," meaning they possessed psychopathic tendencies sufficiently strong to adversely impact relationships or careers. This he estimated to be true of 14 percent of "eminent men," meaning subclinical psychopaths were overrepresented among the powerful and influential: 20 percent of eminent writers and 25 percent of artists. Among politicians, it was just 11 percent, only slightly above the general male population. However, using the less severe measure of having "potentially handicapping traits" of Antisocial Personality Disorder, Post found that this was true of 52 percent of politicians, 50 percent of artists, and 70 percent of writers. Post cautiously estimates that this level

54—Dimitri van der Linden, Edward Dutton, and Guy Madison, "National-Level Indicators of Androgens are Related to the global distribution of number of scientific publications and science Nobel prizes." *Journal of Creative Behavior,* 54 (2020): 134-149.

of psychopathology applies to 16 percent of the male population. Accordingly, it can be averred that moderate Antisocial Personality Disorder is elevated among the highly eminent.[55] So, we should not be surprised that, to a greater extent than was once the case, people who are high in individualism, intelligence, and psychopathic traits should rise to the top.

Such people's rise would be aided if they adopted the group-fitness damaging, Spiteful Mutant-inspired leftist ideas that are currently in vogue, so we would expect them to do that. With their high sex drives and low empathy, we might even expect them to engage in sexual abuse to an elevated degree, including abuse of children because they are such easy prey. Approximately half of those who sexually abuse children are not exclusively attracted to children. Pedophiles, so defined, have strongly elevated levels of poor mental health (something Post also found was high among the very eminent), including mood disorders (66 percent), Obsessive-Compulsive Disorder (25 percent), and personality disorders of various kinds (61 percent), such as Psychopathic Personality.[56] For this reason, evidence of the abuse, especially of young girls, by such males starts to make more sense. Pedophilia and psychopathic personality may be comorbid, because they are both manifestations of developmental instability, resulting from elevated mutational load.[57]

55—Felix Post, "Creativity and Psychopathology," *British Journal of Psychiatry*, 165 (1994): 22-34.

56—Gilian Tenbergen, Matthias Wittfoth, Helge Frieling, *et al.*, "The Neurobiology and Psychology of Pedophilia: Recent Advances and Challenges," *Frontiers in Human Neuroscience* (2015): 344.

57—*Ibid.*

In addition, only pedophiles who are high in psychopathic personality would be likely to act on their proclivities. Those who are high in psychopathic personality are, in evolutionary terms, adapted to a chaotic, unstable environment in which cooperating with people is futile, because such acts might never be reciprocated; you must, therefore, "live fast, die young" and opt to pass on your genes as quickly as possible. This militates in favor of having as much sex as you can with as many fertile (and thus young) females as possible. This is known as a fast Life History Strategy.[58] Having sex with underage, though fertile, girls—"ephebophilia"—would simply be an extreme manifestation of this sexual strategy. There is also evidence that, in such contexts of instability, males who engaged in rape were more likely to pass on their genes, and that gang rape was especially common in prehistory. As a consequence, males, even now, produce more semen during rape, as rape traditionally involved sperm competition. Men also become more aroused by, and produce more semen, when watching violent porn than "vanilla" porn. In other words, men have been selected to be aroused by violence, especially sexual violence.[59] Thus, for some men who abuse underage children, it may not be that they find them attractive; they are turned on by power and dominance. This would be more likely if they were fast Life History Strategists.

In the UK, public fascination with elite pedophilia was sparked in the wake of the death of the extremely popular

58—J. Philippe Rushton, *Race, Evolution, and Behavior: A Life History Perspective* (New Brunswick: Transaction Publishing, 1995).

59—Randy Thornhill and Craig Palmer, *A Natural History of Rape: Biological Bases of Sexual Coercion* (Cambridge: The MIT Press, 2001); Lee Ellis, *Theories of Rape: Inquiries Into the Causes of Sexual Aggression* (New York: Hemisphere Publishing, 1989).

and influential entertainer Sir Jimmy Savile (1926-2011). Evidencing his "Establishment" status, Savile had been given a knighthood in 1990. After Savile died, large numbers of allegations came to light that he had raped and otherwise sexually abused under-age girls throughout his long career and had even been subject to a police investigation about this shortly before his death.[60] A subsequent police inquiry into historic sexual abuse, "Operation Yewtree," as well as concomitant investigations and publicity, led to the downfall or reassessment of many other celebrities and politicians who had received assorted honors such as CBE (Commander of the Order of the British Empire), OBE (Officer of the Order of British Empire), and knighthoods. The investigation led to the jailing of a household name, entertainer Rolf Harris, CBE (b. 1930), for sexually abusing under-age girls; the imprisonment of TV personality Stuart Hall, OBE (b. 1929), on 13 counts of indecent assault against girls aged 9 to 17 between 1967 and 1986; and two posthumous allegations of underage rape, and one of rape of a 17-year-old woman, against deceased TV personality Sir Clement Freud (1924-2009), grandson of the psychiatrist.[61] We will return to the topic of pedophilia and abuse in Chapters 6 and 9.

So, looked at in this way, the idea that the world is run—or at least heavily influenced—by selfish, child-abusing Satanists becomes less than entirely ludicrous. As was noted when Jimmy Savile's proclivities came to light,

---

60—Dan Davies, *In Plain Sight: The Life and Lies of Jimmy Savile* (London: Quercus Books, 2014).

61—Martin Evans, "Clement Freud Accused of Raping Another Teenage Girl as Evidence Mounts That He Was a Predatory Paedophile," *Daily Telegraph* (15th June 2016), https://www.telegraph.co.uk/news/2016/06/15/clement-freud-accused-of-raping-another-teenage-girl-as-evidence/

there must have been so many high-status people who, at best, turned a blind eye to what they knew he was doing and, at worst, enabled him. We can see how people might suspect the same to be true of Jeffrey Epstein, Harvey Weinstein, Michael Jackson (1958-2009), and many others. In general, we exaggerate the extent to which members of an out-group are morally deficient, and we can see how this would become particularly pronounced at a time of extreme polarization and existential stress.[62]

That said, even though the idea that such people can be found among the elite is not entirely ludicrous, it remains a simple fact that, overall, the key predictor of socioeconomic status, when controlling for intelligence, is the "General Factor of Personality," which we explored earlier. This means that, on average, the more elite somebody is, the more mentally stable, the more empathetic, and the more altruistic they are likely to be. It is those who believe in conspiracy theories who tend to be of low socioeconomic status and this is because low intelligence and low GFP (the traits that lead to low socioeconomic status) predict paranoia, black-and-white and dogmatic thinking, and being low in trust.[63]

So, after exploring the rise of spiteful new religions in the postmodern age, we will turn our lens to the fascinating subject of homosexuality, dysphoria, and sexual perversion.

62—Jesse Graham, Jonathan Haidt, and Brian Nosek, "The Moral Stereotypes of Liberals and Conservatives: Exaggeration of Differences across the Political Spectrum," *PLOS One* (2012), https://doi.org/10.1371/journal.pone.0050092.

63—J.W. van Proojen, "Why Education Predicts Decreased Belief in Conspiracy Theories," *Applied Cognitive Psychology,* 31 (2017): 50-58.

CHAPTER 6

THE EVOLUTION OF A TABOO

Homosexuality and Civilization

In 1999, during the summer holiday between finishing school and starting university, I was given a job working in the Islington (north London) offices of the Royal Bank of Scotland. This was set up for me by an acquaintance from the local Conservative Association where I had been Ward Chairman and Secretary of the Young Conservatives. This acquaintance was one of the bank's directors. The building was not yet "online" and the department in which I worked had to process the many documents sent to and from the bank's office every day. As you can imagine, it was exciting stuff.

The utter tedium of the job was rendered bearable by the fact that I wasn't always stuck behind a desk. I would go to the collection point a number of times each day to retrieve the documents that had been received. Two middle-aged Black people worked in this office, and they were always friendly and fun to chat with. One day—I cannot remember why—they were discussing the, at that time, controversial subject of homosexuality. It appalled both of them, especially the woman, who was a churchgoer. I'd never heard either of them swear until this issue came up. The woman spoke forthrightly about "fucking disgusting homos" and "fucking disgusting lezzies." I could see in her face that she was sickened by the very thought of it all. It created a confusion and dysphoria for her. She might even have feared that gay culture, which was increasingly prominent throughout the '90s, would, in effect, "turn people gay."

Her visceral response was also partly due to the fact that she was religious. The Bible is quite clear on this matter: homosexuality, male homosexuality at least, is condemned.

> If a man has sexual relations with a man as one does with a woman, both of them have done what is detestable. They are to be put to death; their blood will be on their own heads.
> **—Leviticus 20: 13**

While we live in an increasingly post-Christian world, ancient commandments like this still carry weight. As already discussed, religious taboos help control behavior; they often promote health, and they ultimately tend to be for the evolutionary benefit of the group, regardless of whether we believe in their divine origins or not. Religion, too, is naturally selected, and it could not persist if it were, on the whole, detrimental to a species' survival. Religions take behaviors that are bad in terms of genetic fitness, for either the individual or the group, and make them taboo. To take one example, religious food taboos tend to involve the forbidding of substances that are likely to be unhealthy, such as pork or shell fish, which corrupt quickly in a warm ecology.[1] Homosexuality obviously discourages reproduction and

---

1—Victor Meyer-Rochow, "Food Taboos: Their Origins and Purposes," *Journal of Ethnobiology and Ethnomedicine*, 5 (2009): 18.

is, at the very least, looked down upon by almost every religious tradition.

But with my colleague at the bank, there was more to it. She expressed a visceral and immediate disgust, even horror, at the thought of homosexuality, which even the most kosher rabbi would not manifest if served a plate of raw oysters. Such strong feelings—which are close to being universal across cultures and classes—must be evolved to a significant degree. This *disgust instinct* has accompanied homosexuality throughout history. While homosexuality can, of course, be depicted as erotic or a "forbidden temptation," it is most often treated as expressing a flawed or deranged character, or as involving the malign seduction of innocents. This can even be seen in the colloquialism "gay"—common up until very recently, when it was declared politically incorrect—which refers to something that is, variously, revolting, weak, lame, effeminate, underhanded, or pathetic—put simply, evolutionarily unfit.

There seems to be a "hardwired" association between disgust and male homosexuality. Researchers have examined the emotions of subjects when images of homosexuals were presented to them accompanied by the release of unpleasant smells:

> An induction of disgust can lead to more negative attitudes toward an entire social group: Participants who were exposed to a noxious ambient odor reported less warmth toward gay men. This effect of disgust was equally strong for political liberals and conservatives, and was specific to attitudes toward gay men—there was only a weak effect of disgust on

people's warmth toward lesbians, and no consistent effect on attitudes toward African Americans, the elderly, or a range of political issues."[2]

So, noxious smells cause people to become more negative about homosexuals. Those who are already negative about them become more so, while those who are positive about them become less so. If you feel disgusted already, then male homosexuals become disgusting to you, implying that disgust makes us more morally judgemental and that we are somehow evolved to find male homosexuality immoral

This reaction, as well as the historical taboos on homosexuality, may, in part, be an issue of disease avoidance. Assuming that homosexual males engage in anal intercourse, which not all of them do, then they are exposed to blood-to-blood contact. For this reason, there are elevated levels of Hepatitis C among homosexual and bisexual men.[3] In this sense, the Biblical prohibition on this practice is similar to the Biblical prohibition on pork, which was imposed, it seems, to avoid parasites.[4] It is making unhealthy practices abhorrent to God, such that God's followers are at an evolutionary advantage. It would follow that generalized disgust towards a practicing homosexual would be fitness elevating. That said, as we shall see, it could be fitness-promoting, at the group level,

---

2—Yoel Inbar, David Pizarro, and Paul Bloom, "Disgusting Smells Cause Decreased Liking of Gay Men," *Emotion*, 12 (2012): 23–27.

3—Fengyi Jin, Gail Matthews, and Andrew Grulich, "Sexual Transmission of Hepatitis C Virus Among Gay and Bisexual Men: A Systematic Review," *Sexual Health,* 14 (2017): 28-41.

4—Victor Meyer-Rochow, "Food Taboos: Their Origins and Purposes, *Journal of Ethnobiology and Ethnomedicine*, 5 (2009): 18.

for homosexuality to stay in populations, as long as it is concomitantly suppressed.

And there can also be little doubt that many homosexuals *are* evolutionarily unfit, even putting aside the basic issue of reproduction. Homosexuals' levels of mental illnesses such as depression are six times that of heterosexuals of the same gender; they commit suicide at eight times the rate of their heterosexual counterparts; and they are far more likely to engage in vices such as illegal drug use and risky sex, something especially true of bisexuals.[5] Today, these unfortunate facts are claimed to be the product of bigotry and bullying, but there seems to be something peculiarly problematic about homosexuals.

Yet it persists. Homosexuality is rare but present throughout human history. How can this be? If the engine of evolution is reproduction, then one might ask how homosexuality was ever selected for at all. We could take this further and speculate on whether the broad acceptance of homosexuality—social pressures in favor of heterosexuality being lessened or reversed—would not lead to a die-off of those who inherited the homosexual predilection? If homosexual men are not just tolerated but publicly celebrated, then fewer and fewer of them would marry people of the opposite sex out of a feeling of duty or social conformism; they would thus not pass on the genes that made them prone to homosexuality. And as we will see, the homosexual phenomenon has multiple layers and potential causes, and it might be selected for *and* against at both the individual and group level.

5—Lisa R. Norman, "Bisexuality," in *Mental Health Practitioners' Guide to HIV/AIDS*, ed. Sana Loue (New York: Springer, 2012), 104.

BORN THAT WAY?

Before we begin, a distinction should be made between homosexual "behavior" and "identity." Homosexual acts can occur in different contexts, many of them when men or women become homosexual on a temporary basis: there are bacchanal atmospheres where "anything goes," and also times when homosexuality serves as a sex substitute when members of the other gender are nowhere to be found, such as on long ship voyages or in prisons.[6] As we will see below, homosexual behavior can feature in ritualized expressions of power and humiliation, as well as in tribal acts and rites of passage. For our purposes, "identity," denotes people who are attracted to people of their same gender in all contexts and express no interest in members of the opposite gender as sexual partners. They understand themselves as homosexual.

Over the past quarter of a century, the gay-rights movement has increasingly stressed identity over behavior. Homosexuals are "born that way," to quote Lady Gaga, and have not "chosen" homosexuality as a lifestyle or passing fad.[7] The concept of "coming out" implies that one is discovering one's true inner nature, not simply taking up a fad or conforming to peer pressure. A British survey in 2016 found that 93.4 percent of the population identified as heterosexual, 1.2 percent as "gay or lesbian," 0.8 percent as "bisexual," and 0.5 percent as "other;" 4.1 percent refused to answer.[8] Different

---

6—Jeffrey Ross and Stephen Richards, *Surviving Prison: Behind Bars* (New York: Penguin, 2002), 86.

7—Lady Gaga, "Born This Way," *Born This Way*, Interscope Record, 2011.

8—*Office of National Statistics*, "Sexual Identity, UK: 2016," https://www.

surveys yield different results, but these findings seem broadly accurate for countries throughout the Western world. Research has shown that homosexuality is, indeed, significantly heritable; it is, at least in part, an inalterable component of who a person is. Male sexuality is heritable in the region of 0.4, while female sexuality is only 0.2 heritable, meaning that female sexuality is far more environmentally plastic.[9]

ARE LESBIANS GAY?

Most people assume that "gays" and "lesbians" are manifestations of the same thing in the two genders, but there is reason to believe that they are distinct phenomena. In the British survey, among men, 1.7 percent identified as gay, whereas only 0.7 percent of women identified as lesbians.[10] This lower percentage likely reflects the more mutable nature of female sexuality in general. The cliché that women "experiment" with lesbianism in college is a cliché for a reason—and notably not a cliché for men. Put simply, women are more likely to have fleeting dalliances with same-sex relationships than males, who will tend to either be "straight" or "gay." In turn, sapphic desire is generally viewed as less toxic or shocking, and more erotic

ons.gov.uk/peoplepopulationandcommunity/culturalidentity/sexuality/bulletins/sexualidentityuk/2016.

9—Niklas Långström, Qazi Rahman, Eva Carlström, *et al.*, "Genetic and Environmental Effects on Same-sex Sexual Behavior: A Population Study of Twins in Sweden," *Archives of Sexual Behavior*, 39 (2010): 75–80; Austin Jeffrey, Todd Shackelford, Virgil Zeigler-Hill, *et al.*, "The Evolution of Human Female Sexual Orientation," *Evolutionary Psychological Science*, 5 (2019): 71-86.

10—Office of National Statistics, "Sexual Orientation, UK," *op cit.*

for both sexes, than male homosexuality. Lesbianism is commonplace in pornography, including that consumed by women. Women French kissing one another has, for a few decades, been featured in music videos and advertising, and often women will engage in public displays of affection with one another "just for fun." Nothing like this features prominently among male behavior.[11]

A literature review has argued that the most parsimonious explanation for greater sexual plasticity in females is polygamy, which was the human norm in prehistory.[12] In this context, wives who were less favored by the husband would have engaged in collaborative "alloparenting" of each other's offspring, something rendered more stable if they could become sexually attracted to each other and thus strongly bonded. This is important because it has been shown that if a child has two parents, then that child is, in effect, more likely to survive childhood and more likely to experience positive life outcomes, including sound mental health.[13] This arrangement would also mean that these co-wives would feel less jealousy towards the more favored wives, helping facilitate a more harmonious arrangement. Women are "hypergamous" and seek to "marry up," as discussed earlier. In line with this model, in female jails, about 60 percent of inmates report being "lesbians,"

11—See Steve Sailer, "Why Lesbians Aren't Gay," *National Review*, May 30, 1994, https://www.unz.com/isteve/why-lesbians-arent-gay/.

12—Austin John Jeffery, Todd Shackelford, Virgil Zeigler-Hill, *et al.*, "The Evolution of Human Female Sexual Orientation," *Evolutionary Psychological Science*, 5 (2019), 71–86.

13—Anthony Volk and Jeremy Atkinson, "Is Child Death the Crucible of Human Evolution?" *Journal of Social, Evolutionary, and Cultural Psychology*, 2 (2008): 103-116.

which few were when they commenced their sentence. In essence, the shortage of high-status males leads to female homosexuality.[14]

A parallel evolutionary theory of lesbianism is that female sexual fluidity has evolved because males are sexually aroused by females, all else being equal, who have a tendency towards bisexuality or towards temporary lesbianism. This would possibly be because if a sexually unsatisfied female had the capacity to become homosexual, this would decrease the probability that this female would cuckold the male.[15] This would also make sense of evidence that men enjoy watching pornography involving feminine lesbians; the kind that are more likely to be bisexual and temporarily so.[16] In terms of understanding exclusive lesbians, known as "butches," the evolutionary explanations seem to cross-over with those advanced for male homosexuality, which we will examine below.

14—If this theory is correct, in that "races" are breeding populations evolved to different ecologies, we might expect there to be race differences in the prevalence of homosexuality. A large scale British survey in 2009 found that non-Whites are less likely to identify as homosexual than Whites, but they are also more likely to refuse to reveal their sexuality. As far as I am aware, there is no study on this matter that controls for the many confounding variables that may be relevant to this difference, such as intelligence or developmental stability. See Edward Dutton, *Making Sense of Race* (Whitefish: Washington Summit Publishing, 2020).

15—Jeffrey, Shakelford, Zeigler-Hill, *et al.*, "The Evolution of Human Female Sexual Orientation," *op cit.*

16—Olga Khazan, "Why Straight Men Gaze at Gay Women," *The Atlantic*, March 8, 2008, https://www.theatlantic.com/health/archive/2016/03/straight-men-and-lesbian-porn/472521/.

DEVELOPMENTAL INSTABILITY

Even though there is evidence for an evolutionary advantage to lesbian inclinations, there is also evidence that female homosexuality is, in many cases, a result of "developmental instability," either due to high levels of mutation ("mutational load"), a sub-optimal environment, or a combination of both factors. Homosexuality correlates with many other markers of developmental instability, such as left-handedness. Humans are generally right-handed and if their brains have developed symmetrically, that is what they will tend to be. Accordingly, left-handedness betokens an asymmetrical brain and, thus, developmental instability, and it correlates with many neurological and auto-immune problems, including asthma and allergies.[17] One study found that 10 percent of females are left-handed, compared to 18 percent of lesbians.[18] Among males, 8 percent of heterosexual men are left-handed, compared to 12 percent of gay men.[19] The difference may be larger among lesbians because they reflect *both* developmental instability and masculinization, and the latter is independently associated with left-handedness.[20] Gay males reflect developmental instability,

17—Ray Blanchard, "Review and Theory of Handedness, Birth Order, and Homosexuality in Men," *Laterality*, 13 (2008): 51-70.

18—Brian Mustanski, J. Michael Bailey, and Sarah Kaspar, "Dermatoglyphics, Handedness, Sex, and Sexual Orientation," *Archives of Sexual Behavior*, 31 (2002): 113–122.

19—Ray Blanchard, "Handedness, Birth Order and Sexual Orientation," *BBC Science*, October 1, 2014, http://www.bbc.co.uk/science/humanbody/sex/articles/results/handedness.shtml.

20—Edward Dutton, Guy Madison, and Dimitri Van der Linden, "Why Do High IQ Societies Differ in Intellectual Achievement? The Role of Schizophrenia and Left-handedness in Per Capita Scientific Publications and

heightening their left-handedness, but their feminization will concomitantly militate against left-handedness.

To give an example of how developmental instability can cause lesbianism, if a mother suffers from congenital adrenal hyperplasia, then this will have the effect of masculinizing her offspring, including females, *in utero*. The result is that females will tend to become highly masculine lesbians—"butches."[21] Mutations tend to be comorbid, so we would expect a mother who suffered from adrenal hyperplasia to suffer from other heritable conditions, which would be reflected in the offspring. Congruous with this expectation, lesbians are far more likely to suffer from depression and contemplate suicide than are heterosexual females.[22] They are also considerably more likely than heterosexual females to smoke, develop alcohol disorders, use illegal drugs, and be obese,[23] with addiction and poor impulse control both being highly heritable.[24] Lesbians are also at elevated risk of breast cancer, but not other cancers, other than cervical cancer, which is generally elevated in childless females.[25] The fact that lesbians are at elevated risk of one particular cancer would be consistent with the hypothesis that

Nobel Prizes," *Journal of Creative Behavior*, (2019).

21—S. Marc Breedlove, "Prenatal Influences on Human Sexual Orientation: Expectations Versus Data," *Archives of Sexual Behavior*, 46 (2017): 1583-1592.

22—Audrey Koh and Leslie Ross, "Mental Health Issues: A Comparison of Lesbian, Bisexual and Heterosexual Women," *Journal of Homosexuality*, 51 (2006): 1.

23—Institute of Medicine, *Lesbian Health: Current Assessment and Directions for the Future* (Washington, DC: National Academies Press, 1999), Chapter 2.

24—Daniel Nettle, *Personality: What Makes You Who You Are* (Oxford: Oxford University Press, 2007).

25—Institute of Medicine, *Lesbian Health, op cit.*

part of the explanation for lesbianism is developmental instability caused by elevated mutational load. It would be probable that this would be more pronounced among "butches," as they are more likely to have had mothers with adrenal hyperplasia.

Another manifestation of developmental instability is autism, a condition marked, in part, by being low in empathy and "theory of mind"—which means one's ability to attribute mental states, like emotions, beliefs, and intentions, in oneself and others. Put simply, autistic people find social situations painfully difficult.[26] Those with autism display reduced levels of heterosexuality and elevated rates of homosexuality, bisexuality, and asexuality.[27] This may be because autism and homosexuality partly reflect the same underlying factor of developmental instability.

It is also possible that, for some homosexuals, their homosexuality is, in effect, a fetish or paraphilia—a form of sexual desire linked, to an abnormal extent, to an object, part of the body, and so on.[28] The development of paraphilia is associated with autism as discussed above,[29] and a formal literature review has found that "homosexuality has a pattern of correlates largely, but not entirely, distinct from those identified among paraphilia. At least, if homosexuality were deemed a paraphilia, it

---

26—Matthew Sarraf, Michael A. Woodley of Menie, and Colin Feltham, *Modernity and Cultural Decline* (Basingstoke: Palgrave Macmillan), 257.

27—Rita George and Mark Stokes, "Sexual Orientation in Autism Spectrum Disorder," *Autism Research*, 11 (2018): 133-141.

28—Martin Kafka, "The DSM Diagnostic Criteria For Fetishism," *Archives of Sexual Behavior*, 39 (2010): 357–362.

29—Matthew Sarraf, Michael A. Woodley of Menie, and Colin Feltham, *Modernity and Cultural Decline, op cit.*

would be relatively unique among them, taxonometrically speaking."[30] It can be cautiously inferred from this that, for some homosexuals, their sexuality may be best understood as a fetish or obsession.

CHILDHOOD DEVELOPMENT AND ABUSE

British evolutionary psychiatrist Bruce Charlton has argued that the optimum development of sexuality involves an extremely complicated sequence—and there is a lot of room for things to go wrong every step of the way. Firstly, there is genetics. Parents with mutant genes are more likely to produce sexually deviant offspring, as noted above. Then there are hormone-induced changes, both *in utero* and in adolescence. There are also critical learning periods, particularly in childhood, in which there is important imprinting and other psychological development. These phases must all be successfully negotiated for sexuality to be adaptive.[31] In this regard, there is evidence that non-heterosexuals are more likely to have experienced sexual abuse as children. Among women, 38.1 percent of lesbians, 43.5 percent of bisexuals, and 14.2 percent of heterosexuals suffered abuse. Among men, 18.6 percent of gays, 19 percent of bisexuals, and only 4.6 percent of heterosexuals, experienced such trauma.[32]

30—James Cantor, "Is Homosexuality a Paraphilia? The Evidence For and Against," *Archives of Sexual Behavior*, 41 (2012): 237-247.

31—Bruce Charlton, "Mutation Accumulation and Modern Western Sexuality," July 20, 2015, *Intelligence, Personality and Genius*, https://iqpersonalitygenius.blogspot.com/2015/07/mutation-accumulation-and-modern.html.

32—Lisa Norman, "Bisexuality," in *Mental Health Practitioner's Guide to*

It can be argued that being non-heterosexual renders sexual predation more likely. It is unclear why sexual abuse is higher among *bisexuals*. This may be because bisexuals have a weak sense of self or identity, meaning that they are not sure about who they are, leading to intense anxiety. Consistent with this, among bisexual females—though not lesbians—involvement in a homosexual community is positively associated with depression and suicidal ideation, implying that their sexuality is a manifestation of an underlying confusion.[33] Further congruous with this, it has been found that Borderline Personality Disorder, which we explored above, is correlated with homosexuality, bisexuality, and frequently changing the sex of one's partner (though not one's sexual identification). Thus, it is associated more with bisexual than with homosexual behavior.[34] Childhood sexual and emotional abuse are key risk factors in the development of Borderline Personality Disorder.[35]

But whatever the reason for higher mental instability among bisexuals, it would seem more probable that sexual abuse of some kind is *causative*. There may also be a symbiotic relationship whereby children who may have homosexual tendencies are more likely to be predated,

HIV/AIDS, edited by Sana Loue (New York: Springer), 104.

33—Ignacio Lozano-Verduzco, Cinthia Cruz del Castillo, and Nélida Padilla-Gámez, "Is Mental Health Related to Expressions of Homonegative Stigma and Community Connectedness in Mexican Lesbian and Bisexual Women?" *Revista Latinoamericana de Psicología*, 51 (2019): 1.

34—D. Bradford Reich and Mary Zanarini, "Sexual Orientation and Relationship Choice in Borderline Personality Disorder over Ten Years of Prospective Follow-up," *Journal of Personality Disorders*, 22 (2008): 564-572.

35—Lucas Ferreira, Fábio Pereira, Ana Benevides, *et al.*, "Borderline Personality Disorder and Sexual Abuse: A Systematic Review," *Psychiatry Research*, 262 (2018): 70-77.

so eliciting these tendencies further. There is a very weak association between having a difficult relationship with the same-sex parent and later homosexuality. But this, again, may be symbiotic in nature. It should be emphasized that the studies that reach these conclusions often involve weak correlations, small samples, and other such deficiencies.[36]

HOMOSEXUALITY AND PEDOPHILIA

There is a clear cross-over between pedophilia and homosexuality. Homosexuality is much more prevalent among men convicted of sex offenses against children than it is among men who are not. The ratio of heterosexuals to homosexuals in the general male population is somewhere between 20:1 and 50:1, depending on the study. Among male sex offenders who have abused children (aged 6 to 11), the ratio is 11:1 and some studies have found it to be as high as 2:1.[37] Indeed an estimated 25-40 percent of pedophiles have a homosexual preference.[38] Put simply, pedophiles have a significantly elevated sexual interest in males.

In itself, this could be explicable in terms of general high mutational load, to the extent that this also causes homosexuality, and we would expect sexual disorders to be

36—J. Michael Bailey, Paul Vasey, Lisa Diamond, *et al.*, "Sexual Orientation, Controversy, and Science," *Psychological Science in the Public Interest*, 17 (2016): 45-101.

37—Kurt Freud and Robin Watson, "The Proportions of Heterosexual and Homosexual Pedophiles Among Sex Offenders Against Children: An Exploratory Study," *Journal of Sex and Marital Therapy*, 18 (1992): 34-43.

38—Ray Blanchard, Howard Barbaree, Anthony Bogaert, *et al.*, "Fraternal Birth Order and Sexual Orientation in Pedophiles," *Archives of Sexual Behavior*, 29 (2000): 463-478.

comorbid. In this regard, pedophilia can be one expression of a general neuro-developmental disorder, and it has a significant genetic component.[39] Homosexual pedophilia is highly distinct from heterosexual pedophilia. Homosexual pedophiles prefer significantly older children, often those that are already pubescent, and the abusers themselves are also more feminine than heterosexual abusers.[40] Taken together, this might imply that homosexual pedophilia should be distinguished from the paraphilia of being attracted to children. Homosexual pedophilia may simply be a form of homosexuality in which youth is found especially attractive, just as heterosexual males tend to sexually select for younger females, including, in extreme cases, those who are only just pubescent. In much the same way, we should distinguish between heterosexual pedophiles who are exclusively attracted to children and heterosexual males with an extreme penchant for female youth. And these should all be distinguished from sexually frustrated opportunists who abuse children because they are easy prey, as well as those who become abusers because their sex-drive is out of control.[41]

Indeed, in some cases, a period of homosexuality may simply be a result of having a high libido and only

39—Gillian Tenbergen, Matthias Wittfoth, Helge Frieling, *et al.*, "The Neurobiology and Psychology of Pedophilia: Recent Advances and Challenges," *Frontiers in Human Neuroscience*, 9 (2015): 344; Collen Berryessa, "Potential Implications of Research on Genetic or Heritable Contributions to Pedophilia for the Objectives of Criminal Law," *Recent Advances in DNA & Gene Sequences*, 8 (2014): 65-77.

40—Vernon Quinsey, "The Etiology of Anomalous Sexual Preferences in Men," *Annals of the New York Academy of Sciences*, 989 (2003): 105-117.

41—See Michael Davis, "Differentiating Child Sexual Abusers," *InPsych*, 35 (2013): 5.

having access to males, in which case the most female-like males would be attractive, which might explain the persistence of pederasty in societies where females are veiled and controlled, as we will explore below. But this all potentially implies that homosexuality—including a propensity to pederasty—may have evolutionary foundations to some extent.

GAY UNCLES

Why and how have gays remained a small but persistent component of populations through the process of evolution by natural selection?[42] Some of the more plausible explanations can be classed under "gay uncle theory." The basic postulate is that a small percentage of homosexual males in the population is actually beneficial in terms of "kin selection." One study found that females with homosexual brothers tend to have higher fertility than those with only heterosexual brothers.[43] The

---

42—American evolutionary psychologist David Barash has proposed that, in pre-history, bisexual males would be so unthreatening that they would be able to copulate with females, without arousing the ire of dominant males, and so pass on their genes. This theory is most improbable. Females strongly sexually select for dominant, high-status males and would thus be most unwilling to copulate with a low-status, effeminate male with homosexual tendencies. Even if this intercourse occurred through gang rape—which is extremely unlikely because if that is what happened, there would still be effete rape gangs in primitive social organizations—Barash's theory does not explain how exclusively *homosexual* preference could have evolved among males either. See David Barash, *Out of Eden: The Surprising Consequences of Polygamy* (Oxford: Oxford University Press, 2016).

43—Andrea Camperio-Ciani, Francesca Corna, and Claudio Capiluppi, "Evidence for Maternally Inherited Factors Favoring Male Homosexuality and Promoting Female Fecundity," *Proceedings in Biological Science*, 271 (2004): 2217–2221.

researchers conclude that material on the X chromosome promotes both fertility and homosexuality. Specifically, females have a strong desire to marry hypergamously—to sexually select for a high-status male, as we have already discussed. This leads to women becoming hyper-female to attract high-status males. The brothers of these hyper-female women might be feminized as well, causing them to be homosexual "gay uncles." In line with this model, male homosexuality is more common as society becomes society stratified. This makes sense because the larger the wealth differences, the more pressure there would be for low-status females to signal their femininity in order to attract the highest-status males.[44]

An extension of this theory is that homosexuality stays in the population due to kin selection. In general, homosexual males don't have offspring themselves and therefore invest resources in their nephews and nieces, meaning that these children are more likely to survive. Some researchers have criticized this hypothesis, however. Two studies have found that homosexuals do not, in fact, provide more care for their kin than heterosexuals do. If anything, they provide less.[45] American psychologists Kayla Causey and Aaron Goetz make the important point that if the "gay uncle theory" were accurate, we would expect

---

44—Julien Barthes, Pierre-Andre Crochet, and Michel Raymond, "Male Homosexual Preference: Where, When, Why?" *PLoS ONE*, 10 (2015): e0134817.

45—Research summarized in Kayla Causey and Aaron Goetz, "The 'Johnny Depp Effect'—An Evolutionary Explanation for Homosexuality," June 10, 2009, *Psychology Today*, https://www.psychologytoday.com/blog/natural-history-the-modern-mind/200906/the-johnny-depp-effect-evolutionary-explanation.

these uncles to be asexual and single.[46] Indeed, having a sexual relationship at all, let alone investing in a sexual partner, would do nothing more than take resources away from their nephews and nieces. Of course, it may be that "gay uncles" who do have sexual relationships are simply sub-optimally group-selected. But this criticism raises the possibility that there may be a better explanation.

TOPS AND BOTTOMS

It's been observed that homosexual couples often appear like refashioned heterosexual couples. That is, in a same-sex pairing, one partner will take on the masculine role, and "wear the pants" in the relationship, while the other acts more feminine. We can see this in stereotypes like "femme" lesbians attracted to "butches," as well as, in the male context, "tops" and "bottoms."

There might, in fact, be two kinds of homosexual: those who are group-selected and those who betoken a breakdown in selection. As already discussed, it has been shown that homosexuality is associated with markers of "developmental instability," such as left-handedness[47] and neurological disorders,[48] and levels of depression and suicide are strongly elevated among homosexual males. They are, in fact, three times higher than among the general adult

---

46—*Ibid.*

47—Michael Woodley of Menie, Heitor Fernandes, Satoshi Kanazawa, *et al.*, "Sinistrality is Associated With (Slightly) Lower General Intelligence: A Data Synthesis and Consideration of Secular Trend Data in Handedness," *HOMO: Journal of Comparative Human Biology*, 69 (2018): 118-126.

48—Ray Blanchard, "Review and Theory of Handedness, Birth Order, and Homosexuality in Men," *Laterality*, 13 (2008): 51-70.

population.[49] It may, therefore, be that some homosexuals exemplify group selection, but they decreasingly do so as Darwinian selection has relaxed since the Industrial Revolution. And Darwinian selection certainly has relaxed. As previously explained, in 1800, the child mortality rate was 50 percent; it is now 1 percent in Western countries, as already noted.[50] Before the Industrial Revolution, those who had mutations (which are almost always detrimental to health) were purged from the population every generation. These mutations of the body, which led to a poor immune system and dying from childhood diseases, were comorbid with mutations of the mind, such as inclinations towards maladaptive sexuality.[51]

This historical change would have several related effects, especially if we refer back to our discussion of Bruce Charlton's model of development. Firstly, there would be more people with fitness-damaging mutations of the mind, such as deviant sexuality. Secondly, these people would be more likely to be maladaptively influenced by hormones *in utero*. Thirdly, society would be influenced, in a maladaptive way, by these maladapted people—these Spiteful Mutants—who would interfere with the development of the sexuality even of some non-mutants. Indeed, some of these Spiteful Mutants might

---

49—Carrie Lee, John Oliffe, Mary Kelly, *et al.*, "Depression and Suicidality in Gay Men: Implications for Health Care Providers," *American Journal of Men's Health*, 11 (2017): 910-919.

50—Volk and Atkinson, "Is Child Death the Crucible of Human Evolution?" *op cit.*

51—Michael Woodley of Menie, Matthew Sarraf, Robert Pestow, *et al.*, "Social Epistasis Amplifies the Fitness Costs of Deleterious Mutations, Engendering Rapid Fitness Decline Among Modernized Populations," *Evolutionary Psychological Science*, 3 (2017): 181-191.

actively encourage easily influenced young people to experiment with homosexuality, to believe homosexuality was "normal," or believe that it was a social good to be homosexual. For these related reasons, we would expect the prevalence of homosexuality to increase.

In addition, there would be two kinds of homosexual male. The stable kind, that there had always been, and the "mutant" kind, who may be becoming more prevalent. In line with this, as we will explore in more detail below, younger brothers are more likely to be homosexual, due to the pregnant mother's immune response to proteins emitted by the male fetus. This results, in effect, in feminizing the fetus—and the mother's response strengthens with each male fetus. Accordingly, if the mother had an overactive immune system, due to mutation, then she would be more likely to produce a homosexual son, even as her first son.[52]

There are also studies indicating a clear distinction between homosexual males who prefer the dominant ("top") or submissive ("bottom") role during anal sex, despite the fact there are many "versatiles," who enjoy both roles. "Bottoms" are more likely to recall having been feminine boys. "Bottoms" are also much more likely to become infected with HIV, due to the bodily fluid of another person entering their anus. They seem to be stereotyped as more feminine in their psychology, and, along with straight females, suffer from higher rates of Neuroticism (feeling negative feelings strongly) and thus depression.[53]

52—Anthony Bogaert, Malvina Skorska, Chao Wang, *et al.*, "Male Homosexuality and Maternal Immune Responsivity to the Y-linked Protein NLGN4Y," *PNAS*, 115 (2018): 303-306

53—J. Michael Bailey, *The Man Who Would Be Queen: The Science of Gender-*

Research from China has substantiated this. "Tops" are psychologically more masculine, behave in more masculine ways, and are higher in "instrumentality," meaning that they are competitive and act decisively.[54] Congruous with "bottoms" being a manifestation of developmental instability to a greater extent, it has been found that they are more left-handed than are "tops."[55] Even among homosexuals, there is prejudice against males who identify as "bottoms." They are regarded as effeminate to an unacceptable degree.[56] According to a gay school friend of mine, who lives in New York, they are known as "hungry pig bottoms."

THE JOHNNY DEPP EFFECT

Males who are slightly feminine can be quite attractive to females. Kayla Causey and Aaron Goetz have espoused a hypothesis for the persistence of homosexuality derived from this, which they call the "Johnny Depp Effect," named after the famously moody, coy, and androgynous actor. Causey and Goetz's thesis is based on the work of

---

Bending and Transsexualism (Washington, DC: Joseph Henry Press, 2003), Chapter 4.

54—Lijun Zheung, Trevor Hart, and Jong Zheng, "The Relationship Between Intercourse Preference Positions and Personality Traits Among Gay Men in China," *Archives of Sexual Behavior*, 41 (2011): 683-689.

55—Ashlyn Swift-Gallant, Lindsay Coome, Ashley Monks, *et al.*, "Handedness is a Biomarker of Variation in Anal Sex Role Behavior and Recalled Childhood Gender Nonconformity Among Gay Men," PLoS ONE (2017), https://doi.org/10.1371/journal.pone.0170241.

56—Thomas Brooks, Stephen Raysen, and Jennifer Shaw, "Smashing back Doors in: Negative Attitudes Toward Bottoms Within the Gay Community," *World Journal of Social Research,* 4 (2017): 129-139.

American economist Edward Miller.[57] Miller argues that male reproductive success can be enhanced by alleles that would lead to typically feminine traits, such as kindness, empathy, and tenderness—in other words, Altruism. An optimum level of these characteristics in males would be attractive to females, meaning they would be selected for. Indeed, we could argue that they would be particularly strongly selected for in an ecology that was more group-selected, in which creating strongly cooperative groups was more important, due to the environment being harsher, an association which has been demonstrated.[58] This is because the females would be more prone to seek signs of a desire to nurture. However, if too many of these feminizing alleles were selected, there would come a "tipping point" where even mate preferences became feminized, leading to males being sexually attracted to other males.

Miller's hypothesis has been successfully tested. Causey and Goetz summarize that Australian psychologist Brendan Zietsch and colleagues found that psychological femininity in men was associated with high numbers of sexual partners.[59] They also note research from Finland that found that heterosexual men with a homosexual twin had more opposite-sex partners and more children than did heterosexual twin pairs, something consistent with Miller's model. In other words, homosexuality occurs due

57—Edward Miller, "Homosexuality, birth order, and evolution: Toward an equilibrium reproductive economics of homosexuality," *Archives of Sexual Behavior*, 29 (2000): 1-34.

58—See J. Philippe Rushton, *Race, Evolution, and Behavior: A Life History Perspective* (New Brunswick: Transaction Publishers, 1995).

59—Brendan Zietsch, Katherine Morley, Sri Shekar, *et al.*, "Genetic Factors Predisposing to Homosexuality May Increase Mating Success in Heterosexuals," *Evolution and Human Behavior*, 29 (2008): 424-433.

to having, in evolutionary terms, "too much of a good thing": alleles that females find particularly attractive. It is unclear how this explanation works in terms of homosexual females, though female sexuality has been found to be much more strongly an environmental issue than is male sexuality, as already noted.[60] It may be that it operates in the same way. Some typically male qualities, such as high levels of spatial intelligence or systematizing ability,[61] may be regarded as attractive, because they may increase survival chances. Males, however, may be less attracted to male qualities in females than is the case *vice-versa*, leading to the lower genetic component of homosexuality in females. Indeed, this is consistent with evidence that males are, in general, less interested in psychological qualities when selecting a mate than are females. They are, as we have seen—and as common sense would tell us—more interested in physical qualities: looks, youth, and signs of fertility.

Miller's model could potentially help to explain the abhorrence for male homosexuality that is seen in Leviticus. In terms of group selection, a group would need to maintain a relatively high level of internal altruism combined with a strong level of external aggression. As already discussed, it has been shown in computer models that, all else being equal, the group that is the most positively ethnocentric (acting cooperatively within the group) and negatively ethnocentric (fighting off outsiders, often with lethal force) eventually comes to dominate groups that are less

---

60—Långström, Rahman, Carlström, *et al.*, "Genetic and Environmental Effects on Same-sex Sexual Behavior," *op cit.*

61—Simon Baron-Cohen, "The Extreme Male Brain Theory of Autism," *Trends in Cognitive Sciences*, 6 (2002): 248-254.

positively and negatively ethnocentric.[62] Accordingly, it would require an optimum level of feminine traits in its male members, in order to be the highly ethnocentric society that would win the battle of group selection. Men who were too feminine, such that they were prepared to practice homosexuality, would thus represent a danger to the group. If they were bisexual, they would likely pass on their highly feminine nature, pushing the group to decrease external aggression. But, in addition, their very presence in the group could help push the group in this direction, by persuading people to be less harsh to the group's perceived enemies. We might also expect homosexuals themselves to be less harsh to the group's enemies, thus reducing the level of negative ethnocentrism.

Consistent with this, American psychologist Gordon Gallup has found that the degree of abhorrence of homosexuals varies according to what they are permitted to do. People feel more comfortable, he notes, with the idea of a homosexual male school teacher than they do about the idea of a homosexual male airline pilot. This, he argues, is because people implicitly regard the homosexual as a feminized male, who would thus be competent at teaching children but incompetent at piloting an airplane, where spatial intelligence and other masculine traits are crucial.[63] And there is evidence that people are correct in their intuitions. Homosexual men really do have significantly worse spatial intelligence than

62—Ross Hammond and Robert Axelrod, "The Evolution of Ethnocentric Behavior," *Journal of Conflict Resolution,* 50 (2006): 1-11.

63—Gordon Gallup, "Attitudes Toward Homosexuals and Evolutionary Theory: The Role of Evidence," *Ethology and Sociobiology,* 17 (1996): 281-284.

do heterosexual men.[64] This being the case, with reference to Leviticus, it would aid the success of the Hebrews to remove from their ranks men who were overly feminine.

Homosexuality is also associated with urbanization and wealth. As groups developed, and founded cities, we would expect that standards of living would increase. Assuming a long period of peace, Darwinian selection—and group selection in particular—would become less intense, at least among the wealthier groups within the society. Wealthier groups would also be less stressed, suffering fewer dangers and experiencing lower child mortality, and thus less instinctive in their behavior. This being the case, we might expect to find increased levels of homosexuality and a greater inclination to accept or at least tolerate homosexual behavior, due to the association between homosexuality and markers of mutational load.

This is precisely what we find in the city-states of Ancient Greece, as well as among the Romans, who reached a similar level of development.[65] It is in cities, such as Sodom and Gomorrah, where the Hebrews found noticeable levels of homosexuality—which their god condemned in the strongest way possible.[66] Indeed, most religions condemn homosexuality. As religiousness is partly a product of group-selection, when this pressure weakens (due to high civilization), societies becomes more tolerant

64—Qazi Rahman, Jonathan Sharp, Meadhbh McVeigh, *et al.*, "Sexual Orientation-Related Differences in Virtual Spatial Navigation and Spatial Search Strategies," *Archives of Sexual Behavior,* 46 (2017): 1279-1294.

65—Thomas Hubbard (Ed), *Homosexuality in Greece and Rome: A Source Book of Basic Documents* (Los Angeles: University of California Press, 2003).

66—See Louis Crompton, *Homosexuality and Civilization* (Cambridge: Harvard University Press, 2003), 36.

of homosexuality and less sexually restrictive in general. To the extent that sexual restrictions elevate ethnocentrism, this, too, declines. (In the concluding sections, we return to issue of why restricting homosexual practice—while keeping homosexual inclination in the population to a small degree—might benefit group selection.)

GAY SHAMANS

There are, however, alternative models that might equally well explain the presence of homosexuality and attitudes towards it. It may be that homosexuality is, indeed, group selected to some extent. Over the past 25 years, the Catholic Church, particularly in America, has been shocked and scandalized by revelations of homosexual pedophilia committed by its priests against young boys. Indeed, homosexuality and other sexually deviant behavior is quite prevalent among religious "celibates," Catholic priests being a prime example.[67] There seems to be a broad tradition of this behavior among priestly types. An effete persona, even transvestitism, is quite common among tribal shamans and Buddhist monks.[68]

In general, homosexual men are more religious than heterosexual men, despite the many prohibitions against homosexuality found in religious texts (or perhaps *because*

67—Ross Benes, "How the Catholic Priesthood Became an Unlikely Haven for Gay Men," *Slate*, April 20, 2017, http://www.slate.com/blogs/outward/2017/04/20/how_the_catholic_priesthood_became_a_haven_for_many_gay_men.html.

68—See Melford Spiro, *Burmese Supernaturalism* (London: Routledge, 2017); Peter Vitesbsky, *Shamanism* (Norman: University of Oklahoma Press, 2001); and John Grim, *The Shaman: Patterns of Healing Among the Obibway Indians* (Norman: University of Oklahoma Press, 1987).

of them).[69] Homosexual men also have twice the rate of schizophrenia and depression than do heterosexual men.[70] Both schizophrenia and bipolar disorder are associated with an elevated propensity towards religious experiences and religiousness in general.[71] Accordingly, it may be that homosexuality renders one more prone to religious experiences and thus more able to be a convincing religious devotee.

Religious devotion might seem quite personal, but it operates on the group level of evolutionary selection. Devotees inspire the group to believe that it is divinely chosen. In this line, it is certainly noteworthy that celibate, world-renouncing religious devotees are a dimension to all major religions, and the development of these celibate castes is ancient in origin. In Christian Europe, there were Roman Catholic priests, as well as monks and nuns, both those cloistered in monasteries and those active in the community. In the 20th century, Spanish priest St. Josemaria Escriva (1902-1973) founded Opus Dei. The group's so-called "numerary members" live ascetic, celibate lives in special Opus Dei houses but pursue secular professions.[72] There are monks and nuns

69—Darren Sherkat, "Sexuality and Religious Commitment in the United States: An Empirical Examination," *Journal for the Scientific Study of Religion*, 41 (2002): 313–323.

70—Shay-Lee Bolton and Jitender Sareen, "Sexual Orientation and Its Relation to Mental Disorders and Suicide Attempts: Findings from a Nationally Representative Sample," *Canadian Journal of Psychiatry*, 56 (2011): 35-43.

71—Harold Koenig, "Religion, Spirituality, and Health: The Research and Clinical Implications," *ISRN Psychiatry* (2012), http://dx.doi.org/10.5402/2012/278730.

72—See Michael Walsh, *Opus Dei: An Investigation into the Powerful, Secretive Society within the Catholic Church* (New York: HarperCollins, 2004).

in Buddhism, *Sadhus* in Hinduism, and *Fakirs* in certain forms of Islam.[73]

These celibates, in the case of cloistered orders, dedicate their lives to praying for the community and adhering to what are perceived as important rituals. Others, more active in the community, perform various charitable works, such as helping to run hospitals. In the case of the *Sadhus*, they publicly perform amazing feats of physical endurance as evidence of their devotion.[74] In the context of a religious community that genuinely believes in the power of prayer, it can be argued to be good for the morale of the community that a caste of people within the society spends its time dedicated to this discipline. And it's not hard to believe that this caste wouldn't have the time and motivation to be so disciplined if it were not celibate.

As we have already seen, there are different ways of passing on your genes. You can do so directly, by having your own children, but you can also do so indirectly. One of the ways you can do this is by investing in your kin, who share a portion of your genes. But you can also do this by investing in the broader ethnic group to which you belong. In much the same way, a religious celibate, whose activities help to reassure and inspire his society to maintain its religiosity—with all the evolutionary benefits that come with that—can be understood to be effectively promoting his genetic interests. As such, it would be to the benefit of a society that it included a small but optimum minority of people who were extremely religious, to the

73—See Paul Hyland, *Indian Balm: Travels Amongst Fakirs and Fire Warriors* (London: Tauris Parke, 2006).

74—See Dolf Hartsuiker, *Sadhus: The Holy Men of India* (New York: Simon and Schuster, 2014).

extent of not wishing to have children. This is good for group selection as, in a religious context, it inspires deeper faith in the group's spiritual cause. Additionally, as there is evidence that homosexuality is associated with elevated intelligence, as mentioned above, there might be an important connection between the priestly class and the fostering of "genius."[75] But it is worth mentioning at this stage that this association may imply that homosexuality remains in the population because it produces a caste of highly intelligent people, whose innovations strongly help their group interests.

It is noteworthy that there is little evidence in shamanistic societies that shamans actually have homosexual relationships with each other. Indeed, the evidence is that they do not, though they are often feminized males. It could be argued that homosexuality, by virtue of promoting religiosity and possibly genius, stays in the population. This only happens, however, because homophobia is likewise selected for. Homosexuality and homophobia, selected together, ensure that homosexuals promote religiosity and group interests but do not invest their energy into homosexual relationships or promote it to the society at large, which would be of little benefit to their group. Instead, they invest their energies in the raising of group morale through inspiring religiousness. I have termed this the "Gay Shaman Theory."[76] At the present stage, this is a speculative theory, but it would

75—Satoshi Kanazawa, *The Intelligence Paradox: Why the Intelligent Choice Isn't Always the Smart One* (Hoboken: John Wiley & Sons, 2012).

76—Edward Dutton, "Why are Non-Heterosexual Males Attracted to Religious Celibacy? A Case for the 'Gay Shaman' Theory," *Mankind Quarterly,* 59 (2018): 197-215.

appear to make sense of the conflicting evidence regarding the evolution of homosexuality. Consistent with it, there is experimental evidence that when people are induced to feel what they perceive as unacceptable and forbidden sexual desires, while also being primed with words relating to damnation and forced to suppress their anger, they become more creative, in effect *sublimating* repressed sexual energy into artistic and other forms of creativity.[77] So there would be an evolutionary benefit to retaining a homosexual caste who were forced, for religious reasons, to repress their "sinful" desires.

A further nuance in understanding the degree to which homosexuality is group selected may be that there are psychological differences behind the kind of homosexual role preferred. If Miller's theory is correct, then it can be argued that those male homosexuals who adopt the submissive role during sex ("bottoms") are more feminized than those who adopt the dominant role ("tops"). There is evidence that the association between homosexuality and mental disorders is much stronger among "bottoms," as already noted. Indeed, homophobia is generally directed towards highly effete homosexuals, those who would be considered obviously gay. This is clearly true in terms of abuse within the Catholic Church. The Catholic priests who engage in abuse almost always take the dominant role. Accordingly, homophobia may also be a means of removing particularly feminized men, who would not be useful in terms of group selection. This process would, however, be less likely to be injurious to

---

77—Emily Kim, Veronika Zeppenfeld, and Dov Cohen, "Sublimation, Culture and Creativity," *Journal of Personality and Social Psychology*, 105 (2013): 639-666.

those who were homosexual in a non-obvious way; those who would be more likely to have the optimum level of personality characteristics, reflecting their homosexuality, which would produce a constant religious devotion.

GAY YOUNGER BROTHERS

Fascinatingly, there exists some cultural variation in attitudes towards particular sexual activities, which may reflect differences in evolutionary strategy. It is generally agreed by Biblical scholars that, in Genesis 38, Onan was killed by God as a punishment for withdrawing during sex and spilling his semen on the ground.[78] This must be taken in the context of the Old Testament, which unquestionably demands that believers have as many children as they can, so long as they raise them properly as devotees of Yahweh and have them in the context of marriage: "Be fruitful and multiply" (Genesis 1: 28).

That said, especially in a polygamous society, there will always be inter-male conflict over the small number of available females. This makes the group less internally cooperative and, thus, less ethnocentric and less group selected. Perhaps homosexuality helps resolve this problem. If so, we can consider the hypothesis that it was selected in polygamous societies to reduce inter-male conflict. In line with this theory, the likelihood of having a homosexual son increases the more sons a woman has already had. This appears to be because the mother's immune system treats male hormones emanating from the fetus as an enemy agent and overwhelms them with female hormones. The more

78—See Peter Allen, *The Wages of Sin: Sex and Disease, Past and Present* (Chicago: University of Chicago Press, 2002).

this happens, the more powerfully her immune system will overwhelm the male fetus, leading to homosexuality.[79] This theory likely makes a contribution, but it does not explain the genetics of homosexuality, especially when the homosexual is not a younger brother.

Like homosexuality, homosexual pedophilia correlates with the number of older brothers (though not older sisters) that a male has.[80] There is no correlation, however, between heterosexual pedophilia and number of older brothers.[81] Regardless, there are reasons to believe that evolution has selected for, on the level of the group, a small, optimal caste of homosexuals.

COMING OF AGE

Disgust towards homosexuality seems to be "hardwired" into almost every human and human society. That said, there are circumstances in which homosexual behavior is tolerated or, in rare but noteworthy cases, integrated into religious ceremonies and rites of passage.

Among the Sambia of Papua New Guinea, for example, boys are initiated into manhood between the ages of 7 and 10. Over this period, they must fellate adult males every day and swallow their semen. The Sambia

---

79—Ray Blanchard, "Review and Theory of Handedness, Birth Order, and Homosexuality in Men," *Laterality*, 13 (2008): 51-70.

80—Martin Lalumière, Grant Harris, Vernon Quinsey, *et al.*, "Sexual Deviance and Number of Older Brothers Among Sexual Offenders" *Sexual Abuse*, 10 (1998): 5-15.

81—Anthony Bogaert, Scott Bezeau, Michael Kuban, *et al.*, "Pedophilia, Sexual Orientation, and Birth Order," *Journal of Abnormal Psychology*, 106 (1997): 331-335.

believe that only through this act can these children obtain semen of their own and thus become men. One possible benefit of such a practice is that it creates bonds between the men and the children who are involved, making it more likely that one will come to another's aid at some later point. In other words, as shocking and distasteful as the tradition may seem to us, it developed because, in effect, it fostered a more ethnocentric society. It might also be argued, and this is likely to be true of any rite of passage, that shared trauma helps make society more cohesive by creating stronger internal bonds, much like the brotherhood found among soldiers and veterans.[82] It should be stressed that, for the Sambia, such behavior is normative and is not regarded as "deviant" in the way that homosexuality is.[83]

The Sambia's activities are effectively a form of pederasty, defined as a sexual relationship between an adolescent boy and an older male. Today in the West, there are few crimes considered more heinous than child abuse, but the fact remains that the practice was common in many pre-modern societies: in Ancient Greece, among tribes in Melanesia, New Guinea, Northeast Asia, and among many Muslim communities in Central Asia during the 19th century, especially in the areas under Russian rule.[84] There is

82—See James Matthews, *Reluctant Warriors: Republican Popular Army and Nationalist Army Conscripts in the Spanish Civil War, 1936-1939* (Oxford: Oxford University Press, 2012).

83— Alan Soble, *Sexual Investigations* (New York: New York University Press, 1997), 124.

84—William Percy, *Pederasty and Pedagogy in Archaic Greece* (Champaign: University of Illinois Press, 1997), 117; Louis Crompton, *Homosexuality and Civilization* (Cambridge: Harvard University Press, 2003); and Adeeb

some evidence that pederasty was taboo among most Celtic, Germanic, and Scandinavian tribes, in which a male proved his manhood through successful hunting and was shunned as effeminate if he hadn't successfully made a kill by a set age.[85] Contra to this, however, there is anthropological evidence from ancient writers that it was practiced among the Germanics, and there was no law against it.[86]

Pederasty was common in pre-Islamic Asia and is widespread in many Islamic countries even to this day, particularly in Afghanistan.[87] In these cultures, age-equal homosexuality—or homosexuality as we know it in the West—is shunned, but pederasty is tolerated. Many males are sodomized as children, and they do the same to others when they become adults. Islam may also play a role, as females are heavily secluded. Indeed, it has been argued that part of the reason for the widespread practice of pederasty in Ancient Greece was the seclusion of females.[88] This theory is consistent with the widely documented phenomenon of males becoming temporarily homosexual if they are isolated from females for long enough periods of time, such as in prison. This presumably occurs because

Khalid, *The Politics of Muslim Cultural Reform: Jadadism in Central Asia* (Los Angeles: University of California Press, 1999), 145.

85—Percy, *Pederasty and Pedagogy in Archaic Greece, op cit.*, 117.

86—David Clark, *Between Medieval Men: Male Friendship and Desire in Early Medieval English Literature* (Oxford: Oxford University Press, 2009), 40.

87—William Kilpatrick, *Christianity, Islam, and Atheism: The Struggle for the Soul of the West* (San Francisco, CA: Ignatius Press, 2015).

88—Stephen Murray, "Some Nineteenth Century Reports of Islamic Homosexualities," in *Islamic Homosexualities: Culture, History, and Literature*, edited by Will Roscoe and Stephen Murray (New York: New York University Press, 1997).

certain kinds of male (those who are not yet masculinized or who are the least masculine) are the closest thing to females that is available or, indeed, visible. In this sense, we can understand why male sexuality would be approximately 60 percent a matter of environmental causes—and why context plays a significant role.

Taking a step back, we can see that there is some benefit to feminized males remaining in the gene pool. They would be more likely to pursue a group-selected role, such as the priesthood, and this might help to explain, in part, the genetic dimension to variance in male sexual orientation. In a context in which there simply are not sufficient numbers of accessible females, the ability to turn to pederasty would reduce inter-male conflict by permitting low-status males a feeling of power. Such men would be unlikely to access females anyway, and they might be of little use to the group other than as cannon fodder. In many Islamic societies, levels of trust and impulse control are relatively low.[89] As such, the seclusion of females is necessary in order to reassure husbands that their children are genuinely their own. This, in turn, helps to foster a more group-selected society that is more positively ethnocentric. But the result of this seclusion of females is the development of (at least temporary) pederasty among unmarried young men. Banning this could potentially lead to such frustration among these young or low-status males that the social order could find itself challenged. As levels of trust increase, the need to seclude women would decrease,

89—See Yael Sela, Todd Shackelford, and James Liddle, "When Religion Makes It Worse: Religiously Motivated Violence as a Sexual Selection Weapon," in *The Attraction of Religion: A New Evolutionary Psychology of Religion*, edited by D. Jason Sloane and James Van Slyke (London: Bloomsbury, 2015).

and pederasty would be less likely to develop; however, as we will see shortly, there is evidence that contradicts this mainly environmental thesis.

DEVIANCY IN THE BRITISH ARISTOCRACY

Winston Churchill caustically observed that the unspoken traditions of the British navy were "Rum, Sodomy, and the Lash." British journalist Christopher Hitchens (1949-2011) added that the three great subjects of English boarding school were "Beating, Bullying, and Buggery."[90] Quips aside, there is a degree to which pederasty, especially in an effectively symbolic form, was tolerated by the British upper class up through the 19th and 20th centuries.

Boys at "prep schools" (for pre-teens) and "public schools" (for teenagers) would be caned or birched on their bare buttocks, often to the point of bleeding. Within certain boundaries, this ritual was entirely accepted. The homo-erotic dimension to this is clear, and it may be that such a punishment evolved because it sends a message of dominance to the person being punished by making him utterly vulnerable and assume the sexual position of the female, a point that has been made by the British zoologist Desmond Morris. Among chimpanzees serious fights are often avoided by the subordinate male presenting his posterior so that the dominant can briefly penetrate him.[91] This symbolic interplay diffuses the conflict, avoids serious harm, and allows those involved to "move on."

90—Christopher Hitchens, *Hitch-22: A Memoir* (New York: 2010).

91—Desmond Morris, *The Human Zoo* (New York: Book Company, 1969).

Some headmasters, however, were considered either overly severe or unreasonable in their beatings, such as Winston Churchill's prep school headmaster, a Latin expert, the Rev. Herbert William Sneyd-Kynnersley (1848-1886). And some actually did sodomize their pupils. For this there were consequences: known homosexual masters were forced to resign to avoid prosecution.[92] One of Sneyd-Kynnersley's favorite pupils, Anglo-German writer Count Harry Kessler (1868-1937), who had far fonder memories of Sneyd-Kynnersley than the badly behaved Churchill, recalled that the headmaster was "driven by empathy for the souls of individual boys which, in his case, as with many great educators since Plato, may well have been homo-erotic in origin."[93] Another, rather unreliable, ex-pupil reported that Sneyd-Kynnersley did actually have homosexual relationships with some of his favorites,[94] and he certainly loved socializing with and entertaining his pupils, often at great effort and expense on his part.[95]

The key point is that there was effectively a system of something like pederasty among the 19th- and 20th-century English upper class. This is consistent with attitudes to homosexuality having slackened as that society became less harsh, especially so for the upper class. Furthermore, Victorian England's Puritanical attitudes towards sexual

---

92—Edward Dutton, *Churchill's Headmaster: The 'Sadist' Who Nearly Saved the British Empire* (Melbourne: Manticore Press, 2019).

93—Laird Easton, *The Red Count: The Life and Times of Harry Kessler* (Los Angeles: University of California Press, 2002), 25.

94—Dutton, *Churchill's Headmaster, op cit.*

95—Virginia Woolf, *Roger Fry: A Biography* (New York: Harcourt, Brace & Co., 1940), 31.

relationships and the exposure of the body meant that females were, in effect, "veiled," which would potentially elevate pederasty, at least among the higher orders, who would likely follow these restrictions more vigorously.

EVOLUTIONARY BENEFITS OF PROHIBITION

In terms of group evolution, the Jewish and Jewish-inspired religions are notable for their absolute prohibition on homosexual relations, including pederasty. This innovation was rare in its time, and there may be some respect to which it proved evolutionarily advantageous. Pederasty was widely practiced during the age of the Early Church among the Jews, despite the clear prohibitions in the Old Testament. St. Paul, however, argued strongly that all pederasts deserved to die:

> Men committed shameful acts with other men,
> and received in themselves the due penalty for their
> error. . . . Although they know God's righteous
> decree that those who do such things deserve
> death, they not only continue to do these very
> things but also approve of those who practice them
> **—Romans I, 27-32**

Philo (c. 25 BC-50 AD), a Hellenistic Jewish philosopher, in his writings on Jewish scriptures, makes a point of stressing that Leviticus condemns both the passive *and* active partner in a homosexual relationship to death. Philo does this because many of his readers would have assumed that the passive partner must be executed but *not* the active partner, because he has not shown himself to be unmanly.[96] It must be emphasized that his audience was Hellenized Jews. These generally city-dwelling Jews were much more liberal than the more traditional rural Jews, who had not embraced Greek *mores* to the same extent.[97]

The inclination to entirely outlaw homosexuality (including pederasty) could have some evolutionary benefits. One possibility is the heightening of investment in the family and in simply having more children. In a context in which homosexual activity is permitted, then men, including married men, are investing energy in and bonding with young males who are not members of their family. It could be argued, as we already noted, that this helps to create strong bonds within society. However, active pederasts may also be investing resources in these young males, subtracting from the resources that they could be investing in their family. Accordingly, from the perspective of kin selection, a societal abhorrence to all forms of homosexuality would effectively compel men to invest in their families or the group. As we've seen, in a polygamous society, this could potentially result in a rebellion at the hands of low-status males with no sexual outlet. However, if they could be persuaded that even God condemned all forms of homosexuality, and enough people were homophobic, then this could perhaps be obviated, and they could be forced into some useful celibate role, such as that of a holy man.

In a situation of strong group selection, all else being equal, the society that was most homophobic

96—Bernadette Brooten, *Love Between Women: Early Christian Responses to Female Homoeroticism* (Chicago: University of Chicago Press, 2009), 257.

97—Celia Brewer Marshall, *A Guide Through the Old Testament* (Louisville: John Knox Press, 1989), 149-150.

would be more likely to triumph—and this repulsion would usefully become higher the more intense were the levels of selection under which the group labored.[98] In a monogamous society, such revulsion would be presumably heightened because there would be very little reason to be homosexual, there being sufficient females for most men. Thus, the males who were homosexual in such a context would likely be so for primarily genetic reasons, meaning they would more adaptively be pushed into a group-selected role. As we have seen, male sexuality is around 60 percent a matter of environmental factors. There may be a degree to which exposure to homosexuality, or rather to its social acceptability, can make a person more likely to be homosexual, as there would be less pressure to try to suppress these feelings, a point that has been made with regard to the acceptability of homosexuality in Ancient Greece.[99] Any group that came to abhor homosexuality would make it less likely that their sons became homosexual, in turn, making it less likely that their investment in their sons would be wasted, by virtue of their sons not passing on their genes. Accordingly, those who held homophobic attitudes would end up with more descendants and their group would be more likely to survive.[100] This may, once more, help to explain the adoption of strict homophobia by the Hebrews and perhaps by some northern European peoples, where group selection may

98—Gordon Gallup, "Attitudes Toward Homosexuals and Evolutionary Theory: The Role of Evidence," *Ethology and Sociobiology*, 17 (1996): 281-284.

99—Miron Baron, "Genetic Linkage and Male Homosexual Orientation," *BMJ*, 307 (1993): 337–338.

100—Gordon Gallup, "Attitudes Toward Homosexuals and Evolutionary Theory: The Role of Evidence," *Ethology and Sociobiology*, 17 (1996): 281-284.

have been particularly intense due to the harshness of the ecology and a state of frequent warfare.

URBANISM, TOLERANCE, AND DECLINE

As alluded to above, once conditions become less harsh, there is a degree to which attitudes to homosexuality appear to soften and homosexuality becomes more noticeable. Homosexuality, in various forms, is tolerated, to a limited extent, in many tribal groups in hot environments where basic needs are met and the environment is relatively unstable. In these contexts (r-selected environments), relatively few resources are invested in partner or offspring.

The Sambia, whom we met earlier, would be a typical example of such a social organization. They tolerate pederasty. In Brazil, Bororo youths engage in homosexual relationships, at least during the period of their rite of passage, when they are secluded from the broader society. Male Yanomamö have sexual relationships with each other until they get married, and this is in a society in which women walk around naked. The same is true of many other tribes. This may be a form of sexual outlet in polygamous societies, because the high-status men control so many of the young women.[101]

Such factors wouldn't, however, explain the tolerance of homosexuality in the later period of Ancient Greece or Rome, which was monogamous. As we move away from this easy ecology towards a much harsher yet more predictable environment, the intensity of selection,

---

101—David Greenberg, *The Construction of Homosexuality* (Chicago: University of Chicago Press, 2008), 68.

especially for investment in offspring and partners, would increase, meaning it would be advantageous to shun homosexuality for the various reasons that we have already outlined. That said, as we move into relatively developed conditions, such as those found in the city-states of the Ancient World, we might expect that the intensity of selection for this strategy and the shunning of homosexuality, would actually decrease.

In other words, people would become more civilized and less warlike. It has been documented, in this regard, that living standards in the cities of ancient Egypt and Mesopotamia were "luxurious," even compared to those of the city-states of ancient Greece.[102] There we find the beginnings of functioning medicine and extremely high living standards in comparison to other societies of the time.[103] In other words, a larger and more genetically diverse population could be produced than was the case among the ancient Jews, who were simple farmers on the borders of these civilizations. Group selection pressure was weaker, religiousness was less intensely selected for, homosexuality became more tolerated. (It must, nevertheless, be remembered that child mortality was high among the ancient Egyptians, and life expectancy was around 35.)[104]

In addition, life would be less stressful, with stress being known to be associated with highly instinctive behavior and,

102—Daniel Rossides, *Social Theory: Its Origins and Contemporary Relevance* (Lanham: Rowman & Littlefield, 1998), 19.

103—John Nunn, *Ancient Egyptian Medicine* (Norman: University of Oklahoma Press, 2002); Barry Kemp, *Ancient Egypt: Anatomy of a Civilisation* (London: Routledge, 2007).

104—Toby Wilkinson, *The Rise and Fall of Ancient Egypt* (London: Bloomsbury Publishing, 2013).

indeed, with religiousness.[105] Thus, any evolved instinct to be repulsed by homosexuality would be less likely to be triggered. Consistent with this, as we have discussed, the Hellenized Jews just after the time of Christ, living in Greek city-states, were far less appalled by homosexuality than their ancestors had been, even believing that the dominant homosexual should *not* be put to death.[106] It might also be argued that urbanized conditions are a strong evolutionary mismatch and that this can induce dysphoria and fitness-reducing behavior at the group and individual level, possibly because it interferes with optimally adaptive development. Humans are not evolved to live in urban conditions, where they must constantly interact with strangers and people who are genetically very dissimilar to them, including foreigners.[107]

Once a civilization urbanizes, selection pressures are weakened due to the fruits of civilization; people become less religious because there is lower mortality salience, society thus becomes less patriarchal, more sexually libertine, more accepting of female rights, and more accepting of homosexuality. Society stops believing in its own unique importance and accepts immigration. It becomes highly materialistic and irreligious and people seem to stop wanting children, due, perhaps, to

105—See Edward Dutton and Dimitri Van der Linden, "Why is Intelligence Negatively Associated with Religiousness?" *Evolutionary Psychological Science*, 3 (2017): 392-403.

106—Bernadette Brooten, *Love Between Women: Early Christian Responses to Female Homoeroticism* (Chicago: University of Chicago Press, 2009), 257.

107—See David Sloan Wilson, *This View of Life: Completing the Darwinian Revolution* (New York: Knopf Doubleday, 2019) and J. Philippe Rushton, "Ethic Nationalism: Evolutionary Psychology and Genetic Similarity Theory," *Nations and Nationalism,* 11 (2005): 489-507.

this evolutionary mismatch discussed earlier. Children become an accident, associated with low intelligence and impulsiveness, and so the civilization goes into decline. In other words, civilizations go through cycles, and these have proven quite predictable.

We can observer this precise process in Ancient Greece, Rome, and Baghdad, each of which experienced pronounced "seasons": growth and fulfillment in the "Spring" and "Summer," followed by harvesting of resources, stagnation, and collapse in the "Autumn" and "Winter." The rise and fall of intelligence is critical in this cycle. In "Winter," once-great societies, separated by distance and time, display the same symptoms: atheism, feminism, materialism, migration, sexual libertinism, and so on. The West may have advanced further than others, due to its being subject to especially intense selection for religiousness and due its being situated in extreme environmental harshness. This meant that mortality salience had to be far lower, and dysphoria far higher, before people started doubting religion and, directly or indirectly, losing the desire to breed.[108] But we have not escaped the cycle.

The key point is that it may be that the group-selection triumph of Christianity can partly be found in its suppression of homosexuality (including pederasty) through religious means, which forced homosexual and single men to invest their energies in their families and the group as a whole. Christianity took a series of

108—See, Edward Dutton and Michael Woodley of Menie, *At Our Wits' End: Why We're Becoming Less Intelligent and What It Means for the Future* (Exeter: Imprint Academic, 2018); John Glubb, *The Fate of Empires and the Search for Survival* (Edinburgh: William Blackwood & Sons, 1976).

evolutionary imperatives, which had developed among desert herders in the Middle East, and rendered them the unquestioned "will of God." It then takes those to an ecology, northern Europe, where it is so cold and stable that the level of selection is intense, even once cities have developed, and where the selection for religiousness is intense as well. As German biochemist Gerhard Meisenberg has argued, this leads to homosexuality remaining taboo through to a much later stage of civilization than we see in the Ancient World.[109] This taboo was also maintained within Islam, which also adopts certain aspects of Jewish thought. But it was clearly preserved to a much lesser extent, evidenced by the acceptability of pederasty in the Muslim world.[110]

SEX AND THE DECLINE OF THE WEST

It is not just homosexuality that is taboo among many religious groups but, to varying degrees, sexuality itself. The Old Testament, for example, makes clear that the act of sexual intercourse is only to take place within marriage. Those who break this rule, such as adulterers or fornicators, are to be severely punished and even killed. The body itself is to be regulated, such that people, especially females, cover themselves and do not reveal too much flesh. The Hebrews often contrasted their culture with other groups, such as the people of Sodom or of Egypt, who were more sexually liberated. This is particularly explicit as we move

---

109—Gerhard Meisenberg, *In God's Image: The Natural History of Intelligence and Ethics* (Kibworth, Leicestershire: Book Guild Publishing, 2007).

110—See Edward Dutton, *Islam: An Evolutionary Perspective* (Whitefish: Washington Summit Publishers, 2021).

into the New Testament and, in particular, the letters of St. Paul. The pagans are portrayed as far more sexually liberal than the puritanical Christians—repression of sexuality being portrayed as a distinctly Christian virtue. In that all religious groups appear to make sexuality taboo to some extent, it is quite probable there is a sound evolutionary reason for doing so.

A long-forgotten English anthropologist, First World War hero, and proto-welfare-state organizer called J.D. Unwin (1895-1936) noticed this while doing research for his doctoral thesis.[111] He also observed that, up to a point, the more developed a society was, the more strongly sex appeared to be repressed. In the book that this thesis led to, *Sex and Culture,* Unwin studied 80 primitive tribes and six known civilizations, spanning a period of 5,000 years.[112] He found a positive correlation between the degree of cultural achievement displayed by a people and the level of sexual restraint they practiced. He further noted that high civilizations will tend to become extremely luxurious, at which point they start to become increasingly sexually liberal. As this change takes place, they lose their cohesion and sense of purpose and collapse back into a more primitive social organization.

How can we explain Unwin's findings? It may be that they are a matter of "correlation, not causation." A society is more likely to develop if it is more cooperative and group-selected, which will naturally result in greater sexual restraint—something that its religiousness is likely to elevate further. To some extent, by virtue of

---

111—E. Ansell, *Admissions to Peterhouse* (Cambridge: Cambridge University Press, 1939), 133.

112—J. D. Unwin, *Sex and Culture* (Oxford: Oxford University Press, 1934).

being high in intelligence, as civilizations tend to be—
and thus higher in trust, pro-social and civic behavior,
and long-term thinking—people will be less likely to
commit adultery or pursue short-term sexual unions.[113]
As the society becomes more and more developed and
luxurious, people will begin to feel less stressed about
external dangers or unpredictable death, meaning that
they will be less religious. They will also feel greater
dysphoria. This will, in turn, lead to more people
becoming less sexually restrained, behavior that generally
trickles down from the higher classes. The weakened
Darwinian selection for the optimum group may
mean a weaker level of selection for traits such as self-
control. Furthermore, contraception, which is generally
innovated in urban environments, will be taken up by
the upper-classes. This will lead to a negative association
between fertility and intelligence and the eventual
collapse of society, maybe the people itself.

Concomitantly, the same high levels of luxury
will lead to the collapse of religion, reduced
ethnocentrism, the acceptance of immigration, and
flagging of the drive to stand-up to foreign invasion.
The resultant multiculturalism on confounded the
matter. Multiculturalism, as Harvard psychologist
Robert Putnam found to his amazement, reduces
social cohesion even between the natives.[114] This is
because some natives will fear that other natives will

113—Richard Lynn and Tatu Vanhanen, *Intelligence: A Unifying Construct for the Social Sciences* (London: Ulster Institute for Social Research, 2012).

114—Robert Putnam, *"E Pluribus Unum*: Diversity and Community in the Twenty-first Century," The 2006 Johan Skytte Prize Lecture, *Scandinavian Political Studies*, 30 (2007): 137–174.

collaborate with foreigners against them to promote their individual interests.

This is the story of the rise and fall of civilizations. D.H. Lawrence (1885-1930) famously wrote,

Men fight for liberty and win it with hard knocks

Their children, brought up easy, let it slip away again, poor fools.

And their grandchildren are once more slaves.[115]

This cycle of optimism and pessimism seems to undergird a popular internet meme.

Hard times create strong men.
Strong men create good times.
Good times create weak men.
Weak men create hard times.

Effectively, the birth of civilization and urbanism is its own worst enemy, as it leads to the degradation of the religious norms and sexual restraint that made it possible in the first place. In this way, liberal sexual morality can be seen as tightly correlated with the rise and fall of civilization—but not a direct *cause* of it. Unwin, however, implies that sexual repression was somehow *causal*. There are a variety of theories that have attempted to explain how this might be so.

German sociologist Max Weber (1864-1920) argued that Calvinist Protestantism acted as an incentive towards socioeconomic achievement and the development of

---

115—D.H. Lawrence, "Liberty's Old Story" (1922), in *The Complete Poems* (New York: Penguin Books, 1993).

capitalism.[116] At the root of Calvinism is the notion of Predestination, that God determines, before time begins, His "Elect" who will go to Heaven. Such a doctrine might seem to inspire a certain fatalism and "devil may care" attitude, since nothing one can do in this world will matter with regard to the next. But this proved to be far from the truth. Calvinists reasoned that God would materially bless His elect, and, in turn, they wanted to be reassured that they were, indeed, part of that most exclusive club. This helped transform them into highly assiduous people, who would attain high socioeconomic status and create more successful societies accordingly. In a similar vein, moral failings would make a person think that they were possibly not part of the Elect. This created a very strong incentive to be morally pure and control and repress any supposedly immoral sexual urges, "assuaging the anxiety produced by them" by strongly focusing on ones work, and thus ensuring that one was materially "blessed."[117]

Sigmund Freud (1856-1939) proposed a related theory. Freud argued that socially unacceptable sexual or aggressive urges would be "defensively sublimated" into socially acceptable productive or creative pursuits. Repressing such ideas would create a kind of energy that could be focused into work of some kind, in particular, into creative work and the arts. So, the taboo nature of sex would lead to a psychological conflict, and consequent neurosis, which could be alleviated by being productive

116—Max Weber, *The Protestant Ethic and the Spirit of Capitalism* (London: Penguin, 2002).

117—Emily Kim, Veronika Zeppenfeld, and Dov Cohen, "Sublimation, Culture and Creativity," *Journal of Personal and Social Psychology*, 105 (2013), 640.

and even daringly artistic.[118] Honoré de Balzac (1799-1850) was known for saying "There goes another novel!" upon completing sexual intercourse.[119]

Obviously, these theories are speculative. However, in 2013 a team at the University of Illinois, led by American psychologist Emily Kim, provided fascinating evidence of causality, looking at whether Protestants, in contrast to Catholics or Jews, were "more likely to sublimate their taboo feelings and desires toward productive ends." They found that Protestant men and women who had sexual problems related to anxieties about taboos and about depraved ideas had greater creative accomplishments, as compared to those with sexual problems unrelated to such concerns and to those reporting no sexual problems. In addition, two laboratory experiments found that Protestants produced more creative art work (such as "sculptures, poems, collages, cartoon captions") when they were "primed with damnation-related words, induced to feel unacceptable sexual desires, or forced to suppress their anger." Significantly, "activating anger or sexual attraction was not enough; it was the forbidden or suppressed nature of the emotion that gave the emotion its creative power."[120]

It should be remembered that this is only one study and, clearly, it would be useful if it were to be replicated and developed. But Kim and her team have provided

---

118—Sigmund Freud, *On Creativity and the Unconscious* (New York: Harper, 1958).

119—Kim, Zeppenfeld, Cohen, *et al.*, "Sublimation, Culture and Creativity," *op cit.*

120—*Ibid.*

evidence for the hypothesis that the relationship between sexual repression and societal accomplishment is, to some extent, *causal*. Societies that regard sex as taboo and encourage people to repress sexual desire, are, as a result, more creative. This finding would potentially help to explain the way in which many religions will tend to present sex in taboo terms: the groups that do this are more successful, all else being equal, in the battle of group selection.

LONDON, SOME TWO DECADES LATER

A great deal has changed in England since 1999 with regard to homosexuality, all of it in a direction that would likely have displeased my colleagues at the Royal Bank of Scotland in Islington. In 1999, the age of homosexual sexual consent was 18, two years higher than that of heterosexual consent. There was no question of pardoning males who had been convicted of homosexual offenses prior to the legalization of homosexuality, which had occurred in 1967. There was no marriage (nor even "civil partnerships") for homosexuals. Homosexual couples could not adopt children. Homosexual men could not serve in the armed forces, and they were banned from giving blood.

Goodbye to all that. Homosexuals now have equal rights with heterosexuals and being homosexual is only taboo in the view of a small minority. In 1999, homosexuality had been so controversial that there was uproar when, the previous year, an openly gay Conservative politician had "outed" Labour politician

Peter Mandelson live on BBC TV's *News Night*.[121] The BBC imposed a blanket ban, for a period, on Mandelson's sexuality being mentioned on their programs.[122] Today, a "closet" or repressed homosexual politician is the exception, not the norm. In 2020, a former small-town mayor, Pete Buttigieg, ran for President with his "personal story" (his homosexuality being paramount) as his chief, if not only, selling point.

Despite the rapidity with which official attitudes to homosexuality have changed, my colleague's visceral reaction to homosexuality—as well as homosexuality itself—appears to have deep evolutionary roots. Under extreme Darwinian selection, groups with an optimum, small homosexual caste were selected for, but so were groups that forced these homosexuals to repress their desires. These Darwinian conditions have now broken down. Homosexuality is not repressed, and its prevalence may be expected to increase in post-industrial, postmodern conditions. We are only now learning what this will mean in terms of social stability, artistic pursuits, and the survival of the group itself.

121—"BBC to Replay Clip of Lord Mandelson Being 'Outed,'" *BBC News*, August 14, 2010, https://www.bbc.com/news/uk-politics-10973463.

122—Jamie Wilson, "BBC Eases Privacy Edict," *The Guardian*, August 21, 2000, https://www.theguardian.com/media/2000/dec/21/broadcasting.uknews.

BORN AGAIN

Gender Dysphoria and Alienation As Identity

I n October 1999, I began my degree in Theology at Durham University. Like Oxford and Cambridge, Durham University (England's third oldest university) is composed of a number of colleges in which you live. Mine was called the College of St. Hild and St. Bede. In the first week of term, there were many "getting-to-know-you" events, to make it easier to become friends with people beyond those who lived on your corridor. Somehow, I got talking to a very unusual young man. He was called Alex Waddell.

We had a few things in common. Alex was from Reading, in the southeast of England, not far from London, where I came from. Like me, he had been to a "state school" (in the U.S., a "public school"), as opposed to a private school, which so many students at the college had attended.[1] Most importantly, Alex was studying Philosophy. This interested me a great deal, and I had toyed with reading a Philosophy degree myself. He'd had a "gap year" in the Czech Republic, teaching English and reviewing cocktails for magazines. This fascinated

---

1—However, his mother's family was part of the "Landed Gentry," England's effective untitled nobility, descending from a German noble family that had migrated to England called the von Kaulbachs. Indeed, Alex's maternal grandmother, Audrey Howard (1916-1994), was the great granddaughter of the brother of the 13th Duke of Norfolk. See, *Debrett's Peerage and Baronetage* (London: Macmillan, 1985), 894.

me because, at the time, I'd only been to France, Spain, and Holland. He also dabbled in writing poetry, as did I. So we had things about which to converse. Making conversation with Alex was rather hard work, however. He spoke in a very idiosyncratic way; a sort of staccato, with pauses in unexpected parts of the sentence. And he tended to deal with everyday statements as though they were philosophical propositions.

"So, are you trying to tell me that you're going to go to the college bar?"

"Yes, Alex, I am."

"And you're asking me if I'd like to come with you to the college bar?"

"That is correct."

"And when you propose going to the college bar, do you mean that we're just going to go there and hang out or are you implying that we're going to go there and have a drink?"

"I'm asking you if you'd like to come with me to the college bar and have a drink, Alex."

"And do you literally mean *a drink*, or is that a term for a more indefinite number of drinks? If so, I might have to go to the cash point . . ."

Alex moved around a great deal, unable to sit still, a habit which was very distracting. He told me that this was due to suffering from curvature of the spine. This had been corrected a few years earlier in a lengthy operation in which metal rods had been inserted into his back. He also mentioned some kind of "syndrome" that caused muscle and abdominal pain. I later discovered that he suffered from fibromyalgia, which causes not just muscle pain and abdominal problems but also sleeplessness and depression. And Alex was a vegetarian, for philosophical reasons, something that was considered extremely eccentric at the time.

The word "eccentric" really encapsulated Alex.[2] The word "autistic" was not yet widely known, but it seems fairly clear now that this is what he was. He had trouble understanding how others might feel, which led him to be socially clumsy, thoughtless, and generally bizarre, but he was also highly analytical in his thinking, congruous with evidence that "systematizing" and "empathy" sit at opposite ends of a spectrum.[3]

In line with this autism diagnosis, Alex was almost child-like in his guilelessness and lack of self-awareness. The small number of us who were his friends—there were two of us at his 21st birthday party in June 2001—euphemistically referred to him as "avant-garde." This "party" was a plaintive affair. His parents had given him a substantial amount of money to take all of his friends out for a meal. But there were only two of us. Our pleas with him to just let us go to McDonalds and then blow all the dosh on gin were not well-received. His parents would be

---

2—Eccentricity and intelligence clearly ran in the family. Alex's father had a Ph.D. in chemistry. Alex's maternal grandfather was Lt. Col. Ronald Kaulback, OBE (1909-1995). After the public school Rugby and then Cambridge University, Kaulback became an explorer, charting then unknown areas of Tibet and Burma in the 1930s. Between 1944 and 1945, the Karen tribal guerilla soldiers, whom Kaulback commanded, managed to kill 13,500 Japanese men with very little loss on their own side. *Daily Telegraph,* "Obituary: Ronald Kaulback," October 7, 1995.

3—Simon Baron-Cohen, "The Extreme Male Brain Theory of Autism," *Trends in Cognitive Sciences,* 6 (2002): 248-254.

displeased, he told us, if they knew that the money had not been primarily spent on eating at a restaurant.

As the first academic year continued, evidence of Alex's autism became increasingly clear. He woke up the entire college out-building in which he lived—Hild Gym—at about 4 o'clock one morning by burning toast in the kitchen and thus setting off the fire alarm. Another time, a girl who lived on his corridor ran herself a bath and then left it, momentarily, to take a phone call. Upon her return, the bathroom door was locked. This was because, while she had been on the phone, Alex had gone to the same bathroom, with the same ablutionary intentions, found that a bath had been run already, and presumably thought to himself, "That's lucky. Someone must have run the bath and then changed his mind." He thus locked the door and hopped in. As the year passed, Alex became withdrawn, stopped washing, grew his hair long, and got shouted down at the Durham Union Society (a debating society) for a laughable and rambling intervention on the subject of prostitution. I remember someone hollering at him, "Sit down, sir!" Every time he tried to speak, the audience clapped, and this continued until he finally gave up and resumed his seat.

The following academic year, we didn't live in college. Most second-years "lived out," in houses in the city, so I didn't see Alex as much. Not having any close friends, he was living with a group of students whom he didn't know. In that academic year (2000-2001), Alex was pursuing an American international student to whom he was attracted. He was also after a girl who studied at the university's campus in Stockton, a sizable industrial town 34 miles away. The two were, effectively, separate universities, so I don't know how Alex had made a connection to Stockton—possibly he had done so by using "the internet," something we normal students tended to eschew. But it transpired that Alex was going to Stockton on the bus, buying cannabis and selling it to students in Durham, where cannabis was more difficult to obtain and thus more expensive. Alex's keen mind had discovered an arbitrage opportunity.

In the Spring term, Alex became president of the Philosophy Society. These student societies usually took your money at "Fresher's Fair" and then did very little. But with philosophy-obsessed Alex at the helm, things were different. He managed, in about October 2001, to persuade the Oxford philosopher of religion Richard Swinburne (b. 1934)—who has been described as "the premier rational defender of Christianity of our time"— to come and speak to the society.[4] Everyone who had done A-Level Religious Studies had read about this giant. His appearance was so wildly popular that Alex hired the Durham Union Society Debating Chamber for it, and it was full to capacity, mostly with people who weren't members of the Philosophy Society and so had to pay to be there. As Alex introduced Oxford University's Nolloth Professor of the Christian Religion, so many people must have been asking themselves: Who was this eccentric— by then sporting a tennis-player's headband—who had managed to achieve this coup? It was the same eccentric that told a group of teenage "locals," from the window of my ground-floor flat, that all "Geordies" (people from Newcastle-Upon-Tyne and its environs, including

---

4—Kelly James Clark, *Philosophers Who Believe: The Spiritual Journeys of 11 Leading Thinkers* (Downers Grove: Intervarsity Press, 1993), 179.

Durham) were stupid, leading to Alex, myself, and two others having to cower in my ground-floor flat while the offended Geordies threw stones at it. And it was the same eccentric who, the following academic year, did something very eccentric, indeed.

I met up with Alex in early October 2001. I didn't see him again, other than at the Richard Swinburne meeting, for the rest of the term. It was December 2001, the night of the Christian Union's Carol Service in Durham Cathedral. The Christian Union was a fundamentalist Christian student society, in which I had many friends. A third of my 15-person out-building in my first year—Bede Gym, a corridor over a gym—had been members, and I ended-up living with "God Squad-ers" for the rest of my time at university. Later, I even wrote my doctoral thesis, and first book, about them.[5] At their encouragement, I always attended their Christmas Carol Service, held in the splendor of Durham Cathedral, which has been voted "the best building in Britain."[6] For some reason, the Christmas Party of the university's LGB (Lesbian, Gay and Bisexual) Society always took place on the same evening as the Christian Union's Cathedral Carol Service. As the two groups couldn't be more different (the Christian Union opposed homosexuality, for a start), and because I was young and pretentious, I made a point, in order to be "avant-garde," of always going to both events: the evangelical carol service and then the LGB party in

5—Edward Dutton, *Meeting Jesus at University: Rites of Passage and Student Evangelicals* (Aldershot: Ashgate, 2008).

6—Jonathan Glancey, "The Votes Are In: Your Favourite British Building," *The Guardian*, September 16, 2011, https://www.theguardian.com/artanddesign/2011/sep/16/britains-best-building-readers-vote-results

the Student Union building.

So this is what I did in December 2001. The tattooed-lesbian, Kerry, who was in charge (tattoos were very rare at the time) was an acquaintance of mine. In the darkened, disco-light-illuminated room, she introduced me to people and, eventually, she led me over to a rather pretty, young girl whom I was immediately convinced I'd met before. She seemed out of place. She was very feminine. She had long hair, make-up, and an ankle-length skirt. She stood in stark contrast to the "butch" lesbians that constituted the bulk of the other females at the party.

"This is Dreya," said Kerry. "This is her first time here."

"Have we met before?" I asked, innocently.

"Um . . . no, I don't think so," came the high-pitched reply.

"I'm sure I recognize you."

"Um . . . no, I don't think we've met."

There was a long pause and then, genuinely shocked, it came to me.

"*Alex! What the fuck is going on?!*"

My memories after this are vague. I recall Kerry telling me that I shouldn't ask what was "going on." "This is a safe space for Dreya," she said. I'd never heard of the concept of a "safe space"—meaning a place where your comforting delusions may not be questioned—that was later to become so ubiquitous. I went upstairs to the bar and told my two friends—one of whom had been at Alex's 21st and who also studied Philosophy—what was "going on." I persuaded Alex to come upstairs and explain himself to them. What had happened?

WHAT IS TRANSSEXUALITY?

We'll return to what happened to Alex later. At this point, he was beginning the process of "transitioning" from being a "male" to being a "female." Cross-dressing, of course, has been perennial throughout human history, usually confined to performative contexts: erotica, satire, theater, camp, or, in some cases, religious and folk rituals.[7] But by the turn of the 21st century, something distinctly new had emerged in the Western world: transgenderism as an *identity*—one that is demographically significant, legally recognized, and, seemingly, on the rise.

It is difficult to be sure what percentage of Western populations are transgender, not least because the numbers are increasing. In 2016, UCLA's Williams Institute estimated that 0.6 percent of the U.S. population (1.4 million people) were transgender.[8] Rates were slightly higher in the states of California, New Mexico, and Georgia. Age also plays a factor: while 0.5 percent of adults over 65 are transgender, the rate is noticeably higher among 18-to-24-year-olds. A recent study of school children from Finland, aged 16 to 18, estimated that 3.6 percent of males, though only 2.3 percent of females, displayed some symptoms of Gender Dysphoria.[9]

7—See, for instance, Jeffrey Gettleman, "The Peculiar Position of India's Third Gender," *New York Times*, February 17, 2018, https://www.nytimes.com/2018/02/17/style/india-third-gender-hijras-transgender.html.

8—Williams Institute, "How Many Adults Identify as Transgender in the United States?" UCLA School of Law, June 2016, https://williamsinstitute.law.ucla.edu/publications/trans-adults-united-states.

9—Riittakerttu Kaltiala-Heino, Marja Työläjärvi, and Nina Lindberg, "Gender Dysphoria in Adolescent Population: A 5-year Replication Study,"

There is also a certain *aggressive* and *assertive* character to the "trans" identity that is hard to miss (though, granted, this quality is not unique in today's political climate). In 2019, a journalist for *The Guardian*, a biological woman, halted and reversed her "transition" to manhood in order to have a baby, then took up her transition once more afterwards. She demanded that a British registrar falsify history by designating her as the child's "father" on its birth certificate. When the registrar refused, this "transman" took the authorities to court. Upon losing her case, she remarked on how "not fair" it all was.[10] A similar determination or spitefulness was seen at the Democratic Socialists of America Conference that same year, when a transwoman made a "point of personal privilege" in order to angrily demand that speakers not use the term "guys" (a typical American colloquialism meaning "everyone") when referring to delegates, which he condemned as "gendered-language."[11]

And this spitefulness has, to a large degree, succeeded in changing the academic and legal arenas. Under English Law, despite the fact that no biological change has taken place, if you "transition" in this way, to the extent of having surgery so that you appear (sometimes convincingly, sometimes not) to be of the "opposite sex,"

Clinical Child Psychology and Psychiatry, 24 (2019): 379-387.

10—Robert Booth, "Transgender Man Loses Court Battle to be Registered as Father," *The Guardian*, September 25, 2019, https://www.theguardian.com/society/2019/sep/25/transgender-man-loses-court-battle-to-be-registered-as-father-freddy-mcconnell.

11—Amanda Prestigiacomo, "Triggering on a New Level: Video Of Democratic Socialists Of America Convention Goes Viral," *Daily Wire*, (August 7, 2019), https://www.dailywire.com/news/triggering-new-level-video-democratic-socialists-amanda-prestigiacomo.

then you are, legally, of that opposite sex and can obtain a "Gender Recognition Certificate" to prove it. A court case in December 2019 found that it was not legitimate to refute or undermine such a change. It became legal to fire somebody if they publicly expressed the opinion that a transsexual could not, in good conscience, assert that they were a member of the sex into which they had transitioned. Specifically, a 45-year-old woman, Maya Forstater, was removed from her job at the Centre for Global Development in London for tweeting "Men cannot become women." She took her employers to a tribunal, claiming that the sacking breached her Human Rights, because she was fired due to her beliefs. She lost the case, though the decision was subsequently overturned.[12]

The Canadian psychologist and author Jordan Peterson rose to fame largely due to his refusal to abide by the state-mandated regime of using the chosen pronouns of transsexual students. This small act of defiance made him a conservative hero. In fact, a cottage industry arose in which conservatives regularly signaled their bravery by calling out transsexuals: "Women are women, and no man is a 'she'!" Regardless of such efforts, pronouns themselves have multiplied in recent years—many have adopted the non-binary "they" as first-person singular—and entered

---

12— Jake Hurfurt, "Britons Have No Right to Ask Whether a Transgender Person is Male or Female, Rules Employment Judge in Landmark Ruling AGAINST Tax Expert Who Was Sacked For Tweeting 'Men Cannot Become Women,'" *Mail Online,* December 19, 2019, https://www.dailymail.co.uk/news/article-7808685/Britons-ask-transgender-person-male-female-judge-says.html; Doug Faulkner, "Maya Forstater: Woman Wins Tribunal Appeal Over Transgender Tweets," *BBC News,* June 10, 2021, https://www.bbc.com/news/uk-57426579.

public consciousness in a way previously unimaginable.[13] Newspapers' style-guides have been altered to accommodate transsexuals, and even non-transsexuals have begun defining their pronouns of choice on their social-media pages. In January 2021, Rachel Levine was appointed by U.S. President Joe Biden as assistant health secretary, making her the first openly transgender federal official.[14] The fact that Levine was tasked with overseeing the national health was, of course, highly symbolic. Everyone, it seems, is encouraged to rethink themselves and the nature of mental health and identity.

A CUCKOO IN THE NEST

As transsexuality has become increasingly prominent, it's only natural that many have grown suspicious that transsexuals are taking on these new identities mendaciously—that is, they are swapping genders as a way of gaining attention or even advantage. In a society in which being a member of a supposedly victimized group is valued—a reversal of what was previously the case— then unscrupulous people are incentivized to reinvent themselves on occasion.

American Rachel Dolezal is the most notorious example of this kind of behavior. A biologically White woman raised in Montana, Dolezal adopted typically

---

13—Avinash Chak, "Beyond 'He' and 'She': The Rise of Non-binary Pronouns," *BBC News*, December 7, 2015, https://www.bbc.com/news/magazine-34901704.

14—Samantha Schmidt, John Wagner, and Teo Armus, "Biden Selects Transgender Doctor Rachel Levine as Assistant Health Secretary," *Washington Post*, January 19, 2021, https://www.washingtonpost.com/health/2021/01/19/rachel-levine-transgender-biden-hhs-pick/.

African-American dress, hair, and speech patterns and, at a relatively young age, became President of the NAACP chapter of Spokane, Washington—a high-status position that, presumably, would not have been open to a White. When Dolezal's deception was revealed, she was excoriated in the media as a liar or con artist—or even, ironically, as the ultimate expression of "whiteness."[15] There is reason to believe that Dolezal genuinely felt that she was part of the Black experience, either through effortful control or, perhaps, childhood psychological trauma.[16] More recently, Dr. Jessica Krug, formerly of George Washington University, did something similar, posing as non-White for years and apparently taking advantage of the "diversity" regime currently dominant in Western academia.[17] So, if you are a White, heterosexual male—and excluded from the new victimhood nobility—you may find yourself drawn towards transgenderism, particularly if you already suffer from the array of psychological problems associated with it, which we will discuss below.

15—See Ijeoma Oluo, "The Heart of Whiteness: Ijeoma Oluo Interviews Rachel Dolezal, the White Woman Who Identifies as Black," *The Stranger*, April 19, 2017, https://www.thestranger.com/features/2017/04/19/25082450/the-heart-of-whiteness-ijeoma-oluo-interviews-rachel-dolezal-the-white-woman-who-identifies-as-black

16—Dolezal's parents were Christian missionaries, who adopted African children. Perhaps Dolezal assumed an African-American identity as part of a symbolic sibling rivalry or attempt to win her parents' affection? Richard Spencer, "Black Like Her," *Radix Journal*, June 18, 2015, https://radixjournal.com/2015/06/2015-6-18-rachel-dolezal-and-the-quest-for-identity/.

17—Guardian Staff, "Jessica Krug: White Professor Who Pretended to be Black Resigns From University Post," *The Guardian*, (September 10, 2020), https://www.theguardian.com/world/2020/sep/09/jessica-krug-professor-resigns-george-washington.

There has been a notable backlash against transwomen entering women's domains, particularly women's sports, but the trend is so advanced that it now seems unstoppable.[18] In 2019, CeCe Telfer became the first transsexual athlete to win a collegiate track-and-field championship in the women's 400-meter hurdles.[19] In March 2022, swimmer Lia Thomas caused a media uproar when she won the 500-yard freestyle championship race in convincing fashion.[20] Both Telfer and Thomas are biological males and "transgender;" they have not undergone sexual-reassignment surgery, but are participating in hormonal therapy. Thompson had been a middle-of-the-pack competitor as a male; after transitioning, she blew her competition out of the water, so to speak. The whole ordeal has forced many people to examine what had been taken for granted: namely sports are segregated by sex for a reason. Biological males have obvious advantages in the areas of strength, size, lung capacity, quickness, and aggression in inter-sexual competition; this rule holds even for biological men under a hormonal regimen. It's worth noting that

18—See Martina Navratilova, "The Rules on Trans Athletes Reward Cheats and Punish the Innocent," *The Times* (London), February 17, 2019, https://www.thetimes.co.uk/article/the-rules-on-trans-athletes-reward-cheats-and-punish-the-innocent-klsrq6h3x; see also Aallyah Wright, "GOP Lawmakers Kickstart New Wave of Transgender Athlete Bans," *Pew*, February 3, 2022, https://www.pewtrusts.org/en/research-and-analysis/blogs/stateline/2022/02/03/gop-lawmakers-kickstart-new-wave-of-transgender-athlete-bans.

19—Gillian R. Brassil and Jeré Longman, "Who Should Compete in Women's Sports? There Are 'Two Almost Irreconcilable Positions,'" *New York Times*, https://www.nytimes.com/2020/08/18/sports/transgender-athletes-womens-sports-idaho.html.

20—Robert Sanchez, "'I Am Lia': The Trans Swimmer Dividing America Tells Her Story," *Sport Illustrated*, March 3, 2022, https://www.si.com/college/2022/03/03/lia-thomas-penn-swimmer-transgender-woman-daily-cover.

America's World Cup-winning women's soccer team lost in an exhibition match (5-2) to a male team of under-15-year-olds, that is, boys who had not completed puberty and development.[21]

Needless to say, these controversies should be put into perspective. Half of one percent of young people are transsexual, and only a fraction of those will ever play competitive sports. Around the time of the Lia Thomas controversy, Utah Governor Spencer Cox vetoed a bill aimed at banning trans athletes. He noted that of his state's 75,000 high-schoolers who participate in sport, only four are transgender, and only one student plays on a girls' team.[22] That said, would it be inappropriate to suggest that some male athletes might simply want to switch genders to gain a competitive advantage—perhaps even to become the greatest of all time? Even if they genuinely feel that they are women, would not this identity formation be, in some way, incentivized by success? Or are many transsexuals, a bit like Alex, trying to be "avant garde" and thus trying to stand out? Rachel Dolezal certainly achieved success as a "trans-racial," before it all fell apart.

We should remember that *deception*—and even *self-deception*—can sometimes be an evolutionary strategy. The cuckoo, for instance, engages in what is known as "nest parasitism": the cuckoo mother lays an egg in the nest of another species, usually after kicking out one of the

21—Anthony Chapman, "The Kids Are Alright—World Cup-winning US Women's Team Suffer Shock 5-2 Defeat to FC Dallas' U-15 Boys Academy Side, *The Sun*, April 6, 2017, https://www.thesun.co.uk/sport/football/3268594/us-women-soccer-dallas-academy-5-2/.

22—Anne Branigin, "Utah Governor Vetoes Transgender Athlete Bill, Citing High Suicide Rates,"*Washington Post*, March 23, 2022, https://www.washingtonpost.com/lifestyle/2022/03/23/utah-cox-transgender-athlete-veto/.

eggs already there. The cuckoo hatchling then proceeds, instinctively, to banish other competing hatchlings from its new nest, becoming its adoptive mother's sole focus. Whether or not the hatchling is "conscious" of its ruthless subterfuge is of academic concern. The fact is that it acts in a way that increases its well-being and ability to survive. If society is structured to incentivize and valorize transsexuals—in other words, that is the environment—then we should not be surprised that it produces more transsexuals, along with a myriad of new ethical and identity dilemmas.

REALITY AND IDENTITY

That being said, even if one takes the most uncharitable view of transgender athletes (or trans-racial leftists), none of that disputes the reality of *dysphoria*—feeling out of place in one's body or in the world—as an intensely felt experience for millions of people in post-industrial society. In this chapter, we will focus on the *causes* of Gender Dysphoria, a condition wherein a person feels profound distress due to what he regards as a mismatch between his biological gender and what he feels like on the inside, or what he feels his gender should be. The sufferer from Gender Dysphoria believes that he can alleviate these feelings by, as much as possible, outwardly becoming his desired gender. Other recognized "dysphoria" include Anorexia Nervosa, which mostly occurs in women. An anorexic is convinced that she is fat, despite the fact that she has made herself dangerously thin through starvation. Mind-Body Integrity Disorder is another prime example; the sufferer believes he is physically mutilated and will often mutilate his own body to make it so.

What are we to make of this? What are the essential causes of this, for many, baffling phenomenon?

A common conception (or you could say cliché) about transsexuals is that they are people "born in the wrong body." This begs an important question: "How did they come to believe this?" How could they become convinced—to the point of drastically changing their appearance and lifestyle and even undergoing medical treatment and surgery—that they have, say, a female "soul" *and* a penis?

Transsexuals could suffer from this conception because they really *do* have the brain of X and the genitalia of Y. They were, in fact, "born into the wrong body." However, if transsexuals also suffer from other delusions and personality disorders, then it is probable that there is some underlying factor that explains why they passionately feel this way. This is particularly true if these delusions and disorders manifest in relatively advanced age.

This is what has been proposed by American psychologist Ray Blanchard in his so-called Transsexualism Typology.[23] Blanchard argues that some "transwomen" (male-to-female transsexuals) are *homosexual transsexuals*. They are highly feminized, and they want to become, as far as possible, heterosexual women. And they show signs of opposite-sex behavior at a very young age. The rest are what he calls *autogynephilic transsexuals*. These are male fetishists who are sexually aroused, or otherwise profoundly satisfied, by the idea of having a female body, something which

---

23—Ray Blanchard, "Varieties of Autogynephilia and Their Relationship to Gender Dysphoria," *Archives of Sexual Behavior*, 22 (1993): 241–251.

correlates with wanting to take action to obtain one, and which becomes an interest for such people during or after adolescence. In other words, autogynephilic transsexuals transform their own body into an object of desire—a kind of erotic loop. More recently, Blanchard has averred that his model is also likely to apply to "transmen" (female-to-male transsexuals), though they are more often lesbians who simply take the "butch" identity to an extreme, generally retaining a vagina.[24] Blanchard has estimated that at least 75 percent of transsexuals are autogynephilic and that percentage is growing, as more and more people "discover" that they are trans.[25]

Not surprisingly, "trans" activists generally find Blanchard's Typology difficult to deal with and often attempt to suppress discussion of it. As American bioethicist Alice Dreger has summarized in her book *Galileo's Middle Finger* (2015):

> There's a critical difference between autogynephilia and most other sexual orientations: Most other orientations aren't erotically disrupted simply by being labeled. When you call a typical gay man homosexual, you're not disturbing his sexual hopes and desires. By contrast, autogynephilia is perhaps best understood as a love that would really rather we didn't speak its name. The ultimate eroticism of autogynephilia lies in the idea of really becoming

---

24—J. Michael Bailey and Ray Blanchard, "Gender Dysphoria is Not One Thing," *4thWaveNow*, December 7, 2017, https://4thwavenow.com/tag/autohomoerotic-gender-dysphoria/.

25—Louise Perry, "What Is Autogynephilia? An Interview with Dr Ray Blanchard," *Quillette*, November 6, 2019, https://quillette.com/2019/11/06/what-is-autogynephilia-an-interview-with-dr-ray-blanchard/.

or being a woman, not in being a natal male who desires to be a woman.[26]

Clearly, my friend Alex was in the autogynephilious category, and this is the far more common of the two.

So let us make sense of the more unusual category first: those who display Gender Dysphoria from a very early age. The earlier a condition manifests itself, the more likely it is to be primarily an expression of genetics, or an epigenetic phenomenon, which has occurred early in development, especially *in utero*. In this regard, the heritability of Gender Dysphoria is relatively low. A review concluded that Gender Dysphoria is about 0.5 heritable in males and 0.4 heritable in females.[27] Another review found that Gender Dysphoria was approximately 0.3 heritable among adults. The authors reviewed three studies of child samples, one of which contradicted the other two. Two of the studies found a heritability of about 0.3.[28] Thus, the common belief that some people are "born into the wrong body" is, broadly-speaking, inaccurate. Gender Dysphoria is as much environmental as it is genetic, if not more so, in males; in females, it is certainly more so.

There is a convincing case for arguing that homosexual transsexuality is a direct result of developmental instability, a concept we have previously explored. Homosexual

26—Alice Dreger, *Galileo's Middle Finger: Heretics, Activists, and One Scholar's Search for Justice* (London: Penguin, 2015); quoted in Perry, "What Is Autogynephilia? *Quillette, op cit.*

27—Kenneth Zucker, Anne Lawrence, and Baudewijntje Kreukels, "Gender Dysphoria in Adults," *Annual Review of Clinical Psychology*, 12 (2016): 217-247.

28—Tina Polderman, Baudewijntje Kreukels, Michael Irwig, *et al.*, "The Biological Contributions to Gender Identity and Gender Diversity: Bringing Data to the Table," *Behavior Genetics*, 48 (2018): 95–108.

transsexuality—and, less directly, Gender Dysphoria in general—appears to be a manifestation of developmental instability. One indication of developmental instability is left-handedness. This correlates with many neurological and auto-immune problems, including asthma and allergies.[29] Blanchard reports that there are elevated levels of non-right-handedness among both homosexual and autogynephilous transsexuals. He also shows that there is elevated left-handedness among homosexuals, pedophiles, and many others whose object of sexual arousal is atypical. Blanchard proposes that these may all be explicable, in part, by developmental instability.

Specifically, in the case of a male homosexual, a pregnant female will react to male hormones, emitted by a male fetus, by releasing female hormones. If she releases too many of these, or if the fetus' immune system cannot protect itself against them—which, in both cases, may be due to mutation—the result may be a highly feminized child, such as a homosexual. In this regard, it has been found that homosexual males, on average, are more physically and mentally feminized than are heterosexual males, yet they still regard themselves as male.

An important piece of evidence in favor of this model is that there is a clear birth order effect on male homosexuality. Every older brother a male has increases his odds of being homosexual by 0.3. This is partly because the mother's immune system will react more strongly with every male pregnancy, and there might be group-level evolutionary benefits, as well: if there are already a large number of boys, then a homosexual

---

29—Ray Blanchard, "Review and Theory of Handedness, Birth Order, and Homosexuality in Men," *Laterality*, 13 (2008): 51-70.

boy will not elevate inter-male conflict any further.[30] Blanchard's model of the causes of homosexuality has been applied to people suffering from Gender Dysphoria. There is a clear birth order effect: male homosexual transsexuals fall into a significantly later birth order than do autogynepilious transsexuals.[31] Consistent with this, it has been shown that the brains of homosexual transsexuals (whether transmen or transwomen) differ significantly from those of the same gender who are not homosexual transsexuals:

> Cortical thickness and diffusion tensor imaging studies suggest that the brain of [Males-to-Females] presents complex mixtures of masculine, feminine, and demasculinized regions, while [Females-to-Males] show feminine, masculine, and defeminized regions.[32]

These data would indicate that the minority of transsexuals who are "homosexual transsexuals" are, to a certain degree, "born into the wrong body." This is principally due to epigenetic processes that occur *in utero*. Homosexual transsexuals are likely to be marked out by the way in which they will have intense difficulty conforming to the expectations of their biological sex from an extremely young age.

30—David Moskowitz, Jonathan Turrubiates, Hector Lorano, *et al.*, "Physical, Behavioral, and Psychological Traits of Gay Men Identifying as Bears," *Archives of Sexual Behavior*, 42 (2013): 775-784.

31—Ray Blanchard and Peter Sheridan, "Sibship Size, Sibling Sex Ratio, Birth Order, and Parental Age in Homosexual and Nonhomosexual Gender Dysphorics," *Journal of Nervous and Mental Disease*, 180 (1992): 40-47.

32—Antonio Guillamon, Carme Junque, and Esther Gómez-Gil, "A Review of the Status of Brain Structure Research in Transsexualism," *Archives of Sexual Behavior*, 45 (2016): 1615-1648.

Further evidence of both forms of transsexuality being manifestations of developmental instability can be seen in the health of transsexuals. Their physical and mental health is far worse than is that of so-called "cis-gender" people. Transwomen, compared to males, report markedly elevated levels of high cholesterol, high blood pressure, vision problems, hearing problems, chronic pain, arthritis, digestive problems, lung problems, kidney complaints, diabetes, Post-Traumatic Stress Disorder, depression, and anxiety. They are also more likely to abuse alcohol, and even hard drugs such as heroin and crack, and engage in commercial sex work. Transmen are elevated in terms of obesity, smoking, asthma, depression, schizophrenia, sexually transmitted diseases, pubic lice, inflammatory conditions, previous menstrual irregularities, and premature or delayed menarche. They are also elevated in hyperandrogenism and, therefore, in a series of complications associated with elevated testosterone in females, including adrenal hyperplasia, and polycystic ovary syndrome.[33]

Transmen also have elevated rates of fibromyalgia (the condition Alex suffered from), though this is not significantly higher in transwomen than it is among the general population.[34] Some of these conditions help to explain why the sufferers are transsexual (as we will see below) or reflect the stresses inherent in being transsexual. But others, such as hearing problems, are likely to simply

33—Sari Reisner, Tonia Poteat, JoAnne Keatley, *et al.*, "Global Health Burden and Needs of Transgender Populations: A Review," *Lancet*, 388 (2016): 412-436.

34—Dana Levit, Jacob Ablin, Valeries Aloush, *et al.*, "Evaluating Fibromyalgia Symptoms in Transgender Patients," *Arthritis and Rheumatology*, 71 (2019): (suppl 10).

reflect the underlying factor of high mutational load and developmental instability.

TRANSSEXUALITY AND FETISHISM

For Blanchard, the kind of transsexual who most attracts public attention—and who are behind the prominence of transgenderism in contemporary public discourse—is the kind who suffers from autogynephilia. This is a fetish, or paraphilia, whereby a man, for example, is "sexually aroused by the thought of himself as a female."[35] Autogynephilia ranges in its severity from mere transvestitism, where a man is deeply satisfied by dressing as a female, to, in its most extreme cases, transsexualism, where a male wants to alter his body such that it is more female-like. Perhaps it could be argued that demanding that society accept them as "real women" with precisely the same rights as "biological females" is an even more extreme manifestation of this paraphilia. Remaining a "she-male" would merely be a partial manifestation of this paraphilia.[36] It can be argued, however, that autogynephilia is more than simply a paraphilia, as there is a strong element of delusion involved in autogynephilia, which is not found in other fetishes. In this sense, as discussed above, autogynephilia is as much an example of dysphoria as it is an example of a paraphilia.

If it is reasonable to conceptualize transsexuality as a paraphilia, then the correlates of transsexuality and other paraphilia should be very similar. The same should be the

---

35—Anne Lawrence, "Autogynephilia: An Underappreciated Paraphilia," *Advances in Psychosomatic Medicine*, 31 (2011): 135-148.

36—Ray Blanchard, "The She-Male Phenomenon and the Concept of Partial Autogynephilia," *Journal of Sex and Marital Therapy*, 19 (1993): 69-76.

case with the correlates of other dysphoria. So, what is associated with more widely experienced fetishes—such as masochism, sexual sadism, or pedophilia? Reviews have consistently found that paraphilia is comorbid with hypersexuality, Autism Spectrum Disorder, Borderline Personality Disorder, Narcissistic Personality Disorder, and Psychopathic Personality Disorder.[37]

HYPERSEXUALITY

Paraphilia experience is placed on a spectrum ranging from no arousal to extreme and exclusive arousal by the paraphilia in question. It has been found that paraphilics have low cerebral serotonin levels, something which leads to high testosterone levels and thus a high sex drive. They report higher levels of sexual arousal, meaning that they might associate non-sexual targets, such as objects, with arousal because they are so easily sexually aroused. They report more diverse sexual interests, greater sexual orientation fluidity, more sexual activity, and a higher number of lifetime sexual partners than do non-paraphilics. In other words, paraphilia involves "recurrent, intense sexually arousing fantasies, sexual urges, or behaviors . . . that involve nonhuman objects, the suffering or humiliation of oneself or one's partner, or children or nonconsenting adults."[38]

These findings are very interesting in evolutionary terms, because they would potentially help to explain

---

37—See *Practical Guide to Paraphilia and Paraphilic Disorders*, edited by Richard Ballon (New York: Springer, 2016).

38—Stephen Kershnar, "Pedophilia" in *Enclopedia of Applied Ethics,* edited by Ruth Chadwick (New York: Academic Press, 2012).

how paraphilia remains in populations.[39] In line with the predictions made by Blanchard's model, it has been found that transsexuality is comorbid with hypersexuality.[40] Hypersexuality, and other sexual dysfunctions, also correlate with anorexia.[41]

AUTISM SPECTRUM DISORDER

Autism Spectrum Disorder (ASD), as already discussed, is associated with deficiencies in empathy and a concomitant propensity towards extreme analytical thinking. It has been conceptualized as the "Extreme Male Brain," and autistic people tend to be physically masculinized, displaying various markers associated with high levels of male hormones.[42] Congruous with this, autistic individuals tend to attach meaning to concrete visual representations: they are interested in "things," rather than people, disliking the unpredictable and unscripted nature of human interaction. You probably know someone

---

39—Christian Joyal and Jan Ankfold, "Paraphilia," in *Encyclopedia of Evolutionary Psychological Science*, edited by Todd Shackelford and Vivian Weekes-Shackelford (New York: Springer, 2017); Michele Heare, Maria Barsky, and Lawrence Faziola, "A Case of Mania Presenting with Hypersexual Behavior and Gender Dysphoria That Resolved With Valproic Acid," *Mental Illness*, 8 (2016): 2.

40—James Cantor and Katherine Sutton, "Paraphilia, Gender Dysphoria, and Hypersexuality," in *Oxford Textbook of Psychopathology*, edited by Theodore Millon, Robert F. Krueger, and Paul H. Blaney (Oxford: Oxford University Press, 2015).

41—Giovanni Castellini, Lorenzo Lelli, Valda Ricca, *et al.*, "Sexuality in Eating Disorders Patients: Etiological Factors, Sexual Dysfunction and Identity Issues. A Systematic Review," *Hormone and Molecular Biology and Clinical Investigation*, 25 (2016): 2.

42—Baron-Cohen, "The Extreme Male Brain Theory of Autism," *op cit.*

who seems highly detached socially, overly logical, and is obsessed with his job, hobby, or something apparently arcane, whether it be video games, online gambling, or evolutionary psychology.

Paraphilia crosses over with autism in the sense that paraphilia involves strong attachment to an object (usually a visual stimulus) and is highly scripted, in the sense that specific situations involving this stimulus can be particularly sexually arousing. It has been found that "high functioning" (intellectually normal) autistic people, particularly those who are male, are more likely to have paraphilic interests than the general population.[43] Consistent with Blanchard's model, it is quite clear that transsexuality is associated with autism. Dutch medic Gunter Heylens and his colleagues found that transgender persons were six times more likely than the general population to suffer from Autism Spectrum Disorder, with transwomen being more likely to have an Autism Spectrum Disorder than transmen.[44] Dutch medic Anna van der Miesen and colleagues, who conducted a systematic literature review, found that children with Gender Dysphoria score higher on all subdomains of Autism Spectrum Disorder than do controls.[45] It is therefore a reasonable conclusion that transsexuality is associated

43—Daniel Schöttle, Peer Birken, Oliver Tuescher, *et al.*, "Sexuality in Autism: Hypersexual and Paraphilic Behavior in Women and Men With High-functioning Autism Spectrum Disorder," *Dialogues in Clinical Neuroscience*, 19 (2017): 381-393.

44—Gunter Heylens, Lore Aspeslagh, Jesper Dierickx, *et al.*, "The Co-occurrence of Gender Dysphoria and Autism Spectrum Disorder in Adults: An Analysis of Cross-Sectional and Clinical Chart Data," *Journal of Autism and Developmental Disorders*, 48 (2018): 2217-2223.

45—Anna van der Miesen, Annelou de Vries, Thomas Steensma, *et al.*, "Autistic Symptoms in Children and Adolescents with Gender Dysphoria," *Journal of Autism and Developmental Disorders*, 48 (2018): 1537-1548.

with Autism Spectrum Disorder. Anorexia, a prominent example of a dysphoria, is also robustly associated with ASD, according to a systematic review of eight studies.[46]

BORDERLINE PERSONALITY DISORDER

Autism is also associated with Borderline Personality Disorder and is characterized by a weak sense of self. Autistic individuals lack the feeling that they are the same person across time and lack the feeling that they are in control of their thoughts and actions. This is possibly because, lacking empathy, they find that they cannot predict the consequences of their actions and, hypersensitive to stimuli, they easily become overwhelmed by the world. The consequence is a chaotic and frightening void, which can result in a coping mechanism whereby you create an extreme and certain identity. Eventually, however, chronic self-doubt results in the collapse of this identity and the adoption of another, sometimes very different one. This, in turn, is the essence of Borderline Personality Disorder (BPD), which is elevated in both paraphilics and autistic people.[47]

BPD is characterized by difficulties regulating emotion, feeling intense emotions, and having problems returning to a stable baseline, frequent mood swings, a fear of abandonment, and a disturbed sense of self.

46—Heather Westwood and Kate Tchanturia, "Autism Spectrum Disorder in Anorexia Nervosa: An Updated Literature Review," *Current Psychiatry Reports*, 19 (2017): 41.

47—Viktoria Lyons and Michael Fitzgerald, "Atypical Sense of Self in Autism Spectrum Disorders: A Neuro- Cognitive Perspective," *InTech Open*, March 6, 2013, doi: 10.5772/53680.

Specifically: "The self is impoverished, poorly developed, or there is an unstable self-image, which is often associated with excessive self-criticism; chronic feelings of emptiness; and dissociative states under stress." Such a person has difficulty developing a sense of self that is stable in terms of beliefs and life goals over time. He can have extreme and polarized self-conceptions, sometimes to the extent of developing multiple personalities. He can lack a coherent image of who he is; he can undergo "explosive shifts into states where the perception of self is distorted and shows weak correspondence with external reality." And he may lack a capacity to flexibly adapt to change. Sufferers experience discontinuity in their development of self, rapidly alter their roles and relationships, and "identify only with their present affective states and have no sense of their continuity over time."[48]

It has been found that sexual masochism is 10 times higher in women with Borderline Personality Disorder than it is among controls.[49] Many other studies, also of men, found a robust association between paraphilic

---

48—Natalie Gold and Michaelis Kyratsous, "Self and Identity in Borderline Personality Disorder: Agency and Mental Time Travel," *Journal of Evaluation in Clinical Practice*, 23 (2017): 1020-1028.

49—Álvaro Frías, Laura González, Cárol Palma, *et al.*, "Is There a Relationship Between Borderline Personality Disorder and Sexual Masochism in Women?" *Archives of Sexual Behavior*, 46 (2017): 747-754. Masochism may reflect a fast Life History Strategy whereby you are attracted to highly dominant people, who would survive in an unstable ecology. They can only prove their dominance by dominating you. Thus, it is potentially adaptive to be sexually aroused by being dominated because you are then attracted to the dominant type who is most likely to ensure that your genes are passed on should you be impregnated by him. This has been discussed in greater depth in Edward Dutton, *Witches, Feminism, and the Fall of the West* (Whitefish: Radix, 2021).

sexuality and Borderline Personality Disorder.[50] It is also associated with Gender Dysphoria. At least two separate studies have found that roughly 80 percent of transgender people display symptoms of BPD or related disorders.[51] Anorexia, as another example of a dysphoria, is also associated with BPD.[52]

NARCISSISTIC PERSONALITY DISORDER

In terms of a strongly distorted sense of self, Borderline Personality Disorder crosses over with the related condition of Narcissistic Personality Disorder. Indeed, in some respects, Narcissism can be understood as an example of Borderline Personality Disorder, though it is more common among males than females. Narcissistic Personality Disorder is characterized by:

- Grandiosity, with expectations of superior treatment from other people
- Fixation on fantasies of power, success, intelligence, or attractiveness
- Self-perception of being unique, superior, and

50—Antonio Prunas, Rossello Di Pierro, and Roberto Bernorio, "The Relationship Between Personality Organization and Sexual Life in a Community Sample of Men," *Psychoanalytic Psychotherapy*, 4 (2016): 345-358.

51—Atefeh Ghanbari Jolfaei, Azadeh Mazaheri Meybodi, and Ahmad Hajebi, "The Frequency of Personality Disorders in Patients With Gender Identity Disorder," *Medical Journal of the Islamic Republic of Iran*, 28 (2014): 90; Kurt Seikworski, Sabine Gollek, Wolfgang Harth, *et al.*, "Borderline Personality Disorder and Transsexualism," *Psychiatrische Praxis*, 35 (2008):135-41.

52—Clive Kelly and Matthew Davies, "A Review of Anorexia Nervosa, Its Relationship to Autism and Borderline Personality Disorder, and Implications for Patient Related Outcomes," *Journal of Psychiatry and Psychiatric Disorders*, 3 (2019): 207-215.

associated with high-status people and institutions
- Needing continual admiration from others
- A sense of entitlement to special treatment and to obedience from others
- Being exploitative of others to achieve personal gain
- Unwilling to empathize with the feelings, wishes, and needs of other people
- Being intensely envious of others, and believing that others are equally envious of them
- A pompous and arrogant demeanor[53]

Narcissistic Personality Disorder has also been found to be a key predictor of paraphilic sexuality.[54] It is also associated with Gender Dysphoria. One study found that, of a male and female sample of people suffering from Gender Dysphoria, 57 percent met the criteria for Narcissistic Personality Disorder and 81 percent, the criteria for some kind of personality abnormality, mainly BPD.[55] A review has found other studies that have highlighted this relationship between Transsexuality and Narcissistic Personality Disorder.[56] It has been found that Anorexia is associated with Narcissistic

53—Hiram Caton, "The Exalted Self: Derek Freeman's Quest for the Perfect Identity," *Identity: An International Journal of Theory and Research*, 5 (2005): 4.

54—Ashley Watts, Madeline Nagel, Robert Latzman, *et al.*, "Personality Disorder Features and Paraphilic Interests Among Undergraduates: Differential Relations and Potential Antecedents," *Journal of Personality Disorders*, 33 (2018): 22-48.

55—Atefeh Ghanbari Jolfaei, Azadeh Mazaheri Meybodi, and Ahmad Hajebi, "The Frequency of Personality Disorders in Patients with Gender Identity Disorder," *Medical Journal of the Islamic Republic of Iran*, 28 (2014): 90.

56—Anne Lawrence, "Shame and Narcissistic Rage in Autogynephilic Transsexualism," *Archives of Sexual Behavior*, 37 (2008): 457-461.

Personality Disorder, specifically with the "vulnerable Narcissism" sub-type.[57] Such people present all of the symptoms of standard Narcissistic Personality Disorder except "grandiosity." This is replaced by "vulnerability," characterized by a constant need for reassurance that one is exceptional, by introversion and by being self-absorbed, high in Neuroticism (feeling negative feelings strongly), and hyper-sensitivity to criticism. In all of these senses, the Vulnerable Narcissist is the opposite of the Grandiose Narcissist, for the latter will be confident that he is exceptional, will be extraverted, and will appear relatively impervious to criticism.[58]

It is easy to see why Narcissism would be associated with transsexuality. Autistic individuals are prone to sexual arousal by objects (fetishes), to a weak sense of self (fundamentally questioning who and what he is), and to Narcissism (as a means of coping with his fundamental sense of fear and chaos). These would come together in his being sexually aroused by the ideal of himself as the "perfect female." Those who questioned his femaleness would, therefore, risk destroying his necessary coping-mechanism, resulting in "Narcissistic Rage." It has been suggested that this makes sense of the often aggressive and furious way in which trans activists seem to respond to those who dare disagree with them.[59]

57—Federico Amianto, *et al.*, "Narcissism and Eating Disorders in Adolescent Population," *EC Paediatrics,* 5 (2017): 58-63.

58—Emanuel Jauk, Elena Weigle, Konrad Lehmann, *et al.*, "The Relationship between Grandiose and Vulnerable (Hypersensitive) Narcissism," *Frontiers in Psychology*, 8 (2017):1600.

59—Anne Lawrence, "Shame and Narcissistic Rage in Autogynephilic Transsexualism," *Archives of Sexual Behavior*, 37 (2008): 457-461.

PSYCHOPATHIC PERSONALITY DISORDER

Psychopathic Personality Disorder, now officially known as "Antisocial Behavioral Disorder," is characterized by,

- Inability to sustain consistent work behavior
- Non-conformity, irritability, and aggression
- Failure to honor financial obligations
- Frequent lying, failure to plan ahead and impulsivity;
- Reckless behavior
- Inability to function as a responsible parent
- Failure to maintain long-term monogamous relationships
- Lack of remorse
- Conduct Disorder in childhood[60]

Psychopathic traits are associated with paraphilia, possibly because of the way in which psychopaths are highly interested in power and control; in the case of males, this causes them to be aroused by voyeurism and sadism.[61] However, it may simply be that psychopathic personality and paraphilia are both expressions of developmental instability. As we would predict, there are elevated levels of psychopathology among transsexuals.[62]

60—Richard Lynn, "Racial and Ethnic Differences in Psychopathic Personality" *Personality and Individual Differences*, 32: (2002): 273-316.

61—Rob van Bommel, Kasia Uzieblo, Stefan Bogaerts, *et al.*, "Psychopathic Traits and Deviant Sexual Interests: The Moderating Role of Gender," *International Journal of Forensic Mental Health*, 17 (2018): 256-271.

62—Cecilia Dhejne, Roy Van Vlerken, Gunter Heylens, *et al.*, "Mental Health and Gender Dysphoria: A Review of the Literature," *International Review of Psychiatry*, 28 (2016): 44-57.

In summary, it can be seen that people who suffer from Gender Dysphoria display all of the key psychological features that are associated with paraphilics. And like paraphilics, they are more likely than controls to be hyper-sexual, suffer from Autism Spectrum Disorder, be diagnosed with Borderline Personality Disorder or Narcissistic Personality Disorder, and display features of Psychopathic Personality Disorder. In addition, we have noted that all of these characteristics are found, to an elevated degree, among those who display another well-researched dysphoria—namely anorexia nervosa.

GENDER DYSPHORIA AND MASCULINIZATION

We are confronted with an additional question. Are late-onset transsexuals suffering from a delusion about themselves? Or are they correct in their assertion that they were "born into the wrong body" but have, for some reason, only recognized this as adolescents or adults? If it is the former (that is, they are delusional), sufferers from Gender Dysphoria should display the same, or similar, correlates to those who suffer from other mind-body dysphoria, such as anorexics. Specifically, they should display evidence of masculinization, and it is masculine traits that are associated with other dysphoria, including anorexia, which is generally associated with females.

A recent study has tested this possibility.[63] The

63— Edward Dutton and Guy Madison, "Gender Dysphoria and Transgender Identity is Associated with Physiological and Psychological Masculinization: A Theoretical Integration of Findings, Supported by Systematic Reviews," *Sexuality Research and Social Policy*, 18 (2021): 788-799.

researchers conducted a series of systematic reviews on original studies in order to test the relationship between Gender Dysphoria and at least one correlate of androgens (male hormones) out of Autism Spectrum Disorder, left-handedness, 2D:4D Ratio (the shape of the hands; males tend to display a relatively smaller difference in finger length compared to females), being male, and male heterosexuality. They found that people with Gender Dysphoria did, indeed, tend to display these signs of masculinization. They were more likely to be left-handed, suffer from Autism Spectrum Disorder, have a low (masculinized) 2D:4D ratio, be male, and want to have sex with females, even if they were male-to-female transsexuals. The researchers' analysis concluded that 65 percent of gender transitions in the U.S. between 2002 and 2013 were male-to-female. They also highlighted research from Finland, from 2019, which revealed that 3.6 percent of male children—but only 2.3 percent of female children—displayed some symptoms of Gender Dysphoria.[64] They further pointed out that a 2015 survey of 3,000 transwomen reported that at least 60 percent claimed to be gynephilious (sexually attracted to women) in their new gender; 27 percent were exclusively gynephilious; and 19 percent exclusively androphilious (sexually attracted to men). Interestingly, the most famous transwoman of them all, Caitlyn Jenner (formerly Bruce Jenner), is reportedly in a relationship with another transwoman.[65]

64—Riittakerttu Kaltiala-Heino, Marja Työläjärvi, and Nina Lindberg, "Gender Dysphoria in Adolescent Population: A 5-year Replication Study," *Clinical Child Psychology and Psychiatry*, 24 (2019): 379-387.

65—Owen Tonks, "Love Is In The Air: Who is Caitlyn Jenner's Partner Sophia Hutchins and How Long Have They Been Dating?" *The Sun*,

Among transmen (female-to-male transition), in contrast, only 12 percent were exclusively gynephilious, while 23 percent were exclusively androphilious, but the proportions of those who were non-exclusively attracted to either sex were not reported. They observed that two percent of the British population claim to be lesbian, gay, or bisexual. So, clearly, transwomen, as the researchers would predict, overwhelmingly retain male sexual desires. And even among transmen, what is effectively lesbianism, which is associated with masculinization, is strongly over-represented.[66] The researchers also found that other dysphoria display similar correlates. Female anorexics, compared to controls, are not only higher in autism but also have a lower 2D:4D ratio (their hands are more masculinized). They further hypothesized that autism may be key to understanding the development of various dysphoria, which are often comorbid. (Among other things, transsexuals have elevated levels of anorexia.)[67] The researchers argue that autistic people tend to have a weak sense of self, making them prone to the disturbed sense of identity, and of reality, that is inherent in all dysphoria. In other words, you believe that you are something that you are not. Autistic individuals would also be more likely to develop fetishes, and it is in its paraphilic nature where

November 26, 2019, https://www.thesun.co.uk/tvandshowbiz/6773717/caitlyn-jenner-girlfriend-sophia-hutchins-age-married/.

66—Edward Dutton and Guy Madison, "Gender Dysphoria and Transgender Identity is Associated with Physiological and Psychological Masculinization: A Theoretical Integration of Findings, Supported by Systematic Reviews," 18 (2020): 788-799.

67—Simona Giordano, "Eating Yourself Away: Reflections on the 'Comorbidity' of Eating Disorders and Gender Dysphoria," *Clinical Ethics* (2017), https://doi.org/10.1177/1477750916661977.

gender dysphoria diverges from other dysphoria. This is consistent with Gender Dysphoria being characterized as a paraphilia of "erotic target identity inversion," whereby people attempt to *become* the object of their desire.[68]

Accordingly, it appears that transsexuality should be characterized both as a paraphilia and a dysphoria and, moreover, that there is considerable crossover between these two disorders in terms of their correlates. Autism itself, for example, has been found to be a manifestation of developmental instability. Not only is it associated with numerous markers of developmental instability, such as sinistrality, but it is robustly correlated with paternal age. This is because, as men age, their semen includes more *de novo* mutations, including those that lead to the development of autism.[69]

ENVIRONMENTAL CAUSES

So, having established that there is a sound theoretical case for understanding transsexuality both as a paraphilia and as a dysphoria, we now need to make sense of its environmental causes. This is crucial. As we saw, in the case of autogynephilious transsexuals, it is significantly a function of environmental factors—though many of these may be influenced by genetics. That transsexuality is strongly environmental is consistent with evidence that

---

68—Anne Lawrence, "Autogynephilia: An Underappreciated Paraphilia," *Advances in Psychosomatic Medicine*, 31 (2011): 135-148.

69—Michael Woodley of Menie, Matthew Sarraf, Radomir Pestow, *et al.*, "Social Epistasis Amplifies the Fitness Costs of Deleterious Mutations, Engendering Rapid Fitness Decline Among Modernized Populations," *Evolutionary Psychological Science*, 3 (2017): 181-191.

it develops in adolescence; generally speaking, the later a phenomenon manifests, the less strongly genetic it is likely to be. Indeed, the persistence of Gender Dysphoria is predicted by how young a person is when they first display symptoms: and the younger it develops, the more persistent it is.[70] A primarily environmental explanation would be congruous with a growing body of evidence that many transsexuals wish to revert back, such that they physically resemble their biological sex, some years after transitioning.[71] Indeed, this would be congruous with transsexuality being a paraphilia, which becomes more or less intense due to environmental variables.

American gynaecologist Lisa Littman has referred to what she calls "rapid-onset Gender Dysphoria," in which adolescents with no previous indication of gender confusion appear to very suddenly declare themselves "non-binary" or transgender. Littman avers that this may be the expression of a "social coping mechanism" for other issues, such as an adolescent homosexual phase. This is rendered increasingly common by "social contagion." Indeed, Littman notes,

> Parents describe that the onset of gender dysphoria
> seemed to occur in the context of belonging to a peer

70—Thomas Steensma, Jenifer McGuire, Baudewijntje Kreukels, *et al.*, "Factors Associated With Desistence and Persistence of Childhood Gender Dysphoria: A Quantitative Follow-up Study," *Journal of the American Academy of Child and Adolescent Psychiatry*, 52 (2013): 582-590.

71—Jack Turban and Alex Keuroghlian, "Dynamic Gender Presentations: Understanding Transition and "De-Transition" Among Transgender Youth," *Journal of the American Academy of Child and Adolescent Psychiatry*, 57 (2018): 451–453; Sara Danker, Sasha Narayan, Rachel Bluebond-Langner, *et al.*, "A Survey Study of Surgeons' Experience with Regret and/or Reversal of Gender-Confirmation Surgeries," *Plastic and Reconstructive Surgery—Global Open*, 6 (2018): 189. doi:10.1097/01.GOX.0000547077.23299.00.

group where one, multiple, or even all of the friends have become gender dysphoric and transgender-identified during the same timeframe. Parents also report that their children exhibited an increase in social media/internet use prior to disclosure of a transgender identity.[72]

Unlike with most cases of late-onset transsexuality, this is a predominantly female phenomenon: 82 percent of a sample of parents who reported having an adolescent child who experienced rapid-onset Gender Dysphoria were referring to a daughter; 41 percent of these had expressed interest in a non-heterosexual orientation prior to declaring their Gender Dysphoria; 62 percent had a history of mental illness; and 38 percent belonged to a peer group of people who had all declared themselves "non-binary" or "trans" at around the same time. In these respects, Rapid-Onset Gender Dysphoria is highly comparable to anorexia. This also seems to occur, in a socially contagious fashion, among adolescent female peer-groups and, as we have discussed, it has the same corollaries as Gender Dysphoria and also correlates with it.[73] It is thus not without good reason that a number of commentators have asked "Is transgender the new anorexia?"[74] This is a perfectly reasonable question to ask, at least with regard to Rapid-Onset Gender Dysphoria.

72—Lisa Littman, "Parent Reports of Adolescents and Young Adults Perceived to Show Signs of a Rapid Onset of Gender Dysphoria," *PLoS ONE*, 13 (2018): e0202330, https://doi.org/10.1371/journal.pone.0202330.

73—Stephen Allison, Megan Warin, and Tarun Bastianpillai, "Anorexia Nervosa and Social Contagion: Clinical Implications," *Australia and New Zealand Journal of Psychiatry*, 48 (2014): 116-120.

74—Robert Tracinski, "Is Transgender the New Anorexia?" *The Federalist*, September 6, 2018. https://thefederalist.com/2018/09/06/transgender-new-anorexia/.

Due to the relative rarity of transsexuality, the studies on its environmental causes are generally clinical studies with small sample sizes, meaning that it behoves us to be cautious of their results. With that caveat, it has been observed that boys who later suffer from Gender Dysphoria tend to be raised in suboptimal environments, in which the parents frequently fight with each other and in which the fathers have low self-esteem and are emotionally distant, while the mothers are high on psychopathology, leading to the boy having an unclear sense of self-value and a high level of anxiety. It has been averred that these conditions may result in sexual identity problems, and that Gender Dysphoria thus has a significant environmental component. Clinical observation of girls with Gender Dysphoria indicates that they tend to have emotionally distant mothers, with whom they are often in conflict and fathers who abuse their mothers, possibly leading the girl to identify as a boy.[75] Another study found elevated levels of Borderline Personality Disorder among the mothers of boys who suffer from Gender Dysphoria.[76]

A study in Taiwan found that students with Gender Dysphoria are more likely to have unaffectionate parents.[77] There is evidence that girls with anorexia tend to have

75—Kenneth Zucker, Susan Bradley, Dahlia Ben-Dat, *et al.*, "Psychopathology in the Parents of Boys with Gender Identity Disorder," *Journal of the American Academy of Child Adolescent Psychiatry*, 42 (2003): 2-4.

76—Sonia Marantz and Susan Coates, "Mothers of Boys with Gender Identity Disorder: A Comparison of Matched Controls," *Journal of the American Academy of Child and Adolescent Psychiatry*, 30 (1991): 310-315.

77—Meng-Chuan Lai, Yen-Nan Chiu, Kenneth D. Gadow, *et al.*, "Correlates of Gender Dysphoria in Taiwanese University Students," *Archives of Sexual Behavior*, 39 (2010): 1415-1428.

emotionally distant mothers as well. Their mothers are more likely to suffer from Alexithymia, that is, having difficulties verbalizing and otherwise expressing emotions.[78] Females with Gender Dysphoria tend not merely to exhibit Autism Spectrum Disorder symptoms but also evidence being higher on measures of psychopathology.[79]

The problem with all of these studies, in terms of understanding the environmental causes of dysphoria, is that they are heavily genetically confounded. If the mothers of transgender boys are high on psychopathology, it may be that being raised by such a mother elevates the likelihood of Gender Dysphoria. But it may also be that such a mother is highly masculinized, or otherwise high in mutational load, and it is this that has led to *in utero* developmental instability, eventually manifesting in a transsexual son, who is also likely to have inherited, to some extent, his mother's psychopathic personality traits.

The same is true with regard to Borderline Personality Disorder, which is elevated among both transsexuals and their mothers. Indeed, 53 percent of mothers of boys with Gender Dysphoria have this disorder compared to six percent of controls.[80] So, it is extremely difficult to tease

---

78—Laura Balottin, Renata Nacinovich, Monica Bomba, *et al.*, "Alexithymia in Parents and Adolescent Anorexic Daughters: Comparing the Responses to TSIA and TAS-20 Scales," *Neuropsychiatric Disease and Treatment,* 10 (2014): 1941-1951.

79—Rittakerttu Kaltiala-Heino, Maria Sumia, Marja Työläjärvi, *et al.*, "Two Years of Gender Identity Service for Minors: Overrepresentation of Natal Girls with Severe Problems in Adolescent Development," *Child and Adolescent Psychiatry and Mental Health*, 9:9.

80—S. Maratz and S. Coates, "Mothers of Boys with Gender Identity Disorder: A Comparison of Matched Controls," *Journal of the American Academy of Child and Adolescent Psychiatry*, 30 (1991): 310-315.

out the environmental causes of Gender Dysphoria. It is possible that there is a symbiotic relationship between genetics, *in utero* developmental instability, and childhood environment, whereby the son of a mother with Borderline Personality Disorder is more likely to manifest this, and thus potentially Gender Dysphoria. This hypothesis, while plausible, needs to be formally tested.

THE BREAKDOWN OF SELECTION AND GENDER DYSPHORIA

This leaves us with a further question: Why has there been a rise, in recent years, in the prominence of transgenderism? This may be partly explicable in terms of the Social Epistasis Amplification Model, which has been presented by Michael Woodley of Menie and his colleagues and which we have already explored.[81] The dramatic change in infant mortality would have a number of related effects. Firstly, there would be more people with fitness-damaging mutations of the mind, such as deviant sexuality or even a propensity towards Gender Dysphoria. Secondly, such people would be more likely to be maladaptively influenced by hormones *in utero*.

Thirdly, society would be influenced, in a fitness-reducing way, by these maladapted people—thus the term "Spiteful Mutants"—who would interfere with the development of some non-mutants. Indeed, some of these Spiteful Mutants might actively encourage easily influenced

---

81—Woodley of Menie, Sarraf, Pestow, *et al.*, "Social Epistasis Amplifies the Fitness Costs of Deleterious Mutations, Engendering Rapid Fitness Decline Among Modernized Populations," *op cit.*

young people to experiment with the idea that they are "non-binary," to believe that this was "normal," or that it was even a social good to be non-binary or transsexual. Spiteful Mutants would act to undermine institutions and ideas that promoted the development of adaptive behavior and ways of thinking, such as religiousness.

In the 1950s, in Western countries, a person would be less likely to know about the existence of transsexuals. If he happened to suffer from Gender Dysphoria himself, he would likely do all he could to repress this, knowing that he would be shunned if he did not. He might, possibly, even believe that such behavior would anger his god. This ability, to force yourself to think in a socially adaptive manner, is known as "effortful control."[82] In the following decade, these social controls, which militated against fitness-reducing thinking and behavior, began to collapse.

At the time of writing, it might be argued that it is "socially adaptive" to force yourself to believe that much in the above discussion must be false, despite the fact that it is based on careful scientific studies, with the results often being widely replicated. This is best exemplified in the firing of Maya Forstater, mentioned above, for stating a scientific fact. As we noted, she originallly lost her Employment Tribunal in which she challenged her firing. Judge James Taylor, presiding over the tribunal, made the following ruling:

> If a person has transitioned from male to female and has a Gender Recognition Certificate (GRC), that

---

82—Kevin MacDonald, "Effortful Control, Explicit Processing, and the Regulation of Human Evolved Predispositions," *Psychological Review*, 115 (2008): 1012-1031.

person is legally a woman. That is not something [Miss Forstater] is entitled to ignore. [Miss Forstater's] position is that even if a trans woman has a GRC, she cannot honestly describe herself as a woman. That belief is not worthy of respect in a democratic society. Even paying due regard to the qualified right to freedom of expression, people cannot expect to be protected if their core belief involves violating others' dignity and creating an intimidating, hostile, degrading, humiliating, or offensive environment for them.[83]

In other words, believing in the empirical truth, and asserting that you believe in the empirical truth, is a stance that is not, in itself, "worthy of respect in a democratic society." There should be no legal protection for those who construct a worldview based on science, reason, and empirical evidence, if aspects of this worldview lead to negative emotions in some people, specifically people who have mind-body dysphoria.

Such a ruling might be seen to strongly incentivize "effortful control" in order to convince oneself that "black is white." In other words, the transsexual movement can be regarded as a sub-component of the Woke crucible of evolution. Those who are strongly genetically healthy will not be drawn into becoming transsexual, whatever the broader culture might promote. Some people, however, will be drawn into it, thus reducing their fitness. This acceptability of transsexuality will foster an evolutionary mismatch, and those with a strong genetic desire to breed,

83—*Maya Foster v. CGD Europe, Center for Global Development, Masood Ahmed*, Employment Appeal Tribunal, 2021.

and a genetic propensity towards highly adaptive thought patterns, such as traditional religiosity, will avoid being sucked into the dysphoria and nihilism that this produces. Thus, the transsexual movement indirectly promotes the genetically healthy and helps to cull the unhealthy. Effectively, it is eugenic.

RETURNING TO ALEX . . . AND DREYA

So, we have substantially made sense of transgenderism, which is best understood as a dysphoria and paraphilia. In this regard, it has the key correlates of both, including severe disturbances of personality. This might best explain the aggressive Narcissism that many have observed in transsexuals. Autism (and thus masculinization), it seems, is the factor that connects everything together.

This brings us back to Alex, my friend from Durham University. There was an irrational and bombastic side to the young man I knew. He attended left-wing protests, where he could be rather rambunctious. My friends and I were dumbfounded by what we discovered about Alex back in December 2001, but perhaps we shouldn't have been. One of my friends, the philosophy student who was also at Alex's 21st, later remarked that such behavior was simply a manifestation of Alex's "avant-garde genius":

> He's going to do it. He's actually going to mutilate his body. Maybe he's not mentally ill at all. Why would anybody who was a man want to become a girl? Most men wouldn't even entertain something so fucking insane. But not Alex. No way! He's too avant-garde! That guy is a fucking avant-garde

genius. I can only conclude that this is some sort of ultimate act of violent, avant-garde artistic sarcasm.

Well, he did do it. And before leaving university, Alex had transformed into "Dreya." Her subsequent academic work evinced a certain arrogance and narcissism—or "avant-garde genius"—that was there from the beginning. Dreya's Master's Thesis, *Logic in Context: Some Considerations Concerning the Philosophy, Sociology and History of Logic* (2006), begins with a quote from the English philosopher A. A. Luce (1882-1977), beneath which she wrote: "I will remark without hesitation that I regard the contents of this quote as arrant and polemical nonsense." Part of the quote is further referred to as "gibberish."[84]

In the student bar that night in 2001, Alex's logical abilities rather broke down in the face of a student of Arabic, who asked him what he hoped to achieve by what he was doing. Alex commented that what he was doing was only logical to other transgender people, to which it was retorted that there's no such thing as subjective logic— something Alex well knew.[85] Alex, and Dreya, could

84—Andrea Waddell, *Logic in Context: Some Considerations Concerning the Philosophy, Sociology and History of Logic* (Master's Thesis, University of Sussex: 2006), 2; *OrnaVerum*, Andrea Joanna Waddell (1980–2009), http://www.ornaverum.org/family/waddell-andrea.html.

85—I have explored elsewhere the runaway individualism, Narcissism, and Neo-Gnosticism that underpins this way of thinking. In essence, as the Gnostics believed, we are sparks of divine light in a world of darkness; we are gods who define ourselves. Nothing can be allowed to cause us "harm" or to question our "equality," not even objective truth. So there is no objective truth; there are just battles between "divine sparks" and "evil gods." Being gods, we define ourselves and this includes defining our own gender. After all, our "spark of divine light" is eternal and could have fallen into any random physical body. See Edward Dutton and J.O.A. Rayner-Hilles, *The Past is a Future Country: The Coming Conservative Demographic Revolution* (Exeter: Imprint Academic, In Press).

could be rather dogmatic. This led, Dreya for example, to present the fallacious argument, in the pages of *Philosophy Now* magazine, that "race" is a purely social construct, simply because "races" have some genes in common.[86] This position, manifestly, fails, due to the fact that races, as examples of humans, will, by definition, have some genes in common. This, however, was the same person who set up a talk at the Durham University Philosophy Society entitled, "Is Feminist Philosophy a Contradiction in Terms?" This event was advertised on a poster featuring Pamela Anderson in black underwear.

Interestingly, in 2008, there was an essay competition in the magazine *Philosophy Now*, where you had to answer the question: "Who is the Best Philosopher?" Rather than advocate for Heraclitus or David Hume, Dreya argued that *she* was. This breathtakingly original tactic meant that she was one of the winners. Her essay was entitled: "The Answer is: Me!"[87]

I didn't see Dreya much in the Spring term. But in my final months at university, the same comical situation kept recurring. I would walk up the road of Victorian houses to the university library, and a slender, pretty blonde girl would smile at me and wave from the other side of the road. "This is my lucky day!" I would think to myself . . . before realizing that it was Dreya. I last saw her in September 2002, when we met up in Bristol in the southwest of England. Just back from a holiday in Malta with her parents, Dreya

---

86—Andrea Waddell, "Race and Science," *Philosophy Now*, February/March 2006, https://philosophynow.org/issues/54/Letters.

87—Andrea Waddell, "The Answer Is: Me!" *Philosophy Now,* November/December 2008, https://philosophynow.org/issues/70/Who_Is_The_Best_Philosopher.

was planning to do a Master's degree in Political Philosophy at the University of Sussex in Brighton, a seaside town in southern England, known for its gay scene. We lost touch.

Years went by. . . In October 2009, I was scrolling through the *Mail Online*, when my attention was drawn to a photograph of a pretty girl wearing a mortar board and graduation robes. I knew her from somewhere. Who was she? It was Dreya. So much had happened in the meantime. She had been working as a prostitute in Brighton, operating out of her own home. And she had been found dead, and the flat, set on fire. The report said nothing about transsexuality.

Once I got over the shock, I knew immediately what must have happened. I could imagine it vividly. Some middle-aged, single man, probably uneducated, a laborer or something, pays Dreya for sex. He comments on how amazingly neat Dreya's vagina is or how uncommonly perfect her breasts are. Dreya, in her autistic innocence, replies, "*Yes. Well, they are very perfect, unnaturally perfect, but that's because I was actually born male and had gender reassignment therapy. So, like, that would explain their near-perfect shape.*" The manly builder, who prides himself on his manliness, realizes that, as far as he's concerned, he's had sex with a man. He completely loses all self-control. He strangles Dreya and then sets fire to the flat in the hope of avoiding detection.

I was sure that this was what had happened. I was so sure that I telephoned the newspaper to tell them so. The News Desk journalist was incredulous at being informed that "Andrea Joanna Waddell" (as was now the name) was once "Alexander John Waddell." He didn't believe me. He asked if anyone could corroborate what I was saying, so I gave him the phone number of a friend from university who did just that. It turned out that my instinct was shared even by the prosecution when the case came to trial in May 2010. The murderer, a 42-year-old Sky TV fitter named Neil McMillan, pleaded "not guilty," but was convicted due to forensic and CCTV evidence. He had paid Dreya £140 for sex but, at some point, also being very drunk, he lost his temper, punched Dreya in the face, and strangled her. Dreya fought back, leading to scratches and cuts on McMillan, but to no avail. We'll probably never know why McMillan murdered Dreya, but the prosecution was convinced that it was likely because McMillan discovered that Dreya was transsexual. The prosecuting barrister, Mr. Russell-Flint, said "McMillan may have attacked her in anger and in drink after discovering she had once been a man."[88]

As the trial progressed, Dreya's naivety became ever clearer. She kept £37,000 in cash at her flat in a filing cabinet in the sitting room. She advertised her services on websites such as one called "Adult Works." Dreya had even contacted the "National Union of Prostitutes" to ask how she could go about paying tax on her earnings.[89] In June 2010, McMillan was handed a life sentence, with the judge instructing that he serve a minimum of 22

88—*Get Reading*, "Andrea Waddell 'Strangled by Her Client,'" May 12, 2010, https://www.getreading.co.uk/news/local-news/andrea-waddell-strangled-client-4226743.

89—Alison Cridland, "£37,000 Found at Murdered Prostitute's Brighton Flat," *The Argus* May 14, 2010, https://www.theargus.co.uk/news/8164339.37000-found-at-murdered-prostitutes-brighton-flat/.

years.[90] Then in November, McMillan was found guilty of having raped a woman in a hotel room in September 2009, just a few weeks before he had murdered Dreya. He was sentenced to be detained at Her Majesty's Pleasure.[91] After the original trial, Dreya's family revealed yet more tragic information about her:

> Her life reads like a catalogue of disasters. She was bullied at school, knocked down by a car in Battersea, mugged in Prague, and once attacked by a gang of young thugs in Reading. While completing her second degree she developed acute ulcerative colitis which was nearly fatal, but she underwent successfully surgery resulting in an ileostomy, which was later reversed.[92]

The family had said, in 2009:

> Andrea was often incapacitated by pain and unable to work, and we know she was concerned about how to make a living and be independent. If her decision on how to achieve this took her down unusual paths, who are we to judge?[93]

90—*Metro*, "Neil McMillan Jailed For 22 Years For Andrea Waddell Murder," June 4, 2010, https://metro.co.uk/2010/06/04/neil-mcmillan-jailed-for-22-years-for-murdering-transgender-prostitute-356623/.

91—*Get Reading*, "Andrea Waddell Murderer Sentenced For Rape," November 22, 2010, https://www.getreading.co.uk/news/local-news/andrea-waddell-murderer-sentenced-rape-4220359.

92—Laura Miller, "Family Tribute to Brave Andrea Waddell," *Get Reading*, June 9, 2010, https://www.getreading.co.uk/news/local-news/family-tribute-brave-andrea-waddell-4225690.

93—Laura Miller, "We Will Never Stop Loving Andrea Waddell," *Get Reading*, October 21, 2009, https://www.getreading.co.uk/news/local-news/never-stop-loving-andrea-waddell-4233931.

I am not so much interested in judging Dreya, either. But we should try to understand her and people like her. This is especially important now that such people are increasingly socially prominent—and particularly now that you can lose your job if you fail to accept their assertions about gender and identity as unconditional facts.

My friend suffered from Gender Dysphoria and Paraphilia. My friend was autistic and seriously physically and mentally ill, points also congruous with these traits being products of developmental instability and high mutational load. Even her left-wing viewpoints have been shown to be associated with evidence of mutational load, as discussed earlier, which makes sense, as they tend to correlate with not having children, meaning that those who hold them are maladaptive.

Of course, saying this may be regarded as a "judgment" (albeit one empirically based), but if more people had "judged" my friend in this way—and, most of all, helped him and her through mental illness, rather than encouraged him and her to make a virtue out of it—Alex may well have been alive today, perhaps writing poetry, reviewing cutting-edge cocktails, and leading a local Philosophy Society.

CHAPTER 8

THE END OF LOVE

Herbivore Men and the Decline of Sex

> *The end of love should be a big event*
> *It should involve the hiring of a hall.*
> *Why the hell not? It happens to us all.*
> *Why should it pass without acknowledgement?*

—Sophie Hannah

In Japan, there is a growing cultural phenomenon that augers very badly for the future of the land of Shoguns, as well as the future of all industrialized countries: *Soshoku Danshi.* The term translates as "Herbivore Men." It was coined in 2007 by Japanese author Maki Fukasawa, as an insulting play on the established term *Nikushokukei Danshi,* meaning "Carnivore Men." Carnivore Men are highly competitive and status-driven, obsessed with ascending the hierarchy of the company that gave them a job for life, as well as with seducing women. These "Carnivores" were usually family men—in the sense that they were married and had children—but, driven by a race to the top, they didn't necessarily spend that much time taking their kids to the park. They were Alpha males and status was what *really* mattered.[1]

1—Tomoko Otake, "Blurring the Boundaries," *The Japan Times,* May

Japan entered a recession in 1990, which continues to this day. And gradually, social commentators began to document the emergence of a new kind of Japanese man, quite the opposite of the "Carnivores," once so prominent: *Soshoku Danshi*. These men are unambitious. Even if they are highly educated, they prefer menial, low-paying, and non-stressful work, which allows them abundant free time to pursue their interests. And their interests are assuredly *not* those that entertain a Carnivore in his limited free time. The Herbivore is effeminate. He spends his money on fashionable clothes and hairstyles, usually of a quite effete and "metrosexual" nature. He enjoys consuming foods that are traditionally indulged in by Japanese females, such as luxury chocolates. And as for women, he really doesn't have much interest in them at all; he does not try to seduce them, or at least is unsuccessful in doing so. The Herbivore is submissive. He is not interested in even the mildest form of competition; this includes, as he sees it, the competition that men must engage in to obtain women. Anyway, this competition will expose him to setbacks, rejections, emotional vulnerability, and even shame. For the Carnivore, these risks are worth it for the potential payoff of sex and status. Not so in the minds of Japan's "New Men."

The *Soshoku Danshi* doesn't even try. He hardly even attempts to develop friendships. These anti-Shoguns have a small number of male friends, but spend most of their time on the internet. Here his sex drive, to the extent that it exists at all, is satisfied by extremely realistic, high-definition pornography. And it is perpetually satisfied

10, 2009, https://www.japantimes.co.jp/life/2009/05/10/life/blurring-the-boundaries/#.XruhUWgzY2x.

because, as we will explore later, males are evolved to desire sexual variety; the ubiquity of free, real-life quality pornographic video means that this is exactly what they can attain, albeit in a digital and not physical form. Porn's realistic nature is now so pronounced that its user is sated, without bothering with the complications and stresses that a "real life" sexual relationship might bring. The Herbivore Man has his counterpart in the lesser known "Carnivore Woman"—*Nikushoku Joshi.* She is a woman with the mind of a Carnivore Man. Status-driven and ambitious; she "takes the initiative in life and in love."[2]

The result of all this is a sex crisis in Japan, one that, fascinatingly, is not even limited to the Herbivores. According to data from 2015, 42 percent of Japanese men and 44 percent of Japanese women aged between 18 and 34 are virgins. In 1992, 22 percent of women and 20 percent of men in this age range had never had sex. Narrowing it down to those aged 30 to 34, in 2015, 11.9 percent of Japanese women and 12.7 percent of Japanese men were still virgins. In 1992, by the same age range, 6.2 percent of women and 8.8 percent of men were still virgins.[3] The phenomenon of middle-aged virgin males is now so common that a term has been coined: *Yaramiso.* The word is a combination of *yaruzu* ("not doing it") and *misoji* (an old-fashioned term for someone who is "past it").[4] Even within marriage, sex in Japan is collapsing. A

2—Kittredge Cherry, *Womansword: What Japanese Words Say About Women* (Southbridge: Stonebridge Press, 2018).

3—University of Tokyo, "First National Estimates of Virginity in Japan: One in 10 Adults in Their 30s Remains a Virgin," *Medical Xpress,* April 8, 2019, https://medicalxpress.com/news/2019-04-national-virginity-japan-adults-30s.html.

4—Cherry, *Womansword, op cit.*

2014 survey which reported the rise of Japanese virginity also found that Japanese marriages were, increasingly, sexual deserts. In 2014, 47 percent of married Japanese people hadn't had sex for at least one month. In 2004, a mere 31.9 percent of married Japanese of either gender had been a month or more without "doing it."[5]

WHY IS THIS HAPPENING?

Why is this happening? Why are the Japanese losing their virginity later and later and then having less and less sex once they are married? Why have a growing number of Japanese males become effete pushovers, who have lost all interest in obtaining sex, let alone a girlfriend? And could this dire situation migrate to Western countries? As we will now see, it has already made inroads into the West. What is happening in Japan, and why it happened in Japan first, makes perfect sense in evolutionary terms.

Put simply, Darwinian selection has collapsed, leading to more and more people with fitness-damaging ways of seeing the world.[6] The Spiteful Mutants have helped to undermine institutions that promote adaptive behavior—such as traditional religiosity—and through this and other means, they have spread their maladaptive ideas to other people. This has also created an evolutionary mismatch,

---

5—Charlotte England, "Half of Japanese Couples in 'Sexless Marriages,'" *Independent*, February 15, 2017, https://www.independent.co.uk/news/world/asia/japan-couples-sexless-marriages-half-low-birth-rate-long-working-hours-family-planning-children-a7581061.html.

6—Michael A. Woodley of Menie, Matthew Sarraf, R. Pestow, and Heitor Fernandes, "Social Epistasis Amplifies the Fitness Costs of Deleterious Mutations, Engendering Rapid Fitness Decline Among Modernized Populations," *Evolutionary Psychological Science*, 3 (2017): 181-191.

as previously discussed, which will have caused even the sexuality of some relatively "normal" people to develop sub-optimally. In addition, the speed of technological change has created an additional mismatch: we are simply not adapted to the current situation in which we find ourselves. Evolved to an agricultural society of a very specific kind, our inclinations become strongly fitness-damaging in the current, radically different, zoo in which we now live. The explosion of the internet has rendered these inclinations even more problematic, and done so virtually overnight. The consequences have been seen first in Japan because, for reasons we will explore, Japanese people have evolved to be highly pro-social and very strongly adapted to a highly competitive ecology; they are thus profoundly sensitive to environmental change. The undermining of adaptive institutions—the growth of Spiteful Mutants and their influence—an increasing evolutionary mismatch—all have become more pronounced. We are seeing the beginnings of a Japanese-style situation in Western countries.

HOW SEXUALITY CAN GO AWRY

As we have discussed, the Spiteful Mutant is only "spiteful" because of the impact that he has on the wider breeding population, especially on its more genetically adaptive members. We would expect, therefore, the Spiteful Mutant to undermine the optimal development of sexuality among members of his group. How would he do this?

Bruce Charlton has highlighted the potential impact of mutational load on sexual development.[7] Charlton

---

7—Bruce Charlton, "Mutation Accumulation and Modern Western Sexuality," *Intelligence, Personality and Genius,* July 20, 2015, https://iqpersonalitygenius.

argues that the optimum development of sexuality involves an extremely complex sequence with ample room for things to go wrong at every step of the way, as noted earlier. Crucial to understanding what is happening in Japan are the "critical learning periods," particularly in childhood, in which there is important imprinting and other psychological development. For example, children would, under Darwinian conditions, have been told that there were "men" and "women" and it was wrong for one to try to behave like the other. These phases must all be successfully negotiated for sexuality to be adaptive. The breakdown of Darwinian selection means that all of these phases are less likely to be successfully negotiated by a growing percentage of the population.

Congruous with genetic changes, between 1989 and 2004, there was a substantial and age-independent decrease in average levels of serum testosterone in American males.[8] The researchers found that there was

---

blogspot.com/2015/07/mutation-accumulation-and-modern.html.

8—There is ongoing debate over the causes of this fall in testosterone among males. One proposal is that there has been an increase in recent decades in endocrine-disrupting chemicals in the environment and that these partly explain the decline. There are, however, many serious limitations to the studies that have found this, such as incomparable samples. See Hueiwang Anna Jeng, "Exposure to Endocrine Disrupting Chemicals and Male Reproductive Health," *Frontiers in Public Health*, 2 (2014): 55. Another possibility is that human societies, as with other pack animals, go through hormonal cycles across set time periods. These cause generations to vary in behavior and size, so giving the species an advantage against predator and prey, both of which will adapt to humans being of a certain modal type. According to this model, Western humans, born in the 1990s, were exposed to relatively low levels of testosterone, as this period was the trough of the testosterone cycle. See Janne Miettinen, "Cyclical Metapopulation Mechanism Hypothesis: Multiannual Animal Population Cycles are Created and Driven by a Multiannual Hormone Cycle," (2022). https://jannemiettinen.fi/FourthTurning/.

no apparent environmental factor that could explain this.[9] They did not look, however, into the possibility that males being constantly denigrated and placed in an evolutionary mismatch, and thus high stress, might act to reduce testosterone levels, which we would expect it to.[10]

Indeed, a number of other studies have also found dramatic declines in male testosterone levels, potentially too rapid to have a plausible genetic explanation, such as in Denmark and Finland.[11] These trends appear to be ongoing, and they are found among young American men in unpublished research that substantially controls for health.[12] Consistent with testosterone decline, whatever its causes, sperm counts among Western males fell by 59.3 percent between 1973 and 2011, a decline of about 1.6 percent per annum. There was, however, no significant fall among a Non-Western sample.[13] A number of studies have also found that Western males are becoming

9—Thomas Travison, Andre Araujo, Amy O'Donnell, *et al.*, "A Population-Level Decline in Serum Testosterone Levels in American Men," *Journal of Clinical Endocrinology and Metabolism,* 92 (2007): 196-202.

10—See, Jim Penman, *Biohistory: The Decline and Fall of the West* (Newcastle: Cambridge Scholars Publishing, 2015).

11— Anna-Maria Andersson, Tina Jensen, Anders Juul, *et al.*, "Secular Decline in Male Testosterone and Sex Hormone Binding Globulin Serum Levels in Danish Population Surveys," *Journal of Clinical Endocrinology and Metabolism*, 92 (2007): 4696-4705; Antti Perheentupa, Juuso Mäkinen, Tiina Laatikainen, *et al.*, "A Cohort Effect on Serum Testosterone Levels in Finnish Men," *European Journal of Endocrinology*, 168 (2013): 227-233.

12—Kristie Kahl, "Testosterone Levels Show Steady Decrease Among Young US Men," *Urology Times,* July 3, 2020, https://www.urologytimes.com/view/testosterone-levels-show-steady-decrease-among-young-us-men.

13—Hagai Levine, Niels Jørgensen, Anderson Martino-Andrade, *et al.* "Temporal Trends in Sperm Count: A Systematic Review and Meta-regression Analysis," *Human Reproduction Update*, 23 (2017): 646-659.

physically weaker, as measured by their "grip strength." These findings are among child samples, so the results cannot simply be put down to males being less likely to pursue physically arduous work than was once the case.[14]

To the extent that mutation is a factor, it is relevant that if you have a weak immune system, which you will if you have high mutational load, then your body must work harder to fight off disease, which reduces testosterone levels.[15] Disease, which you will be less able to fully fight off if you have high mutational load, reduces testosterone levels, and we are an increasingly genetically sick population. This is why Covid-19 reduces male testosterone levels.[16] Being obese, an increasing Western problem, which is also highly genetic, reduces male testosterone levels as well,[17] though obesity rates are very low in Japan, so it is not a comprehensive explanation.[18]

14—Elizabeth Fain and Cara Weatherford, "Comparative Study of Millennials' (age 20-34 years) Grip and Lateral Pinch with the Norms," *Journal of Hand Therapy*, 29 (2016): 483-488.

15—William Lassek and Steven Gaulin, "Costs and Benefits of Fat-free Muscle Mass in Men: Relationship to Mating Success, Dietary Requirements, and Native Immunity," *Evolution and Human Behavior*, 30 (2009): 322-328.

16—Selahittin Çayan, Mustafa Uğuz, Barış Saylam, *et al.*, "Effect of Serum Total Testosterone and Its Relationship with other Laboratory Parameters on the Prognosis of Coronavirus Disease 2019 (COVID-19) in SARS-CoV-2 Infected Male Patients: A Cohort Study," *The Aging Male*, 1 (2020): 10.1080/13685538.2020.1807930.

17—Mark Fui, Philippe Dupuis, and Mathias Grossmann, "Lowered Testosterone in Male Obesity: Mechanisms, Morbidity and Management," *Asian Journal of Andrology*, 16 (2014), 223–231.

18—Brian Senauer and Gemma Mashiko, *Why Is the Obesity Rate So Low in Japan and High in the U.S.? Some Possible Economic Explanations* (University of Minnesota: The Food Industry Center, 2006).

It should also be noted that we have gone beyond such mutants arising as a result of very low child mortality. With *in vitro* fertilization, we take sperm that are so unhealthy that they are not able to successfully fertilize an egg under natural conditions, and we facilitate fertilization—potentially of an egg that is also unhealthy. Consequently, we would expect the products of this process to, themselves, have relatively poor genetic health. Under natural conditions, they would have not merely died as infants; they would never have been born. And there are many health problems that are more likely among those born using IVF, including high blood pressure, advanced bone age, and thyroid disorders.[19]

It should, therefore, be no surprise that, controlling for parental characteristics, children conceived using IVF have elevated levels of psycho-social problems compared to those conceived naturally as already noted. Secondly, as already noted, our Brave New World results in more and more mothers who have hormone imbalances, and these will interfere with the development of the sexuality of their offspring *in utero*. To give another example, a woman who produces elevated levels of feminizing hormones in response to male hormones produced by a male foetus is more likely to have a son who is homosexual or even a son who is a homosexual pedophile.[20]

It is this critical learning phase, highlighted by Charlton, which is the most fascinating in understanding

---

19—Roger Hart and Robert Norman, "The Longer-term Health Outcomes for Children Born as a Result of IVF Rreatment: Part I—General Health Outcomes," *Human Reproduction,* 19 (2013): 3.

20—Anthony Bogaert, Scott Bezeau, Michael Kuban, *et al.,* "Pedophilia, Sexual Orientation, and Birth Order," *Journal of Abnormal Psychology,* 106 (1997): 331-335.

Herbivore Males. Humans are a strongly social species, and we are evolved to develop alongside genetically adaptive humans. Under Darwinian conditions, we developed our own environment—partly controlled by us—that was optimally tuned to our survival and reproduction, including being calibrated to conditions that would ensure the optimal development of sexuality. One of the institutions that ensured the optimum development of sexuality was religion, which, in effect, made adaptive behavior, including adaptive sexual behavior and development, the "will of the gods." All of the established traditions of a society under harsh Darwinian conditions would push people towards being optimally successful in evolutionary terms, and this would include sexual development. If these conditions changed, then we would expect problems to ensue in relation to the development of human sexuality. They *have* changed and, as we would predict, problems have, indeed, arisen.

We would expect that, for genetic reasons, there would be more people with deviant sexuality, which appears to be the case. Due to the influence of Spiteful Mutants and runaway individualism, the influence of institutions that would previously have suppressed aberrant sexuality, or which would have branded it as deeply abnormal or worse, would be heavily reduced. Thus, more and more people who might already have the potential to develop in a sexually maladaptive way, due to rising mutational load in the population, would be exposed to maladaptive sexuality as something "acceptable." The consequences of this can possibly be seen in the "social contagion" associated with transgender identity. As explored earlier, gynaecologist Lisa Littman has referred to what she calls "rapid-onset Gender Dysphoria," in which adolescents with no previous indication of gender confusion appear to very suddenly declare themselves "non-binary" or "transgender." The spiteful promotion of maladaptive sexuality has consequences for those undergoing key growth periods.

INTERNET PORNOGRAPHY

Children and adolescents are now exposed to sexuality like never before in Western history. Internet porn has reached a state of ubiquity, if not omnipresence. Though it might still be frowned upon in some quarters, online porn is so widely consumed that it can only be considered "mainstream." Reportedly, 35 percent of the entire internet is dedicated to porn; 40 million Americans regularly visit porn sites; 10 percent of Americans and (perhaps surprisingly) 17 percent of women admit to an addiction to porn.[21] The median age for first viewing of porn is, according to one study, 14 years and can occur as early as nine.[22]

Traditionally, organized religion has suppressed sexuality and erotica, though, perhaps, it is more accurate to say that it has *channeled* it. Religion sanctifies sexual relations through marriage and match-making; it will condemn licentiousness but then also preside over certain

---

21—Megan Hull (Ed.), "Pornography Facts and Statistics," *The Recovery Village*, https://www.therecoveryvillage.com/process-addiction/porn-addiction/pornography-statistics/.

22— Aleksandra Diana Dwulit and Piotr Rzymski, "Prevalence, Patterns and Self-Perceived Effects of Pornography Consumption in Polish University Students: A Cross-Sectional Study," *International Journal of Environmental Research and Public Health*, May 2019, 16(10): 1861

"Dionysian" sexual expressions. In Western countries, until relatively recently, public discussion of sex was taboo, and it was socially unacceptable to have sexual intercourse outside of marriage. Adult (though not child) nudity was not tolerated. As recently as the 1950s, the exposure of a female's upper leg in public was considered shocking; at the beginning of the 20th century, it was unacceptable for anything other than a woman's hands and head to be exposed.

Until the rise of the internet in the late '90s, access to images of adult nudity was still heavily restricted with males who wished to obtain such images having to go through the shame of purchasing a "dirty" magazine from a newsagents' top shelf, or getting a glimpse of the female form in a peep show or kinetoscope. This had a strong deterrent effect. There were strip clubs, but, again, there was a great deal of social stigma associated with needing to go to such places at all. They were for "sexual inadequates" and "dirty old men," who could not persuade attractive females to have sex with them. The internet means that men can access extreme, high-definition pornographic photography and, more importantly, video, wherever and whenever they want them, including when they are very young.

When I was a teenager, in the 1990s, there was, essentially, no access to completely nude female images (or the bare breasts, vagina, or completely naked buttocks) other than occasionally finding discarded "porn mags" behind bushes, which, we would joke, had been left there by the "porn fairies." My parents were both sometime Art teachers and, as a result, there were art books in my house that included 1970s naked photographs or realistic paintings of female nudes. This made some of my friends rather keen to visit my home at weekends, so rare and dear such images were at the time.

Our current situation, of easy access to very realistic sexual stimulation, is an evolutionary mismatch to a pronounced degree. It could be argued that males in developed countries have effectively evolved to an ecology in which you only see female nudity when you are in a sexual relationship with a female, brothels and prostitution aside. Consequently, we would expect female nudity to have an extremely potent effect on such males; it should strongly arouse them, and it should easily sate their desires. Until relatively recently, if men sought sexual satisfaction, in almost all cases, they had to contract a relationship with a female.

Males and females operate different sexual strategies, as noted earlier. The male has nothing to lose from the sexual encounter, so he sexually selects for youth, as an indicator of fertility, and physical beauty. This is because the ability to be conventionally "beautiful" is a marker of sound genetic health. You have managed to maintain a symmetrical and proportioned phenotype in the face of disease, meaning you have a good immune system, among other things. The female *does* have something to lose from the sexual encounter, because she can become pregnant. She and her offspring are more likely to survive if the male invests in them and looks after them. So, she will select more for status (or the ability to attain it) and for evidence of a desire to commit.[23] This means that the male will only

---

23—David Buss, *The Evolution of Desire: Strategies of Human Mating* (New York: Basic Books, 2003); Edward Dutton and Guy Madison, "Why Do Finnish Men Marry Thai Women but Finnish Women Marry British men? Cross-National Marriages in a Modern Industrialised Society Exhibit Sex-have his sexual desires satiated, as a rule, if he commits to the female, traditionally through lifelong marriage. And many religions will often preach that anything else is contrary to divine will. Specifically, they tend to promote patriarchy, as discussed earlier.

If females sexually select for status, then the males must engage in a status competition in order to obtain the most desirable females, or any female at all. Women's abhorrence of very low-status males is such that they would often rather not have sex at all than copulate with such people. The result is that very low-status males will sometimes resort to rape in order to satisfy their desires, or even to reproduce. In polygamous societies, there are large numbers of single men because of the way in which multiple females will want to marry the highest-status males. The result is a culture of "gang rape," in which low-status males band together to obtain sex from a woman who is, for whatever reason, not chaperoned.[24] Obtaining social status is, for males, in significant part, an unconscious means of obtaining sexual satisfaction. If, however, males no longer need to obtain social status in order to be sexually satisfied, you might expect many of them to increasingly drop out of the race to do so.

Due to the evolutionary mismatch of having porn on-demand—which tricks the mind into thinking it genuinely has a willing female, to the extent that a male can orgasm via such images—the male can be sexually satiated without the need for the perils of status

Dimorphic Sexual Selection According to Primordial Selection Pressures," *Evolutionary Psychological Science*, 3 (2017): 1-9.

24—Randy Thornhill and Craig Palmer, *A Natural History of Rape: Biological Bases of Sexual Coercion* (Cambridge: The MIT Press, 2001).

competition, or even social interaction with real females. He has at his fingertips the male evolutionary dream: an almost infinite number of sexually attractive females. Novelty and diversity are also important. Men will often want to have sex with many different kinds of female. In evolutionary terms, this is a "bet hedging" strategy. In the unstable ecologies of our hunter-gatherer past, if you had sex with lots of women, who were all genetically quite different from each other, then one of them might have a genetic adaptation that would better permit the resultant offspring to survive. For the same reason, many men tire of an attractive wife and may be highly aroused by a novel female, even if she is not as alluring as his stable partner.[25] The internet is a kind of sex paradise—but one that has had acutely fitness-damaging consequences on both men and women.

There is a growing body of evidence that this is exactly what is happening, as set out in a thorough literature review.[26] Pornography is so sexually rewarding for males—the payoff being so high and the investment, so low—that it becomes addictive.[27] As with any addiction, pornography involves a "law of diminishing returns." As you become more addicted to a substance, you require a

25—Elisa Ventura-Aquinoa, Alonso Fernández-Guasti, and Raúl G. Paredesa, "Hormones and the *Coolidge* Effect," *Molecular and Cellular Endocrinology*, 467 (2018): 42-48.

26—Pascal Emmanuel Gobry, "A Science-Based Case for Ending the Porn Epidemic," *American Greatness*, December 15, 2019. https://eppc.org/publications/a-science-based-case-for-ending-the-porn-epidemic/.

27—Matthias Brand, Christian Laier, Mirko Pawlikowski, *et al.*, "Watching Pornographic Pictures on the Internet: Role of Sexual Arousal Ratings and Psychological-psychiatric Symptoms for Using Internet Sex Sites Excessively," *Cyberpsychology, Behavior and Social Networking*, 14 (2011): 371-377.

stronger dose of the stuff—or, in the case of pornography, greater novelty and variety—to obtain the same effect. Thus, there is evidence that frequent porn users effectively become desensitized to erotic images ("vanilla porn").[28] This has to be taken with evidence that environmental factors can alter a person's sexual interests to some extent. A survey in Belgium found that 49 percent of men who frequently viewed online pornography reported searching for sexual content that was not previously of interest to them, or even that they previously regarded as revolting.[29]

A study in 2007 on sexual arousal in young males found that males under the age of 30 had difficulty becoming aroused by the kind of old-fashioned, pre-internet pornography to which the researchers exposed them. Desensitized to pornography via frequent exposure from a relatively young age, they required pornography that was far more extreme.[30] Studies that control for key confounds have found that people in relationships where the male frequently uses pornography report lower relationship satisfaction; additionally, there is some association between frequent porn use and erectile dysfunction, with males requiring pornography to help them attain an erection in order to have real-life sexual

28—Paula Banca, Laurel Morris, Simon Mitchell, *et al.,* "Novelty, Conditioning and Attentional Bias to Sexual Rewards," *Journal of Psychiatric Research,* 72 (2016): 91-101.

29—Aline Wéry and J. Billieux, "Online Sexual Activities: An Exploratory Study of Problematic and Non-problematic Usage Patterns in a Sample of Men," *Computers in Human Behavior,* 56 (2016): 257-266.

30—Erick Janssen and John Bancroft, "The Dual-control Model: The Role of Sexual Inhibition and Excitation in Sexual Arousal and Behavior," in *The Psychophysiology of Sex,* edited by Erick Janssen (Bloomington: Indiana University Press, 2007).

intercourse. Consistent with this, evidence indicates a significant increase in erectile dysfunction among young males in recent years.[31]

This does not prove that there is a connection between internet pornography and sexual dysfunction and declining libido, but it implies that this may be what is happening. And from an evolutionary perspective, we would expect something like this to occur due to the way in which internet pornography creates such an evolutionary mismatch. Indeed, insomuch as males are increasingly addicted to porn, it makes sense that real-life sexual encounters would be less fulfilling. The addicts are constantly saying "Hit me again!" and seeking out increasingly bizarre and depraved sexual imagery.[32]

These findings have interesting implications for parts of the Muslim World, in which all females, other than very close relatives, must be covered in the presence of men at all times. This would mean that Muslim males from countries such as Afghanistan can be expected to be extremely sensitive to, and easily aroused by, even partial female nudity. Congruous with internet pornography reducing male testosterone levels, it has been found that sexual desire positively predicts testosterone, while fulfillment negatively predicts it.[33] Abstaining from ejaculation for seven days causes a sizeable rise

---

31—Gobry, "A Science-Based Case for Ending the Porn Epidemic," *op cit.*

32—Brand, Laier, Pawlikowski, *et al.*, "Watching Pornographic Pictures on the Internet," *op cit.*

33—David Puts, Lauramarie Pope, Alexander Hill, *et al.*, "Fulfilling Desire: Evidence for Negative Feedback Between Men's Testosterone, Sociosexual Psychology, and Sexual Partner Number," *Hormones and Behavior*, 70 (2015): 14–21.

in testosterone, which would make sense of why many religions tend to condemn masturbation.[34] This adds up to a sound case for the argument that internet pornography is interfering with Western male testosterone levels.

WHY JAPAN?

But why is this process of the breakdown of sexual intercourse so far advanced in Japan compared to other highly developed countries? The answer may lie in East Asia's Life History Strategy, a concept we explored in Chapter 2. In his 1995 book, *Race, Evolution, and Behavior,* British-Canadian psychologist J. Philippe Rushton (1943-2012) presented what he called the Differential-K theory.[35] Rushton presented a large body of evidence that, on numerous markers, the three largest racial groups—Blacks, Caucasians, and East Asians—differ in terms of their modal Life History Strategy. Blacks are the most r-selected; East Asians, the most K-selected; Whites are intermediate, though closer to East Asians. The relationship is not perfect, and there are some measures of LHS where Whites are slower than East Asians. This is likely the case because, as the ecology becomes harsher and more stable, you must increasingly find an ever narrower evolutionary niche. This means that at extreme levels of harshness and stability, the positive relationship between the different components of K becomes weaker. The optimum means of survival might

34—Ming Jiang, Jiang Xin, Qiang Zou, *et al.,* "A Research on the Relationship Between Ejaculation and Serum Testosterone Level in Men," *Journal of Zhejiang University-SCIENCE* A, 4 (2003), 236-240.

35—J. Philippe Rushton, *Race, Evolution, and Behavior: A Life History Perspective* (New Brunswick: Transaction, 1995); see Edward Dutton, *Making Sense of Race* (Whitefish: Washington Summit Publishers, 2020), Chapter 6.

be a highly *K* strategy overall, combined, very specifically, with being highly aggressive towards outsiders. That said, overall, on numerous measures—twinning, maturation rate, age at puberty, age at first pregnancy, criminality, marital stability, intelligence, personality, secondary sexual characteristics, intercourse frequency, and more—Rushton's model works.[36]

Slow Life History Strategists are more environmentally plastic than fast Life History Strategists, meaning that they are more influenced by their environment. This sensitivity allows the organism to be optimally adapted to its environment at any given time, giving it a competitive edge in the merciless ecology that produces a slow LHS.[37] For this reason, much less is "hard-wired" in *K*-strategists. When a crab is born, it has the inbuilt instinctive drives to simply get on with life; it rarely deviates from its course, nor does it question its fate. This is not the case with a human. Not only is it helpless when born, but it has to be taught how to behave. As such, the adaptive development of a *K*-strategist is far more reliant on a precisely optimum environment than is the adaptive development of an r-strategist. If this environment deviates from the one in which development is evolved to take place, we would expect extreme *K*-strategists to become far more psychologically maladapted.

The Japanese are extreme *K*-strategists, and, so it follows, they are extremely environmentally sensitive.

36—Edward Dutton, *J. Philippe Rushton: A Life History Perspective* (Oulu: Thomas Edward Press, 2018).

37—Christopher Kuzawa and Jared Bragg, "Plasticity in Human Life History Strategy: Implications for Contemporary Human Variation and the Evolution of Genus *Homo*," *Current Anthropology*, 53 (2012): 369-383.

This means that a small deviation of their developmental environment from the evolutionary optimum will have far profounder effects on the development of their sexuality than it would on the development of the sexuality of Whites or Blacks. But as the White environment becomes increasingly suboptimal, we will begin to see the same kind of phenomena in Western countries that can already be observed in Japan—such as the reaction to widespread pornography. That said, Japan is generally likely to remain on the vanguard of fitness-compromising behavior due to the Japanese being so environmentally sensitive.

MOUSE UTOPIA AND THE HERBIVORE MALES

The degradation of human sexuality under conditions in which Darwinian selection has essentially collapsed shouldn't really be a surprise to us. The same phenomenon has been thoroughly documented with mice. Indeed, the parallels with humans—and especially with Japan's Herbivore Males—are simply uncanny.

In 1968, John B. Calhoun (1917-1995), of the University of Maryland, began his long-term experiment in rodent society, which lasted until 1973. "What would happen," he wondered, "over the generations, if you took away Darwinian selection, as has increasingly happened with humans since the Industrial Revolution?" Mice were placed in conditions where there was, essentially, no purifying Darwinian Selection: no inclement weather, no predation, no serious illnesses, and ample access to nutritious food and medical care. This paralleled the way in which the Industrial Revolution brought inoculations, effective medicine, cheaper food, and an ever-improving standard of living. As with humans, there was an initial population explosion, but then population growth began to slow down as fewer and fewer mice had offspring. Eventually, the population plateaued and, as with developed countries where there is little or no immigration, such as Japan, it then went into decline.

This population decline was paralleled by the observation of very unusual forms of behavior. Females expelled their young from the nest too early, so that they weren't sufficiently socialized to be able to deal with other mice. Females also became increasingly masculinized, aggressive, and uninterested in breeding, even attacking their own young. Slightly later, a startling group was noticed among the males. Known as "the Beautiful Ones," they were remarkably effeminate. They didn't fight for territory, had no interest in females, and spent all of their time grooming each other. Calhoun described them thus:

> Autistic-like creatures, capable only of the most simple behaviors compatible with physiological survival, emerge out of this process. Their spirit has died ('the first death'). They are no longer capable of executing the more complex behaviors compatible with species survival. The species in such settings die.[38]

Eventually, after many generations, all the mice were either "Beautiful Ones," masculinized females, or socially inept. Consequently, no more mice were born, and the colony died out. Michael Woodley of Menie and

---

38—John Calhoun "Death Squared: The Explosive Growth and Demise of a Mouse Population," *Proceedings of the Royal Society of Medicine*, 66 (1973): 80-88, 86.

colleagues show that the colony was nowhere close to being overcrowded when the population growth began to slow down. Thus, the simplest explanation is that mutant genes, causing fitness-reducing behavior in mice, were no longer being expunged from the population. This led to "mutational meltdown," where the percentage of the maladapted in a population is so high that the society collapses. Woodley of Menie and colleagues argue that the collapse of the Mouse Utopia was partly due to Spiteful Mutants, of which the Beautiful Ones were a prime example.[39]

It turns out that the Beautiful Ones' urine was communicating to other mice that they were in a situation of intense stress, even though they were not. The urine of the Beautiful Ones contained a particular pheromone, which is extremely costly—in terms of energy—to produce; it is generated by normal mice only at times of intense stress. This pheromone was becoming mixed-in with the general urinary miasma of the colony, leading normal mice to become profoundly anxious. These normal mice were, therefore, miscarrying, expelling their offspring from the nest too young, misdirecting aggression and generally being driven mad. In the world of mice, the Beautiful Ones were helping to destroy the sense of order and relative peace within the community by altering what the community smelt like. Mice communicate information through urine; humans have culture and "memes"—ideas, behaviors, and worldviews that spread

---

39—Michael A. Woodley of Menie, Matthew Sarraf, Radomir Pestow, *et al.*, "Social Epistasis Amplifies the Fitness Costs of Deleterious Mutations, Engendering Rapid Fitness Decline Among Modernized Populations," *Evolutionary Psychological Science*, 3 (2017): 181-191.

and replicate like genes.[40] The memes Spiteful Mutants produce can affect and infect us all.

A series of problems have been found with Calhoun's experiment, including failure to replicate.[41] But its results do bear an uncanny resemblance to what is happening in the "Human Zoo"[42] that is the modern world, with its very weak conditions of harsh Darwinian selection.

THE BREAKDOWN OF MATING IN THE WEST

Among advanced nations, Japan's sexual degradation is the most noticeable, due to a combination of technological advancement and a highly environmentally plastic people. That said, the increasingly extreme environmental mismatch that now exists in the West— due to a combination of technology and the influence of Spiteful Mutants—means that the Japanese sexual situation is increasingly becoming noticeable in Western countries. We have already discussed rising levels of erectile dysfunction and addiction to pornography. In addition, those who are referred to as part of generation *i-Gen*— born in the 1990s and thus never having known a world without the internet—lose their virginity later, leave home later, start dating later, are less sexually promiscuous, and have less sexual intercourse than was the case with the

---

40—Richard Dawkins, *The Selfish Gene* (Oxford: Oxford University Press, 2016 [1976]), Chapter 11.

41—Matthew Sarraf, Michael A. Woodley of Menie, and Colin Feltham, *Modernity and Cultural Decline: A Biobehavioral Perspective* (Basingstoke: Palgrave Macmillan, 2019).

42—Desmond Morris, *The Human Zoo* (New York: McGraw Hill, 1969).

previous generation.[43] Many are destined to never have sexual intercourse at all.

According to American psychologist Jennifer Twenge and her colleagues, Americans born in the 1980s and 1990s (categorized as Millennials, Zoomers, and iGen) were more likely to report having no sexual partners since the age of 18 (implying they were virgins), compared to Gen-Xers (born in the 1960s and 1970s) in the General Social Survey. Among those aged 20–24, more than twice as many Millennials born in the 1990s (15 percent) were virgins compared to Gen-Xers born in the 1960s at the same age (6 percent). Fascinatingly, the team found that the effect is not very pronounced on Black people, something congruous with Black people being relative r-strategists and, thus, less environmentally plastic.[44]

British people—aged controlled—are having considerably less sexual intercourse than they used to, including once they have a long-term partner. British women, aged 16 to 44, reported having sex four times a month in 1991 and 2001; by 2012, this was down to an average of 3 times a month. Analysis of other measures found that the frequency of those having had sexual intercourse in the last month increased between 1991 and 2001, possibly due to liberalizing attitudes to sex across the period and even an increasing social pressure

43—Jennifer Twenge, *iGen: Why Today's Super-Connected Kids Are Growing Up Less Rebellious, More Tolerant, Less Happy—and Completely Unprepared for Adulthood—and What That Means for the Rest of Us* (New York: Atria Books, 2017).

44—Jennifer Twenge, Ryne Sherman, and Brooke Wells, "Sexual Inactivity During Young Adulthood Is More Common Among U.S. Millennials and iGen: Age, Period, and Cohort Effects on Having No Sexual Partners After Age 18," *Archives of Sexual Behavior*, 46 (2016): 2.

to be sexually active and thus to over-report. Levels dramatically decreased, however, between 2001 and 2012. For example, 20 percent of the sample reported having had sex 10 or more times in the last month in 2001; by 2012, this was down to just 13 percent in women and 14 percent in men. The steepest declines in sexual activity were found among married or cohabiting couples.[45] This would all be consistent with the declining testosterone levels that we examined earlier.

SOY BOYS AND SIMPS

The West is, more and more, moving in the same direction as Japan. We can glimpse our own Herbivore Males and their female equivalent in many popular internet memes. An obvious example is the stereotypical "Soy Boy." This term refers to a highly feminized, though usually heterosexual, male. He is physically weak and adopts lifestyles generally associated with females, such as vegetarianism and veganism, apparently profoundly concerned about the welfare of animals. Politically, he is the stereotypical SJW, emphasizing his concern about any subject that might allow him to virtue signal his way to social status in the Church of Multiculturalism: women's rights, racism, animal rights, trans rights, etc. According to the *Urban Dictionary:*

> The average soy boy is a feminist, nonathletic, has never been in a fight, will probably marry the first

45—Kaye Wellings, Melissa Palmer, Kazuyo Machiyama, *et al.*, "Changes in, and Factors Associated with, Frequency of Sex in Britain: Evidence From Three National Surveys of Sexual Attitudes and Lifestyles (Natsal)," *British Medical Journal,* (2019): 365:1525.

girl that has sex with him, and likely reduces all his arguments to labeling the opposition as 'Nazis.'[46]

The Soy Boy literally cries, like a girl, over issues such as "toxic masculinity" and "xenophobia." This was exemplified on January 29, 2020, when the European Parliament debated and then ratified the bill permitting Britain's exit from the European Union. Male Labour Member of the European Parliament (MEP) Rory Palmer (b. 1981), who is married with a daughter,[47] was pictured almost in tears, being consoled by a masculine-looking female Labour MEP.[48]

The term "Soy Boy" derives from the belief that Soy, consumed by vegetarians, can reduce your sex drive due to it supposedly containing estrogen.[49] Whether or not that is true, "Soy Boy" is used to refer to feminized, leftist heterosexual men. Those who are accused of being such have been known to become enraged—online, rather than face-to-face—at the accusation, terming their accusers "Nazis."[50] Such a visceral reaction usually implies there is

---

46—*Urban Dictionary.* "Soy Boy," https://www.urbandictionary.com/define. php?term=Soy%20Boy.

47—Dan Martin, "Former Leicester Deputy Mayor Rory Palmer Reveals Daughter's 'Heartbreaking' Battle with Viral Meningitis," *Leicester Mercury,* May 10, 2018. https://www.leicestermercury.co.uk/news/leicester-news/ former-leicester-deputy-mayor-rory-1543741.

48—*Thomson Reuters,* "Cheers, Tears and Auld Lang Syne: European Parliament Approves Brexit Withdrawal," *CBC,* January 29, 2020, https:// www.cbc.ca/news/world/eu-parliament-brexit-vote-1.5444759.

49—James Hamblin, "Why Men Think Plant-Based Meat Will Turn Them into Women," *The Atlantic,* February 3, 2020, https://www.theatlantic. com/health/archive/2020/02/why-men-are-afraid-soy-will-turn-them-women/605968/.

50—Mark Dice, *Liberalism: Find A Cure* (Independently Published, 2018).

some truth to the accusation. It is an example of cognitive dissonance. This occurs when a person's fervently held worldview, which is important to their sense of identity and self-worth, is challenged and they recognize, on some level, that their whole way of thinking might be wrong. This will often "trigger" them. It will cause them to react in an emotional and aggressive fashion in order to suppress the person, and the ideas, that are making them feel uncomfortable.[51]

These people, though some may be in sexual relationships with left-wing women, are, in key respects, similar to the Herbivore Men. They are unlikely to be especially attractive to females, because although females favor some feminine qualities in males such as "caring,"[52] they are ultimately attracted to high-status males with the masculine qualities—including testosterone-induced drive and competitiveness—which tend to lead to high status.[53] They can be regarded as manifestations of falling male testosterone, occurring for both environmental and genetic reasons. Soy Boys are likely, by virtue of attracting left-wing females, to have relatively few, if any, offspring, due to the documented negative association between leftist ideologies and fertility.[54] This may be partly mediated by

---

51—Leon Festinger, *A Theory of Cognitive Dissonance* (Stanford: Stanford University Press, 1957).

52—Edward Miller, "Homosexuality, Birth Order, and Evolution: Toward an Equilibrium Reproductive Economics of Homosexuality," *Archives of Sexual Behavior*, 29 (2000): 1-34.

53—Allen Mazur and Theodore Lamb, "Testosterone, Status, and Mood in Human Males," *Hormones and Behavior,* 14 (1980): 236-246.

54—Martin Fieder and Susanne Huber, "Political Attitude and Fertility: Is There a Selection for the Political Extreme?" *Frontiers in Psychology* (2018), https://doi.org/10.3389/fpsyg.2018.02343.

factors such as lack of traditional religiosity (meaning there is no god or religious community instructing them to multiply) and feminism (meaning women's most fertile years are dedicated to a career). It may also be that fitness-damaging worldviews—such as anti-natalism, atheism, and feminism—are comorbid, because they are all underpinned by high mutational load.[55]

Related to the Soy Boy, to some extent, is the idea of the "Simp." This term sounds like it is derived from the word "simper," but is supposedly an acronym for "Sucker Idolizing Mediocre Pussy." According to London newspaper *Metro*:

> It's the type of person who, instead of trying to attract the opposite sex through being attractive and interesting, is more sycophantic and fawning. They use faux niceness and concern in the hope that it will one day result in pity sex or a relationship out of guilt. Essentially, they give to get, even if it means losing some dignity or their original values in the process.[56]

In other words, a Simp is a male with very little self-respect, who allows females to exploit and humiliate him in the desperate hope of a few crumbs of affection, or even just attention. He is an emasculated male, under the control of females. Unlike Herbivore Males, he is, in a sense, competing for females, he is doing so in a

---

55—Matthew Sarraf, Michael Woodley of Menie, and Colin Feltham, *Modernity and Cultural Decline: A Biobehavioral Perspective* (Basingstoke: Palgrave Macmillan, 2019).

56—Jessica Lindsay, "What is Simping and What is a Simp?" *Metro*, January 4, 2020, https://metro.co.uk/2020/01/04/what-is-simping-and-what-is-a-simp-12001620/.

way that makes him everything females are evolved to despise: effete, psychologically weak, and of low status in the view of other men. In this sense, he is even more maladaptive than the Soy Boy, who may attract a certain kind of female by virtue-signaling and even attaining social status, as clearly occurred with former MEP Rory Palmer. The Simp's sexual strategy is thus maladaptive as it is very likely to fail. It is best encapsulated in the phenomenon of female internet personalities running a system of ersatz prostitution, whereby males will give them money in return for small amounts of attention. In one infamous case, in 2019, such a woman, a 19 year-old American, sold her followers bottles of her soiled bath water, something which made international news.[57] Not to be outdone, reality TV star Stephanie Matto began selling jars of her own flatulence, before stopping the practice after such excessive gas production led to her having to go to hospital.[58] The Simp is an exploited, low testosterone male. In that Agreeableness is correlated with traditional religiosity, he may simply lack the social skills to pursue a normal relationship with a female.

MGTOWS AND INCELS

In the classic musical number "Kids" from *Bye Bye Birdie* (1963), an exasperated parent laments,

57—Katie Bishop. "Who is Paying $30 for 'Gamer Girl' Belle Delphine's Bath Water?" *The Guardian,* July 12, 2019, https://www.theguardian.com/technology/2019/jul/12/belle-delphine-gamer-girl-instagram-selling-bath-wate.

58—Bruce Y. Lee, "90 Day Fiancé Star Sells Her Farts In Jars Then Suffers Health Scare," *Forbes,* January 8, 2022, https://www.forbes.com/sites/brucelee/2022/01/08/90-day-fianc-star-sells-farts-in-jars-then-suffers-health-scare/?sh=2f2f866936fc.

Kids! I don't know what's wrong with these kids today!

Kids! Who can understand anything they say? [...]

Kids! They are just impossible to control!

Kids! With their awful clothes and their rock an' roll![59]

Every generation, it seems, sees the next as lacking in restraint, respect, taste, and discipline. And most parents would love for their biggest worry about their teenagers to be "awful clothes and rock n' roll." For most of the 20th century, parents fretted over their children being sexually libertine and engaging in dangerous behavior, like drugs and violence.

In the 21st century, generational *angst* has been transformed. As mentioned earlier, children are participating in significantly less sexual activity than their parents did at the same age. Indeed, the lament from respectable outlets has become, "Why are young people having so little sex?":

> From 1991 to 2017, the Centers for Disease Control and Prevention's Youth Risk Behavior Survey finds, the percentage of high-school students who'd had intercourse dropped from 54 to 40 percent. . . . Meanwhile, the U.S. teen pregnancy rate has plummeted to a third of its modern high. When this decline started, in the 1990s, it was widely and rightly embraced. But now some observers are beginning to wonder whether an unambiguously good thing might have roots in less salubrious developments. Signs are gathering that the delay in teen sex may have been the first indication of a broader

59—Charles Strouse, Lee Adams, and Michael Steweart, *Bye Bye Birdie*, 1963.

withdrawal from physical intimacy that extends well into adulthood. . . . People now in their early 20s are two and a half times as likely to be abstinent as Gen Xers were at that age; 15 percent report having had no sex since they reached adulthood.[60]

The Covid-19 pandemic only accelerated this development. Millennials and iGen or Gen-Z are starved for physical intimacy and connection, and as a result, family formation is collapsing.

This new situation has, among other things, birthed the "Incel" phenomenon: "involuntary celibates" who seem resigned to their joyless fate and are deeply resentful of all women and the few men who are actually getting laid. Incels' "social life" revolves around participating in anonymous online forums and video chat rooms dedicated to inceldom.[61] The Incels hold that contemporary sexual relations are breaking down into a kind of 80/20 rule: 20 percent of the men ("Chads") are sexually active with 80 percent of the women (the beautiful "Stacys," along with nerdy, feminist "Beckys"). The Chads are cleaning up: securing all the relationships and random hook-ups, while the Incels are left with nothing, longing for a new age of "mandatory monogamy." Obviously, all this is hyperbole, but the Incels are right to notice that sexual relations seem to be reverting to a kind of neo-polygamy. Not surprisingly, some Incels have lashed out at the world.[62]

60—Kate Julian, "Why Are Young People Having So Little Sex?" *The Atlantic*, December 2018, https://www.theatlantic.com/magazine/archive/2018/12/the-sex-recession/573949/.

61—See *Incels Wiki*, https://incels.wiki/w/Main_Page.

62— Jonathan Griffin, "Incels: Inside a Dark World of Online Hate," *BBC News*, August 13, 2021, https://www.bbc.com/news/blogs-

Most notoriously, in 2014, Elliot Rodger (1991-2014) killed six people and injured 14, assaulting a sorority house with guns, knives, and his vehicle, attacking the very people he viewed as sexually successful. At the end of the rampage, he committed suicide.[63]

Alongside Incels, there is the "MGTOW" movement. This stands for "Men Going Their Own Way." I am aware of no detailed study on MGTOW, but one gets the impression that they are more aggressive and stereotypically masculine than Soy Boys, Simps, or Incels. They are, as it were, "Incels with an attitude." Indeed, due to their hostility towards women, and feminism in particular, some left-wing commentators classify MGTOW as right-wing extremists.[64] In effect, MGTOWs claim that females are unpleasant and manipulative and should be avoided. According to a manual authored by "MGTOW American": "Let the chads, cuckolds and simps suffer from female manipulation. There's plenty to go around."[65]

Neither of these are going to be successful sexual strategies. The MGTOW, like the effete Herbivore Males, have simply given up, and they present arguments to rationalize their evolutionary failure—at least in the direct sense of attaining females and passing on your genes. It is, of course, possible to pass on your genes indirectly, as we have discussed.[66] But in most

trending-44053828.

63—See Julia Ebner, *Going Dark: The Secret Social Lives of Extremists* (London: Bloomsbury, 2020).

64—*Ibid.*

65—MGTOW American, *MGTOW: A Minimalist Guide to Becoming a Healthy Happy MGTOW* (Page Publishing, 2019).

66—Frank Salter, *On Genetic Interests: Family, Ethnicity and Humanity in an*

circumstances, the optimum strategy is to have children yourself, and MGTOWs are, so they claim, resigned to barrenness. They have attempted to make a moral virtue out of their apparent inability to attract desirable females. The Incel doesn't espouse the benefits of being an Incel, but he appears to identify himself as incapable of attracting women and seems to have developed a deep hatred towards them, which females he may meet—with their much superior empathy compared to males—are likely to pick up on.[67] Accordingly, the Incel is unlikely to pass on his genes, rendering his behavior maladaptive. Again, we seem to have people with poor social skills, as predicted by their deviation from traditional religiosity and group-orientation.

It could, perhaps, be argued that both MGTOWs and Incels are operating at the level of group selection. Eschewing relationships with females, perhaps it could be averred that they invest their energies in helping to make the group more patriarchal. There is no agreed definition of patriarchy, but it has been defined by evolutionary psychologists as such:

> [T]he control by males of female sexuality in the form of a system of implicit and explicit rules of conduct, of power structures, and of belief systems that support male control over women's reproduction.[68]

Age of Mass Migration (New Brunswick: Transaction Publishers, 2006).

67—Christopher Soto, Oliver John, Samuel Gosling, *et al.*, "Age Differences in Personality Traits from 10 to 65: Big Five Domains and Facets in a Large Cross-Sectional Sample," *Journal of Personality and Social Psychology,* 100: 330-348.

68—Rachel Grant and V. Tamara Montrose, "It's a Man's World: Mate Guarding and the Evolution of Patriarchy," *Mankind Quarterly,* 58 (2018): 384-418.

As already discussed, it has been shown that patriarchy is adaptive because it reduces inter-male violence: if females are controlled, males will have less paternity anxiety. This elevates positive ethnocentrism, that is, in-group cooperation. As mentioned, computer models have shown that groups that are highest in positive and negative ethnocentrism will tend to dominate other groups, all else being equal.[69] This is why many religions will tend to promote patriarchy as divinely ordained; it is adaptive at the level of group selection.[70] Accordingly, there seems to be a case of separating MGTOWs and Incels from Soy Boys and Simps. It is the latter that are comparable, though not exactly comparable, to Japan's Herbivore Males. It may be that MGTOWs and Incels have similar attitudes to traditional religious celibates living in religious houses, such as Orthodox monks in Russia or Greece or where traditional religiousness is less left-wing oriented than in Western traditions. There is certainly abundant evidence that misogyny was an important motivation, historically, in choosing to become a monk.[71] According to literary scholar Nicole Nolan, "Sidhu Buddhist" monks' "authority is predicated on misogyny, since freedom from the malign influence of women is a key element in the monk's claim to objectivity and wisdom."[72]

69—Ross Hammond and Robert Axelrod, "The Evolution of Ethnocentric Behavior," *Journal of Conflict Resolution,* 50 (2006): 1-11.

70—Grant and Montrose, "It's a Man's World," *op cit.*

71—See Jack Holland, *A Brief History of Misogyny: The World's Oldest Prejudice* (London: Hachette, 2012).

72—Nicole Nolan Sidhu, *Indecent Exposure: Gender, Politics, and Obscene Comedy in Middle English Literature* (Philadelphia: University of Pennsylvania Press, 2016), 115.

The development of these assorted "herbivore men of the West" is likely to have similar causes as those in Japan: rising mutational load, the subversion of institutions and traditions that lead to optimal sexual development, and other evolutionary mismatches that result in sexual and psycho-sexual development going awry. The adaptive strategy would be for males to drop these identities. But, presumably, they cannot, because they have developed maladaptively, due to a sequence of factors. For example, for most of human history, masculine behavior has been promoted as morally good, natural, and the "will of the gods." Now, it is "toxic." For a developing male to imbibe such information as a fact would be a clear example of an evolutionary mismatch, rendered all the more problematic if he already had high mutational load pushing him towards fitness-compromising ways of thinking and behaving. Only males with low mutational load, or who are strongly genetically resistant to fitness-damaging ideas and strongly inclined to breed, will survive these new "evolutionary crucibles."

"NO EGGS"

Having looked at sexually maladaptive males, we now turn to females. The key predictors of not passing on your genes are being left-wing but, also, having a high IQ, something which is associated with being highly educated. This negative association between IQ and fertility is more pronounced among women than it is among men. This is because intelligent women will increasingly dedicate all of their 20s—and even the first half of their 30s—to their careers, limiting their fertility due to menopause.[73] Intelligence doesn't simply predict *reduced* fertility among women. The more intelligent a woman is, the more likely she is to have no children at all. Moreover, the more intelligent a woman is, the more likely she is to simply *not want* to have them.[74] In other words, the stereotypical female Social Justice Warrior—the extreme left-wing university graduate—does not desire children and will tend not to have children. She has been inculcated with a fitness-damaging way of seeing the world. It becomes difficult even if they *do* want children. Feminist ideology has brought about a situation where, in many Western countries, females are more educated than males. This is because females tend to fair better in the education system, due to having higher Conscientiousness than males and due to male-female IQ only differing because there are more *outlier* high-IQ males.[75]

As we have discussed, females are strongly evolved to sexually select for social status—or evidence of the ability to attain it—in males. They are evolved to want to marry *hypergamously*: socially upwards, to somebody of higher status than themselves.[76] Education level is a key marker of the ability to attain social status and, indeed,

73—See Edward Dutton and Michael Woodley of Menie, *At Our Wits' End: Why We're Becoming Less Intelligent and What It Means for the Future* (Exeter: Imprint Academic, 2018).

74—Satoshi Kanazawa, *The Intelligence Paradox: Why the Intelligent Choice Isn't Always the Smart One* (Hoboken: John Wiley & Sons), 179.

75—Edward Dutton, "The Male Brain, Testosterone and Sex Differences in Professional Achievement," *Mankind Quarterly,* 58 (2017): 93-100.

76—Edward Dutton, "Women Marry Up," in *Encyclopedia of Evolutionary Psychological Science*, eds. Todd K. Shackelford and Viviana Shackelford-Weekes (New York: Springer, 2018).

accords social status. The result is that the more educated a woman is, the fewer males there are who are even *as* educated as she. This means there are not enough highly educated males to go around, resulting in highly educated women—who will tend to be left-wing, as academics, for example, overwhelmingly are[77]—not being able to find an attractive mate.

Clearly, such a situation, in which so many females are of higher status than males, is highly novel; it is an evolutionary mismatch and a result of females no longer being directed towards adaptive ends by the group. This inability to find a mate is more likely the case if they are physically unattractive, because males strongly sexually select for physical attractiveness. It is also more likely the case if these females are "past their prime," as men sexually select for youth. And these females are likely to be "past their prime" if they have dedicated their 20s and most of their 30s to their careers, at the expense of finding a husband.

Accordingly, when it comes to females, adoption of anti-traditional, fitness-compromising worldviews will, to some extent, reflect mutational load, meaning that such females may have other fitness-damaging desires, such as anti-natalism. Such views, however, lead to maladaptive consequences when adopted by relatively low mutational load females, because they will result in their being unattracted to the available males and being unattractive to the kinds of males they desire. The sexuality of females is strongly environmentally influenced, and it has been shown that, in the absence

---

77—Noah Carl, "Lackademia: Why Do Academics Lean Left?" *Adam Smith Institute*, March 2017.

of desirable males, females have an evolved tendency to become lesbians, as discussed in Chapter 7. It has been proposed that this may be because humans overwhelmingly lived in polygamous societies until relatively recently. In this context, wives who were less favored by the husband engaged in collaborative "alloparenting" of each other's offspring, something rendered more stable if they could become sexually attracted to each other and thus strongly bonded.[78] On this basis, we would predict that such females—when not believing in traditional religiosity—might be more likely to contract lesbian relationships. And there is evidence that this is increasingly happening.[79]

Moreover, we might expect females, when faced with an evolutionary mismatch, to make more maladaptive decisions than do males, because they are more evolved to be adaptively directed by the group, and the group is now maladaptively directing them. Greek psychologist Menelaos Apostolou has argued that we are evolved to a situation in which patriarchy is prevalent, as those who reject patriarchal values would have been shunned by the group or even killed. Being adapted to patriarchy, females are adapted, to a greater extent than males, to a situation in which choices are made for them, usually by their parents and particularly by their fathers. Traditionally, the female desire for power would be directed towards a suitable match by their family; a match would be likely

78—Austin John Jeffery, Todd Shackelford, Virgil Zeigler-Hill, et al., "The Evolution of Human Female Sexual Orientation," Evolutionary Psychological Science, 5 (2019), 71–86.

79—See F. Roger Devlin, "Sexual Utopia in Power," The Occidental Quarterly, Summer 2006, vol. 6, no. 2.

to be from among their social circle and thus genetically similar and, usually, of slightly higher status.

Females, in such a situation, would, thus, have a similar level of power and resources to their husbands, backed-up by their families. Left to their own devices, women are, accordingly, more likely to make maladaptive choices, as noted above, no longer being pushed by religion and society to marry and have children.[80] They will also gravitate towards much higher-status males. On the other hand, males—who are less picky—are more than happy to take advantage of these sex and power dynamics, ultimately settling down with the female with the best mate value both in terms of looks and access to financial resources. Thus, such females will end-up failing to find a hypergamous mate and failing to breed. These choices would be rendered even more fitness-damaging by Spiteful Mutants positively encouraging them to make maladaptive choices, and by the dysphoria produced by runaway individualism, which would promote ever-more fitness-destroying ways of thinking.

Consistent with this, it has been found that more intelligent people express a preference to remain childless when they are young, but only more intelligent women actually do so. This is the case even when controlling for factors that might limit female fertility, such as education and earnings (and the consequent trading of fertility for a career).[81] This implies that females are more maladapted than males in a non-patriarchal environment. Only those

---

80—Menelaos Apostolou, *Sexual Selection Under Parental Choice: The Evolution of Human Mating Behavior* (Hove: Psychology Press, 2014).

81—Satoshi Kanazawa, "Intelligence and Childlessness," *Social Science Research.* 48 (2014): 157-170.

strongly genetically inclined to breed will, thus, overcome this. Additionally, working, and competing with, males in a work environment is a severe evolutionary mismatch for both men and women.

THE NEW CHURCH LADIES

In a sense, female SJWs are what writer Jim Goad has called "The New Church Ladies."[82] They are unmarried, unattractive, infertile, and dedicated to a moralizing, dogmatic ideological group in which they attempt to gain status by virtue (or should we say "purity"?) signaling. There are, however, key differences between SJW females and Church Ladies.

A century ago, a significant proportion of the population might be adult virgins because they were unmarried and sex before marriage was socially unacceptable in a society in which Christianity was still dominant. There was a "spinster crisis" in Britain in the 19th century, and again after World War I, due to there being far more middle-class females than there were males of similar status. This had various causes, such as middle-class males delaying marriage for career reasons, leaving Britain for the Empire, and being more likely than working-class men to die in war, due to officers being from middle-class backgrounds and these officers— leading the troops—more likely to be killed in battle.[83] In World War I, for example:

82—Jim Goad, *The New Church Ladies: The Extremely Uptight World of Social Justice* (Stone Mountain: Obnoxious Books, 2017).

83—Virginia Nicholson, *Singled Out: How Two Million Women Survived Without Men After the First World War* (Oxford: Oxford University Press, 2012).

[O]fficers were selected from the men from the middle and upper classes deemed to be of officer material. . . . Offensive operations were led by officers and consequently casualty rates among officers, and in particular among lieutenants and captains in the infantry, were twice those of men in the ranks. . . . [W]orking class military participation and war losses were proportionately lower than middle-class war losses. . . .[84]

As these middle-class females did not wish to "marry down"—and so many of the men they could have married had been killed—there was a generation of "old maids." But this was involuntary. These were females evolved to hypergamy, living in a sexually puritanical society in which there weren't enough upper-middle- and upper-class males to go round. They would often deal with this by becoming intensely religious and heavily involving themselves in the local Anglican Church. In this sense, it could be argued that they were operating at the level of group-selection. But the "New Church Ladies" advocate ideologies that are damaging to group-selection. They are the inversion of the Church Ladies. And they avoid reproduction in a completely different context.

FEMINISM AND EVOLUTION

We now live in a context in which patriarchal controls on female sexuality—due to feminist ideology—have broken down. The result is, in effect, the return of polygamy. Females want to have sex with a small number of high-

---

84—Jay Winter, "Demography," in *A Companion to World War I*, edited by John Horne (Oxford: Wiley-Blackwell, 2010), 252.

status males and, being more educated than men on average, will find that there are relatively few of these to go around. They will also suffer from the dysphoria caused by not living in the patriarchy to which they are evolved. If they have internalized the current feminist ideology, then they will focus on their career to the detriment of their fertility. This will be especially the case, anyway, among more intelligent females, as intelligence has been shown to predict adopting and accepting the current ideology, as a means of better getting on in life.

Intelligence is associated with the "effortful control" that permits you to force yourself to believe something; in other words, you are better able to come up with ways to convince yourself of the veracity of it.[85] The women who are likely to reject feminism are those who are, for genetic reasons, highly religious and patriarchal, precisely the kind of females who predominated under conditions of harsh Darwinian selection. They are more inclined to breed, and, indeed, they do. And, as discussed, traditional religiosity is associated with genetic health. Thus, "feminism," for females, is a new crucible of evolution. It recreates Darwinian pressures and removes genetically unhealthy females. In a quite ironic way, it is a return to nature.

Feminism is a crucible of evolution for males, too. It creates an intense evolutionary mismatch. From a young age, men are told that masculinity is evil; they are encouraged to be female-like (and thus unattractive to females); they are forced to live in a society increasingly dominated by women and feminine interests, such as "empathy" and "equality." Monogamy is undermined. An evolutionary mismatch creates stress, and it has been found that stress, particularly about low status and losing—with males being constantly told that masculinity is bad—reduces testosterone levels, making more males behave in a more feminine way, reducing their drive.[86] To make matters worse, a society that focuses on "equality" plays down, among males, the need to win in competitions and feel dominant over other people, from a very young age. It is, however, the knowledge that you have won, and the feeling of dominance, that boosts testosterone.[87]

But Western males are not only discouraged to compete in these ways, but society tells them that they have "lost"—something hammered home with every commercial where a White female has a non-White husband or every time they see a foreign male or woman in a position of power, something which the media heavily exaggerates. With female dominance of the workplace, work becomes a less competitive space, at least in the overt male sense, creating an extreme mismatch and reducing male testosterone. To make matters worse still, females in the workplace interfere with sexual selection because they cause so many females to be themselves of higher status than so many males, when females sexually select for status.

This results in more and more males not being able to obtain females, with the collapse of restrictions on female

---

86—Leo Kreuz, Robert Rose, and Richard Jennings, "Suppression of Plasma Testosterone Levels and Psychological Stress: A Longitudinal Study of Young Men in Officer Candidate School," *Archives of General Psychiatry*, 26 (1972), 479-482.

87—Alan Booth, Greg Shelley, Allan Mazur, *et al.*, "Testosterone, and Winning and Losing in Human Competition," *Hormones and Behavior*, 23 (1989): 556-571.

sexuality also meaning that these females either have fleeting relationships with promiscuous higher status males or turn to lesbianism in their absence, so strong is their revulsion for lower-status men. Males are, anyway, preoccupied, if not overwhelmed, by highly realistic porn. The kind of males that will get through this abusive environment will be those that are highly resistant to absorbing left-wing ideas about feminism, because they are genetically highly traditionally religious. They will also be those who are not prone to mental illness and the resultant dysphoria, and those who have a genetic strong desire to have children. In other words, only males who are strongly adaptive, for genetic reasons, and thus cannot be pushed awry in this manufactured hellscape, will end up passing on their genes.

In this narrow sense, feminism is effectively eugenic, though its overall effect is massively dysgenic, due to it persuading intelligent women to heavily limit their fertility. Regardless, feminism, and all that goes with it, will have dramatic demographic consequences in the West. Future polities will have a dramatically different character than the ones in which feminism flourished.

CHAPTER 9

HIDING IN PLAIN SITE

The Normalization of Pedophilia

In November 1996, I was walking home from school one grey afternoon, when I noticed a sticker on a lamp-post. It read, "*Protect Our Young. Hang Paedophile Scum.*" In the Britain of 1996, traditional, religiously-sanctioned morality was still clinging on. Homosexuality remained taboo and very few Members of Parliament dared to be openly gay.[1] Government ministers who contracted extra-marital affairs usually had to resign. Transsexuals were widely dismissed as mentally ill. A few years earlier, the Conservative Prime Minister, John Major, had instigated a campaign to restore traditional morals called "Back to Basics."[2] And there was nothing more morally repugnant than sex with children.

Since 1996, the last vestiges of traditional sexual morality have gradually collapsed through a movement to "problematize" and "question" all traditional moral, social, and even scientific structures. Status is gained in this movement of "Social Justice Warriors" by signaling your "Wokeness"—your desire to deconstruct ever more fundamental traditions—as much as you can, without

---

1—Donald MacIntyre, *Mandelson: The Biography* (London: HarperCollins, 1999), 429.

2—Earl Reitan, *The Thatcher Revolution: Margaret Thatcher, John Major, Tony Blair, and the Transformation of Modern Britain, 1979-2001* (Oxford: Rowman & Littlefield, 2003), 147.

being so extreme that you inspire a public backlash or offend traditionalist parties still in positions of power, and thus "damage the cause." The result has been a war of attrition against all traditional structures, morals, and ideas. The next step, so it seems, is to "normalize" pedophilia, such that the attitudes underlying the sentiments in that sticker seem as out-dated and socially unacceptable as those that motivated jailing male homosexuals for "gross indecency," before the love-that-dare-not-speak-its-name was legalized in Britain in 1967.

As we will see, there is evidence that this normalization of pedophilia is well underway. And it can be best understood in terms of the on-going collapse in harsh Darwinian selection. This system's most prominent manifestation so far was in 2019 with the case of Desmond Napoles. Desmond, who was 11 at the time, is an American child drag queen. His mother had been arranging for Desmond to perform in gay clubs in which this prepubescent child provided his audience with risqué dancing and quasi-strip-teases, while gay men threw dollar bills at him. The mother was shocked, apparently, to discover that a convicted pedophile had been openly expressing his lustful desires for little Desmond online.[3]

In June 2020, it emerged that a group of anonymous online pedophiles were attempting to re-brand themselves as "MAPs"—"Minor Attracted Persons." Imitating the tactics so successfully employed by homosexuals and transsexuals, they created their own "MAP Pride" flag with some members, arguing that MAPs "should be celebrated

---

3—Daniel Payne, "Drag Kids" Attract Pedophiles, Which Is No Surprise," *National Review,* July 8, 2019, https://www.nationalreview.com/2019/07/drag-kids-attract-pedophiles-which-is-no-surprise/.

as a niche group alongside the LGBT community." They started memes on social media including "Gay MAPs are amazing," and presented cartoon characters stating: "Repost if you think MAPs should be able to date minors."[4] Britain's "MAPs" had previously been defended by Stephen Harper, a psychologist at Nottingham Trent University, who has researched the group. Harper told a newspaper that:

> I think that the MAP community is essential. We know that people who are minor attracted face a lot of stigma in society. We also know that a lot of them don't commit any offences at all. So actually having that community where they can support each other—and their mental health—gives them a sense of identity.

Harper added:

> As a heterosexual male it doesn't mean because I see a female in the street I'm automatically going to commit an offence. I think it's a common misconception that minor attracted people have no self-control. They have the same levels of self-control as anyone else.[5]

This is inaccurate. According to *The Diagnostic and Statistical Manual of Mental Disorders,* a paraphilia, by

---

4—Katherine Denkinson, "Outrage as Paedophiles Rebrand Themselves as 'Minor-Attracted Persons' in Chilling Online Propaganda Drive," *Mail Online,* June 27, 2020, https://www.dailymail.co.uk/news/article-8466899/Paedophiles-rebrand-minor-attracted-persons-chilling-online-propaganda-drive.html.

5—Charlie Wolf and Hannah Mitchell, "Nottingham Academic Says Non-offending Paedophile Community is 'Essential' to Help Stop Offenders," *Nottinghamshire Live*, June 4, 2019, https://www.nottinghampost.com/news/nottingham-news/nottingham-academic-says-non-offending-2940755.

definition, involves "recurrent, intense sexually arousing fantasies, sexual urges, or behaviors . . . that involve nonhuman objects, the suffering or humiliation of oneself or one's partner, or children or nonconsenting adults."[6] By this definition, those who are slightly attracted to children, such that they can easily control their urges, are not pedophiles.

BRITAIN'S PEDOPHILE PANIC AT THE DAWN OF THE MILLENNIUM

You couldn't have imagined this in the Britain of 1996. At the time, Britain was in the midst of a "moral panic" about pedophilia, understood as the predatory sexual abuse of children, especially by socially and sexually inadequate males. On the morning of March 13, 1996, a 43-year-old pedophile and loner called Thomas Hamilton (1952-1996) had walked into Dunblane Primary School, in southern Scotland, and shot dead 15 children, all aged five. He also killed their teacher and managed to injure 15 other children and staff. Hamilton, a former Scout Master and Boys' Club leader, who had used these positions to sexually abuse minors, then killed himself. Britain was in shock and the media remained obsessed with pedophilia for years afterwards.[7]

In July 2000, with this moral panic having spiraled out of control over the preceding years, Sarah Payne (1991-2000), an 8-year-old girl from a working class

6—See S. Kershnar, "Pedophilia," in *Encylopedia of Applied Ethics*, ed. Ruth Chadwick (New York: Academic Press, 2012).

7—See David Wilson, *My Life with Murderers: Behind Bars with the World's Most Violent Men* (London: Hachette, 2019).

background, was murdered by 41-year-old pedophile Roy Whiting in Pulborough in West Sussex, south of London. The result was an explosion of public fury.[8] There were anti-pedophile marches, especially in rundown council estates occupied by working class British people.

These were, to some extent, incited by the "For Sarah" campaign run by the salacious Sunday tabloid *The News of the World.* Beginning on July 23, 2000, and continuing for two weeks, *The News of the World* published the names, photographs, and addresses of convicted child sex abusers. It publicly exposed 83 of the 150 pedophiles on whom it had information, before dropping the campaign.[9] The front page headline on July 2, 2000 was simply "Named, Shamed."[10] The result was a string of vigilante attacks on men who were, or were wrongly believed to be, pedophiles. On the night of August 3, for example, 150 people rioted outside the home of a convicted pedophile in Portsmouth on the south coast. During the three hours of violence, the pedophile's flat was pelted with stones, a car was overturned and set ablaze, one policeman was hospitalized, and another one took a brick to the face.[11] In one case, a "paediatrician" was forced to flee her home

---

8—Bill Thompson and Andy Williams, *The Myth of Moral Panics: Sex, Snuff, and Satan* (London: Routledge, 2013), 276.

9—Matt Born, "Paper Drops Paedophile Campaign," *The Telegraph,* August 5, 2000, https://www.telegraph.co.uk/news/uknews/1351615/Paper-drops-paedophile-campaign.html.

10—Terry Thomas, *The Registration and Monitoring of Sex Offenders: A Comparative Study* (London: Routledge, 2011).

11—Staff and Agencies, "News of the World Suspends Name-and-Shame Campaign," *The Guardian,* August 4, 2000, https://www.theguardian.com/society/2000/aug/04/childprotection.

in South Wales because vigilantes had concluded that this must be another word for "paedophile," this being the British spelling of the word.[12]

At the time, there seemed to be nothing more likely to evoke visceral emotion in Britain than pedophilia. This is why, in July 2001, the "Brass Eye Paedophile Special," broadcast on nakedly leftist station Channel 4, created a media storm greater than any program ever broadcast on British television. It remains the most complained about single program in UK television history.[13] *Brass Eye* focused on cutting edge, and highly intelligent, social satire, presented as spoof news programs. It had previously explored issues such as "Sex" and "Drugs," but its "Paedophile Special" took on new levels of comedic and satirical brilliance. "Why can we no longer think of the 'British Isles' without the word 'Paedoph' in front of them?" the presenter asked at the beginning. He then reported on the "notorious pedophile Sydney Cooke," who was

> blasted into space to spend the rest of his life on a one-man prison vessel, posing no further threat to children on Earth. But it was revealed that an 8-year-old boy was also placed on board by mistake and is now trapped alone in space with the monster. A spokesman said, 'This is the one thing we didn't want to happen.'

The program, performed and partly written by Chris Morris, drew attention to the hypocrisy and inconsistencies

---

12—Rebecca Allison, "Doctor Driven Out by Vigilantes," *The Guardian*, August 30, 2000, https://www.theguardian.com/uk/2000/aug/30/childprotection.society.

13—Eric Burman, *Developments: Child, Image, Nation* (London: Routledge, 2008), 118.

in public and media attitudes to the sexual exploitation of children. One sketch—in order to highlight the exposure of youngsters to sexualized pop music that glorifies serious criminality and even the sexual abuse of females—presented a white rapper called "J.L. Bait," who "dates girls as young as seven." We see his music videos being fawned over by two British prepubescent female fans. Another piece lampooned American child beauty pageants with a report on the supposed trend of American parents giving their female toddlers breast implants. Showing them off to their impressed friends, we see a couple expose their toddler's breasts, before the father comments, "They jiggle." The episode culminated in prepubescent girls singing a sugary piece, addressed to pedophiles, about when they can have sex with them: "Not today, not even tomorrow," they sing, before a preteen girl finishes with, "But maybe the day after that" and smiles coquettishly. The outer limits of edgy humor were tested on national television.

TOO NEAR THE BONE

Strong emotional reactions—of the kind induced by the "Brass Eye: Paedophile Special"—are often manifestations of "cognitive dissonance," the distance between what the empirical evidence is telling you is reality and what you profoundly wish to be true. This causes you to question how the world works and who you are, leaving you existentially insecure and anxious, often doubting whether or not you are a good person. Sometimes, people react to this cognitive dissonance by changing their worldviews. But, frequently, they become extremely aggressive, in an attempt to insulate themselves from their perceived critics and to make these critics shut up and go away, such that the deeply uncomfortable feelings the critics have induced might go away as well.[14] This is what happened in response to this notorious episode of *Brass Eye*.

Morris, in effect, pointed out that many British people are extraordinarily hypocritical in their attitudes to pedophilia. Pedophiles sexualize children but, in 2001, British (and, more broadly, Western) culture had long been sexualizing children. The pubescent girl singing, "Not today, not even tomorrow . . . but maybe the day after that," could be interpreted as a satire of "barely legal" and heavily sexualized female pop stars at the time, such as Billie and Britney Spears. It has been noted that such pop stars had a strong child-following, and their videos frequently involved images of sexual behavior, which children could be expected to imitate.[15] "J.L. Bait," clearly a satire of Eminem, also drew attention to the way in which children are exposed to sexuality at younger and younger ages, because they are raised in a society in which promiscuity is promoted as "normal," with religious taboos having long since broken down.

The working-class parents rioting in front of the pedophile's home in Portsmouth would have included many women who had become pregnant as teenagers, and whose daughters would go on to become pregnant as teenagers, with teen pregnancy being, overwhelmingly,

---

14—See: Leon Festinger, *A Theory of Cognitive Dissonance* (Stanford, Stanford University Press, 1957).

15—Christine Sanderson, *The Seduction of Children: Empowering Parents and Teachers to Protect Children from Sexual Abuse* (London: Jessica Kingsley Publishers, 2004), 312.

a working-class phenomenon in Britain.[16] These parents would have allowed their pubescent daughters to have dressed in a sexually provocative fashion and given them free rein to "hang around" in teenage street gangs, only to get knocked up by older men. There is an extent to which the sketch about breast implants for toddlers lampoons the way in which some parents sexualize children, whether passively or, like pedophiles, actively. In that sense, the riot in Portsmouth was a classic example of "projection," where we cope with negative feelings about ourselves by projecting them onto others.[17]

THE PAEDOPHILE INFORMATION NETWORK

Another issue that was satirized in the program was attitudes towards pedophilia in 1970s Britain, with the insinuation that people condemning child abuse in 2001 turned a blind eye to it only a few decades before. This was achieved via a pastiche, seemingly of the band *T-Rex*, in which an androgynous vocalist sings about his sexual desires for youngsters in a song entitled "Playground Bang-a-Round." One cannot read the minds of the sketch writers, but this may have been an exaggerated reference to the relative acceptability of under-age sex in the 1970s, especially as then rumored to have been indulged in by certain celebrities, including pop stars. A string of revelations came to light in this regard following the death of the eccentric British entertainer and "National Treasure"

16—Gillian Evans, *Educational Failure and Working Class White Children in Britain* (London: Palgrave Macmillan, 2006), 41.

17—See, Mary Ann Mattoon, *Jungian Psychology in Perspective* (New York: Simon and Schuster, 1985), Chapter 8.

Sir Jimmy Savile in 2011, as noted earlier. Upon his death, not only did it become clear that Savile had been a serial abuser of young girls, but so had other prominent British celebrities, and even in 2001, the child abuse committed by "glam rocker" Gary Glitter was already public knowledge.[18]

In the 1970s, Britain witnessed relatively open discussions of far more unorthodox views than it being okay to have sex with 13-year-old school girls. In 1974, the "Paedophile Information Exchange" (PIE) was established, and it remained an official organization for 10 years. PIE was founded in Edinburgh as a special interest group within the "Scottish Minorities Group," which campaigned for gay rights in Scotland. In 1975, the group relocated to England, where it campaigned to "alleviate the suffering of many adults and children" by the abolition of the age of sexual consent.[19] It is clear that there were people on what is sometimes termed the "libertarian left" who were sympathetic to PIE. For some time, PIE was affiliated to the National Council of Civil Liberties (NCCL), a group which campaigned for "civil rights" for perceived persecuted minorities such as homosexuals. While it was connected to this organization, PIE argued that child pornography, in which no harm has come to the child, should be decriminalized. In 1978, Harriet Harman—NCCL's legal officer and later the Labour Party's Acting Leader of the Opposition—lobbied parliament with such proposals.[20]

18—See Dan Davies, *In Plain Sight: The Life and Lies of Jimmy Savile* (London: Quercus Publishing, 2014).

19—Christian Wolmar, "Looking Back to the Great British Paedophile Infiltration Campaign of the 1970s," *Independent,* February 27, 2014, https://www.independent.co.uk/news/uk/politics/looking-back-to-the-great-british-paedophile-infiltration-campaign-of-the-1970s-9155610.html.

20—Martin Beckford, "Jimmy Savile: Labour Faces Embarrassment Over

In 1975, the left-wing newspaper *The Guardian* published a not unsympathetic piece explaining what "paedophilia" was to its readers. Its main source, used relatively uncritically, was PIE leader Keith Hose, who was quoted by one newspaper as saying, "I am a paedophile. I am attracted to boys from about 10, 11, and 12 years of age. I may have had sexual relations with children, but it would be unwise to say." In 1977, the Campaign for Homosexual Equality passed a resolution condemning "the harassment of the Paedophile Information Exchange by the press." In response, the president of the Young Liberals, Peter Hain—who was later a Labour Cabinet Minister—described pedophilia as "a wholly undesirable abnormality." To this, a fellow Liberal activist retorted, "It is sad that Peter has joined the hang 'em and flog 'em brigade. His views are not the views of most Young Liberals." In other words, he was implying that Hain was a bigoted reactionary. When a journalist for *The Guardian* wrote in support of Hain, the columnist "was inundated with mail from people—many willing to give their name—who defended sex with children."[21]

PIE members portrayed themselves as being in favor of "liberation"—the liberation of children and adults from old-fashioned, restrictive laws, which had once criminalized homosexuality. This evidently appealed to some influential gay-rights campaigners and others on the left. A 1977 piece in *The Guardian* opined, unhappily, "in

Former Child Sex Claims," *Telegraph*, October 17, 2012, https://www.telegraph.co.uk/news/uknews/crime/jimmy-savile/9614516/Jimmy-Savile-Labour-faces-embarrassment-over-former-child-sex-claims.html.

21—Tom de Castella and Tom Heyden, "How Did the Pro-paedophile Group PIE Exist Openly for 10 Years?" *BBC News*, February 27, 2014, https://www.bbc.com/news/magazine-26352378.

another five years or so, their aims would eventually be incorporated into the general liberal credo, and we would all find them acceptable."[22] By the early 1980s, however, there was an increasing media backlash against PIE, and in 1984 it was disbanded.

PIE IN A NEW FORM

As already discussed, there was a period of many decades, beginning in the 1980s, in which pedophilia was both widely discussed in the media and also completely socially unacceptable. So, how did we get to the point where the sexualization of children has increasingly become acceptable once again? No prominent organization is advocating—as did PIE—that the age of sexual consent be abolished and paedophilia, legalized. But what we are seeing is a slow normalization of a once-abhorred practice. As already alluded to above, the process is explicable in terms of the concept of the "Spiteful Mutant" promoting fitness-destroying ways of thinking, as well as runaway individualism. In effect, once everybody accepts transsexuals, we must move on to the next supposedly marginalized group as a means of signaling how much we "care" and desire "equality." We would expect leftists to be attracted to subverting traditional systems of child-rearing. But we would also expect pedophiles to be attracted to doing so, because they are also high in mutational load and because so doing provides them with easier sexual access to children.

Let us define the "pedophile" as an adult who is exclusively sexually attracted to pubescent or pre-

22—*Ibid.*

pubescent children, as opposed to sexual opportunists, who will sexually abuse children simply because they are easy to take advantage of. Approximately half of those who sexually abuse children are not exclusively attracted to children. Pedophiles, so defined, have strongly elevated levels of poor mental health, including mood disorders (66 percent), Obsessive Compulsive Disorder (25 percent), and personality disorders of various kinds (61 percent), such as Borderline Personality Disorder and Psychopathic Personality Disorder.[23] It is, therefore, empirically inaccurate to assert that pedophiles "have the same levels of self-control as anyone else."

Pedophiles show evidence of problems in the development of certain brain structures. They are more likely to be left-handed, which is an accepted marker of mutational load. They are more likely to have older mothers. Old parents are also associated with mutational load, because greater mutational load is passed on with age. Pedophiles are also more likely to have suffered brain damage as children through serious knocks to the head. This would be consistent with pedophilia being a product of developmental instability, one of the causes of which is high mutational load.[24] In addition, pedophiles are more likely than controls to display "Minor Physical Abnormalities," these being an obvious sign of mutational load as they are deviations from symmetry.[25]

23—Gilian Tenbergen, Matthias Wittfoth, Helge Frieling, *et al.*, "The Neurobiology and Psychology of Pedophilia: Recent Advances and Challenges," *Frontiers in Human Neuroscience*, (2015): 344.

24—*Ibid.*

25—Kirsten Jordan, Tamara Wild, Peter Fromberger, *et al.*, "Are There Any Biomarkers for Pedophilia and Sexual Child Abuse? A Review," *Frontiers in Psychiatry* (2020), https://doi.org/10.3389/fpsyt.2019.00940.

It has been found that, in many people, homosexuality evokes a disgust response. Indeed, having a strong general disgust response—that is, becoming easily disgusted—correlates with becoming disgusted by homosexuals and lesbians. It has been found that disgust sensitivity is associated with the five Moral Foundations that appear to predict differences in attitudes: care, fairness, loyalty, authority, and sanctity.[26] High scores in authority and sanctity predict being disgusted by homosexuality, and it has been found that high sanctity scores mediate (cause) the association between disgust sensitivity and being disgusted by homosexuality.[27] It has also been found that people feel more disgusted towards homosexual men the more likely those men are to come into contact with their children, such as through being doctors or teachers. And there is evidence that boys, though not girls, who are sexually abused by someone of the same sex are more likely to later become homosexual, and that homosexuality is heavily over-represented among pedophiles.[28] It would, therefore, follow that disgust towards homosexuality, and especially towards male homosexuality, is adaptive. Those who lacked this disgust-response, to put it simply, ended up with a higher percentage of homosexual sons and thus

26—See Jonathan Haidt, *The Righteous Mind: Why Good People Are Divided By Politics and Religion* (London: Penguin, 2012).

27—Ruile Wang, Qi Yang, Peng Huang, *et al.*, "The Association Between Disgust Sensitivity and Negative Attitudes Toward Homosexuality: The Mediating Role of Moral Foundations," *Frontiers in Psychology*, 10 (2019): 1229.

28—See Gordon Gallup and Susan Suarez, "Homosexuality as a By-product of Selection for Optimal Heterosexual Strategies," *Perspectives in Biological Medicine*, 26 (1983): 315-322; Gordon Gallup, "Attitudes Toward Homosexuals and Evolutionary Theory: The Role of Evidence," *Ethology and Sociobiology*, 17 (1996): 281-284.

with fewer descendants.[29] As we have already discussed, those who are high in "individualizing" foundations—which map on to being liberal—are not only prone to runaway individualism, but are lower in generalized disgust, especially in sexual disgust.

THE NORMALIZING OF PEDOPHILIA

As we have explored, with the collapse of harsh Darwinian conditions, we see a rise in mutational load among the products of industrialized societies. In genetic terms, the resultant populations would shoot off in every direction from the preindustrial "norm" that had permitted survival in a strongly Darwinian context. All of these Darwinian "norms"—natalism, sexual attraction to fertile and healthy members of the opposite sex, traditional religiosity, inclination towards group selection, mental health, physical health, and much more—would be bundled together and thus genetically inter-related. Similarly, the deviations from this would tend to be co-morbid as well, though there could be exceptions with certain individual traits.

The overall consequence of this would be a rising number of Spiteful Mutants, who would never have survived under harsh conditions, who would be programed to want to undermine and destroy everything that promoted group fitness. They would be motivated by a "death wish" for the ethnic group. In addition, the form of Multiculturalist Religion, of which this process is a part,

---

29—For a summary of the debate, see Jess Bering, "Natural Homophobes? Evolutionary Psychology and Antigay Attitudes," *Scientific American*, March 11, 2011, https://blogs.scientificamerican.com/bering-in-mind/natural-homophobes-evolutionary-psychology-and-antigay-attitudes/.

sets up a system where you will increasingly "virtue-signal" in order to gain status within the New Church. As myself and a colleague have noted in relation to ideologically driven academics, this involves a form of intellectual risk-taking, whereby they showcase their devotion to multiculturalism by daring to question or confront a perceived example of oppression that had previously been ignored. They must be careful in this regard. If they are *too* radical, they may create a hostile backlash from the masses, as occurred in relation to PIE in the '80s. So they, carefully and slightly, move the culture in the direction of further undermining adaptive behavior, such that it seems like a perfectly reasonable progression. They take a small risk for a small pay off in terms of showcasing your credentials.[30] These "salami tactics" allow a "Cultural Revolution" to advance relatively smoothly, avoiding violent upheavals.

This process can be seen in the history of the West since the mid-19th century. They begin by questioning the country's religion, which will tend to promote what is group-adaptive as the will of God. As people begin to lose faith in this, they start questioning the patriarchal system that ensures that females are motivated to want to have children, and the class system that promotes group-selected traits such as ethnocentrism and obedience to traditional authority. Along with traditional religion, they undermine traditional taboos on sexuality and traditional models of the family. They create a society that is evermore sociosexual and one in which marriages

---

30—Edward Dutton and Dimitri van der Linden, "Who are the 'Clever Sillies'? The Intelligence, Personality, and Motives of Clever Silly Originators and Those who Follow Them," *Intelligence,* 49 (2015): 57-65.

can be easily dissolved, exposing children to insecurity, disruption, and the danger of abusive step-parents.[31] This is despite the fact that, according to criminologists, "Step-parenthood *per se* remains the single most powerful risk factor for child abuse that has yet been identified."[32]

Once women are reasonably empowered—and the Woke can no longer gain status by calling for their empowerment—they move onto the issue of "racism." They instill the population with guilt about the crimes of their ancestors; they endorse mass immigration, something which has been shown to destroy in-group cooperation and undermine trust even between natives.[33] And ethnocentrism (part of which is in-group cooperation) has been shown to be key to the survival of groups that battle with other groups in the process of group selection.[34]

Once almost everyone professes "anti-racism," they can either become ever more extreme in your professions of anti-racism, or move to something else. This is what some people did, in the form of homosexual rights, and then the public acceptance of homosexuality, including

31—Child abuse is massively elevated at the hands of step-parents, for obvious evolutionary reasons. In the U.S., a child under the age of 2 is 100 times more likely to be killed by a step-parent than by a biological parent. David Barash, *Revolutionary Biology: The New, Gene-centered View of Life* (London: Routledge, 2017), 162.

32—Martin Daly and Margo Wilson, *Homicide: Foundations of Human Behavior* (London: Routledge, 2017), 87-88.

33—Robert Putnam, "*E Pluribus Unum*: Diversity and Community in the Twenty-first Century," The 2006 Johan Skytte Prize Lecture, *Scandinavian Political Studies*, 30 (2007): 137–174.

34—Ross Hammond and Robert Axelrod, "The Evolution of Ethnocentric Behavior," *Journal of Conflict Resolution* 50 (2006): 1-11.

teaching school children that this was "normal," despite evidence that homosexuals are high in mental and physical illnesses and that there is an extent to which homosexuality is environmentally mediated.[35] Then they move on to transsexuals, whom they also attempt to normalize. In doing so, they attack the biological distinction between "male" and "female." They celebrate "transwomen" as no different than women. They expose children to such mentally unstable and provocative people at schools. They stop the puberty of children who may simply be going through a passing phase of sexual insecurity and encourage them to believe that they are actually transsexual. In stopping their puberty, of course, you treat these children as adults, who are intellectually capable of making life-altering decisions, which will, in many cases, render them either infertile or needing to have children via IVF.[36]

The population is increasingly in an "evolutionary mismatch." We are evolved to be with genetically normal humans, who are mentally healthy, and shun those who are not. We are evolved to a situation of hierarchy, often with hereditary and religiously sanctioned leadership. We are evolved to live in a religious society, as well as a patriarchal society, with clear sex roles. We are evolved to live in a homogenous society. This is our "evolutionarily familiar"

35—See Chapter 6.

36—In vitro fertilization is a problematic process that has been shown to produce mentally damaged and unhealthy children who are considerably more likely to have psychiatric problems. This may be partly because IVF avoids the adaptive process of intense sperm selection. See Malene Svahn, Marie Hargreave, T.S.S. Nielsen, et al., "Mental Disorders in Childhood and Young Adulthood Among Children Born to Women with Fertility Problems," *Human Reproduction,* 30 (2015): 2129-2137.

THE NORMALIZATION OF PEDOPHILIA

environment, and animals tend to become unhappy and stressed if placed outside familiar structures, leading to depression and anxiety, which leads to infertility—a sense that nothing is worth it.[37] People do not enjoy living in an "evolutionary mismatch," no matter what they might feel they should say in public.

Once they've got this far, what is the next step? With the breakdown of traditional religiosity, the society is already strongly sociosexual. So, perhaps the next "oppressive structure" they should question is the adaptive distinction between "adult" and "child." They can use the same tactics that you might with "race." What do we mean by "child"? Is there a clear border between "adult" and "child"? Do not different societies have different conceptions of what constitutes a "child"? Is not "child" a very "Western" concept? Children are oppressed, shouldn't we liberate them from this oppression? Didn't you know that there is evidence that even very young children have sexuality? Shouldn't expression of sexuality be a "human right"?

As we saw with PIE, when these kinds of questions were asked in the 1970s, British society remained sufficiently evolutionarily adaptive that it knew to dismiss them out of hand as the ravings of Spiteful Mutants. But that was almost half a century ago. Now, pedophilia can be gradually normalized such that a few decades hence, people might find it amazing that their parents never allowed them to have relations with adults. Of course, this will simply create further dysphoria, chaos, and psychological damage to children. It will be a form of psychological selection-pressure, with only the most psychologically resilient, and

37—Satoshi Kanazawa, "Intelligence and Childlessness," *Social Science Research.* 48 (2014): 157-170.

thus genetically healthy, at least in part, being likely to pass on their genes in the face of it.

POSTSCRIPT

In June 2021, a few months after I wrote this chapter, some of my predictions came true: a bold attempt was made to normalize pedophilia. Allyn Walker, a gender fluid transman academic (pronouns: they/them) at Old Dominion University in Virginia, published a book entitled *A Long, Dark Shadow: Minor-Attracted People and Their Pursuit of Dignity*.[38] Having interviewed 42 non-active pedophiles, Walker compared pedophilia to heterosexuality and argued that Minor-Attracted Persons ("MAPs") should, as long as they don't break the law, be given full equality. They shouldn't be made to feel ashamed of their sexual orientation, as this could stop them seeking counseling. There should be "MAP" role-models in the media to help young, marginalized MAPs. After all, MAPs, the author argued, are in the same positions transsexuals previously were. They are marginalized, lacking in "privilege" and it is, in effect, time for them to be accepted.

Consistent with compulsion being an aspect of pedophilia—as it is with most fetishes—one of Walker's subjects, Isaac, "had gone to a small island where he 'saw children running around naked' in public. Isaac immediately went online to seek help from others who would understand." Isaac told Walker, "It was a bit of a challenge for me." But the online communities told him, "'You can do it, [Isaac]!' By this, they meant he could

---

38—Allyn Walker, *A Long, Dark Shadow: Minor-Attracted People and Their Pursuit of Dignity* (Oakland: University of California Press, 2021).

refrain from offending."[39] Isaac is akin to a heterosexual man on a nudist beach, who feels such a compulsion to rape every woman in sight he has to seek help to keep himself under control. He is not simply a person "attracted" to minors.

This is the key problem with the concept of MAPs. In desiring sexual relationships with minors, MAPs are effectively akin to men who are exclusively aroused by rape or, at best, aroused only by having sex with women who are so drunk as to be incompetent. Of course, it may be that Walker's sample—in reaching out for help to online communities—are not representative of the average MAP. Perhaps the average MAP is better at suppressing, or coping with, his desires or feels them less acutely. It seems, however, the West is not ready for the normalizing of pedophilia quite yet. The enormous backlash publicity for the book caused in November 2021 resulted in Walker resigning from Old Dominion University.[40]

39—*Ibid.,* 118.

40—Sam Baker, "Trans Professor, 34, who Defended Pedophiles as 'Minor Attracted Persons' Finally RESIGNS After 15,000 People Signed Online Petition," *Mail Online,* November 25, 2021, https://www.dailymail.co.uk/news/article-10241745/Trans-professor-34-defended-pedophiles-Minor-Attracted-Persons-RESIGNS.html.

CHAPTER 10

THE FUTURE PAST

Our Social Apocalypse

The normalizing of pedophilia may be the relatively immediate future, but it is not unreasonable to try to look a little further. As we have seen, Wokeism—and all that it brings about—is the new "crucible of evolution." It discourages people from having children, or even passing on their genes indirectly through elevating group fitness. Wokeness does this via indoctrination, via the creation of a sub-optimal environment, and, in particular, by the creation of an extreme evolutionary mismatch and thus a kind of dysphoria which leads to maladaptive, fitness-damaging behavior.

As discussed, the Woke have relatively low fertility. So, the kinds of people who will survive the Zombie Apocalypse are those who, for genetic reasons, can resist it. These will be people who, for genetic reasons, very strongly desire children, or somehow end up having them, even in the face of the most suboptimal possible environment. And there is evidence that desiring your own children and to be pregnant with them—or "baby fever"—is intense, not uncommon, is heritable, and more genetic in younger age cohorts. This implies that sexual and other selection pressures mean that a portion of a self-aware population that understands, as all populations seem to, "where babies come from," has an adaptive desire to strongly want their own babies and that this is being selected for in a context in which people can control their fertility with contraception.[1]

Who are these people who are having children? They seem to divide into two distinct kinds: very fast Life History strategists and very slow Life History Strategists, or extreme individualists and extreme collectivists. We would expect such people to be strongly genetically distinct, and thus to dislike each other. As I have explored in an earlier book, *At Our Wits' End,* the first group that breeds is people with low intelligence. There is a -0.2 correlation in developed countries between fertility and intelligence, and the relationship exists even when controlling for socioeconomic factors. This may seem like a small relationship, but the result is that Western Europe lost about 15 IQ points between 1880 and the year 2000; this is the difference between a policeman and a high school teacher, or between the same teacher and a science professor. Such a change means that the percentage of the population with very high intelligence—an IQ of above 130: the highly influential and leading academics, lawyers, doctors and politicians—falls from 14 percent of the population to just 2 percent. Those directing the society, in other words, become dramatically stupider. And it is a society where more people need to be managed and directed, because those who are mentally retarded—with an IQ of below 70—increases from 2 percent to 14 percent.

This relationship exists because, in our evolutionary mismatch, many people appear to have lost the instinct to have children at all. Accordingly, large families tend to be

1—See A. Rotkirch, "'All That She Wants Is (A)nother Baby'? Longing for Children as a Fertility Incentive of Growing Importance," *Journal of Evolutionary Psychology*, 5 (2007): 89-104.

the accidental product of low intelligence. Low IQ people are too impulsive and too low in future-orientation to use contraception, or they are too low in intelligence to use it efficiently, so they end up with lots of children. In addition, low IQ women do not delay fertility in order to have a career, as they are less easily indoctrinated with the current ideology and will, anyway, perform poorly at school and dislike formal education. Thus, they will be grandmothers by the time their more intelligent contemporaries start breeding, meaning they create more generations, not just larger families. In Britain, only those who are on welfare and also require interventions from the police and social workers, with an IQ of about 80, have above replacement fertility.

This decline in IQ can be seen on numerous correlates of intelligence: reaction times are getting longer with an element of intelligence being processing speed, memory is getting shorter; per capita major innovations—having peaked in 1870—have declined back to where they were in 1600; and the population prevalence of alleles indirectly associated with very high IQ is falling. Since about 1997, IQ scores have been in decline on the most genetic components of intelligence. This decline had previously been cloaked by massive rises on specialized abilities, which are weakly associated with intelligence, and which are measured by the IQ test. This is the so-called Flynn Effect.[2] Our increasingly scientific and technolgical society has pushed these abilities to their phenotypic maximum so quickly that it showed up as

---

2—See James Flynn, *What Is Intelligence?: Beyond the Flynn Effect* (Cambridge: Cambridge University Press, 2007); Edward Dutton, *Making Sense of Race* (Whitefish: Washington Summit Publishers, 2020), Chapter 7.

an IQ score rise across generations, due to the imperfect nature of the IQ test. But with this limit reached, we have widespread Negative Flynn Effects; IQ scores are precipitously declining.[3]

This is important because every aspect of civilization—law and order, levels of corruption, public health, democracy, peace, education, development, and so on—is associated with national level IQ, and these have been shown to be fair, highly reliable, and strongly correlated with other relevant measures, such as national prevalence of alleles associated with high intelligence. As we explored in our discussion of homosexuality, civilizations go through cycles and it appears that our civilization is now in its "winter" phase. It is gradually collapsing back into something rather less civilized, significantly due to the intelligence decline which its innovations have created. Historically, when civilizations collapse, you see the rise of new religions and even new ethnic groups and it would be hubris to suppose that something like this will not occur in our case. Indeed, as we will see below, it is very likely already well under way.

Democracy, to the extent it ever develops, is always lost in a civilization's "winter." Why have democracy and freedom of speech declined? They are associated with intelligence and trust. However, religiousness—which might suppress freedom due to its strong focus on the "holy" and "binding" values—is elevated at times of stress. Thus, what may have occurred is that our mortality salience collapsed quite rapidly, leading

3—Edward Dutton and Michael Woodley of Menie, *At Our Wits' End: Why We're Becoming Less Intelligent and What It Means for the Future* (Exeter: Imprint Academic, 2018).

us to be less religious, sufficiently intelligent to question religion, and also relatively high in both intelligence and trust, itself a correlate of intelligence. This permitted a period of freedom and low religious influence, because there was an optimum balance between "binding" and "individualistic" values, in the form of weak traditional religiousness. This period could only be fleeting. The decline in religiousness meant a decline in ethnocentrism, resulting in immigration and multiculturalism, and, so, declining trust. The collapse in child mortality led to greater genetic diversity, in the sense that there are more gene-forms due to weakened purifying selection, and, therefore, to declining trust, with trust associated with genetic similarity.[4]

This process has also led to the rise in the influence of females and thus a greater emphasis on "equality" and "harm avoidance" over systematizing and truth-seeking—systematizing being the essence of the "male brain."[5] This has helped to bring about increasing restrictions on free speech. The entire situation led to an increasing evolutionary mismatch, higher levels of mental illness, greater paranoia, and thus declining trust. Declining intelligence itself meant a decrease in the value placed in democracy, declining trust, and increasing dogmatism. Genetic diversity also permitted more and more depressed and individualistic people, who would be low in trust and black-and-white in their thinking, to push society away from beliefs in freedom of speech and democracy. With

---

4—J. Philippe Rushton, "Ethic Nationalism: Evolutionary Psychology and Genetic Similarity Theory," *Nations and Nationalism,* 11 (2005): 489-507.

5—Simon Baron-Cohen, "The Extreme Male Brain Theory of Autism," *Trends in Cognitive Sciences,* 6 (2002): 248-254.

no group-selection pressure to keep society united and with traditional religiousness being weak, these people could hijack the culture—due to the way in which group-oriented people sympathize with individualists, as a consequence of conservatives valuing all five Moral Foundations and individualists only valuing two, as we saw above—pushing it in an extreme individualistic direction, and so challenging democracy and free speech. But this situation, itself, will also be fleeting, mainly due to fertility.[6]

Fertility is also associated with certain components of a fast Life History Strategy, which arises in an easy yet unstable environment.[7] That it would only be certain components makes sense, because the post-industrial world is an easy and *stable* ecology: the threat of being wiped out by an act of nature as been overcome in advanced societies; deadly floods, droughts, or hurricanes are exceptional, not the expected events that defined an r-selected environment. This means that the components of a fast LHS are going to break up. Thus, Conscientiousness, in females, is negatively associated with fertility, probably due to those who are low in Conscientiousness being too impulsive to use contraception or plan for the future. Extraversion, which involves feeling positive feelings strongly and thus risk-taking, is also associated with fertility, possibly for the same reason.[8] And although fertility is negatively

---

6—Adam Perkins, *The Welfare Trait: How State Benefits Affect Personality* (Basingstoke: Palgrave Macmillan, 2015).

7—See Chapter 2.

8—Markus Jokela, "Birth-cohort Effects in the Association Between Personality and Fertility," *Psychological Science,* 23 (2012): 835-841.

associated with Neuroticism, it is positively associated with certain expressions of a fast Life History Strategy.

Thus, people who are "incentive-seeking and selfish" have more children than controls.[9] This may be because in many developed countries there are financial incentives to have large families, largely in the form of welfare payments, which in theory are to be spent on the children. It may also be because people tend to look up to and admire people for having children.[10] Indeed, males seem to be attracted to women with Borderline Personality Traits so long as they are physically attractive, because it may lead to a thrilling, short-term relationship, which may, naturally, result in accidental pregnancy.[11] And the fertility of non-White immigrants in Western countries is often considerably higher than that of natives. The average Somali family in Denmark has five children, compared to fewer than two for the average Danish family.[12] On many, though not all, measures, these immigrants are faster Life History Strategists. Low intelligence—as well as low Conscientiousness and, indeed, r-strategy in general—predicts low socioeconomic status.[13]

9—Fernando Gutiérrez, Miguel Gárriz, Josep Peri *et al.*, "Fitness Costs and Benefits of Personality Disorder Traits," *Evolution and Human Behavior,* 34 (2013): 41-48.

10—See, Perkins, *The Welfare Trait, op cit.*

11—Alyson Blanchard, Thomas Dunn, and Alex Sumich, "Borderline Personality Traits in Attractive Women and Wealthy Low Attractive Men are Relatively Favoured by the Opposite Sex," *Personality and Individual Differences,* 169 (2021): 109964.

12—Emil Kirkegaard, "Predicting Immigrant IQ from their Countries of Origin, and Lynn's National IQs: A Case Study from Denmark," *Mankind Quarterly,* 54 (2013), 151-167.

13—Perkins, *The Welfare Trait, op cit.*

On the other hand, as we have already discussed, traditional religiousness is correlated with fertility. And so are a number of factors that cross-over with this, including Agreeableness.[14] This may be because altruistic people want to have children whom they can nurture. In addition, a number of aspects of K-strategy—the essence of which is the desire to nurture—have been shown to be associated with fertility.[15] As already discussed, this suite of traits is associated with high socioeconomic status. On this basis, we would predict increasing polarization as extreme individualists and extreme collectivists tend to breed while the center is hollowed out, and this is consistent with research that the West is highly polarized.[16]

Genetic diversity is increasing in contemporary Western societies, due to relaxed Darwinian selection and the collapse of infant mortality, as well as immigration and multiculturalism. As this evolutionary mismatch becomes ever more extreme, with more and more people feeling intense dysphoria, "backlash" politics will be the norm. The "cultural war"—which plays out on the level of politics but has much deeper roots, as the name implies—is fought between groups that are geographically separated, don't trust and generally despise one another. Episodes like the insurrection attempt on January 6, 2021, in Washington, DC, or the Canadian "Trucker

---

14—Jokela, "Birth-cohort Effects," *op cit.*

15—Michael Woodley of Menie, Tomas Cabeza de Baca, Heitor Fernandes *et al.*, "Slow and Steady Wins the Race: K Positively Predicts Fertility in the USA and Sweden," *Evolutionary Psychological Science*, 3 (2017): 109-117.

16—Peter Turchin, *Ages of Discord: A Structural-Demographic Analysis of American History* (Mansfield: Beresta Books, 2016).

Protest" (which got started just before this book went to press) are both notable examples of this trend.

In the 20th century, the United States experienced two related phenomena, which occurred in succession and would define demographics and politics for decades: "White flight" and "gentrification." The first occurred as White Americans moved to the suburbs. This was made possible through the expansion of the interstate highway system and massive investment in real-estate development; it was sparked, in large part, by the mid-century racial integration of schools, as well as protests and riots in urban areas that accompanied this. The second phenomenon occurred as many Whites—stereotypically wealthy, educated, and liberal Whites—returned to the abandoned cities and transformed them into bohemian paradises. White flight supported family formation and fertility; gentrification did not. Both are indicative of the "Big Sort" and the Red/Blue divide, in which liberals predominate in urban centers, and Republicans, in much of the rest of the country. "Reds" and "Blues" live in separate places, pursue separate cultures, and largely co-exist in a state of political and psychological apartheid. Both groups feel "under siege," by the "liberal elites" or "racist rednecks," respectively.

Conservative Americans, who live in rural and suburban areas, are animated by ethnocentrism, more traditional religiosity, and other forms of collectivism. Though they might talk about "secession," or engage in dysfunctional protests like that of the Canadian truckers, their political expressions are enveloped by the idea of nationalism and "saving" their respective countries. Conservative, uneducated, rural Americans remain high in fertility, if no longer family formation. On the other hand, the evolutionary crucible of Wokeism will dictate that those that are most woke (transsexual, homosexual, or those who succumb to debilitating levels of "White guilt") will simply die off.

Perhaps all of this parallels what happened the last time Western civilization collapsed. It did not completely fall. Rome, and its civilization, held on in the Near East, in what came to be Byzantium. Intelligent people from all around Europe escaped the chaos and breakdown into small and violent polities, making their way to Constantinople and, in a sense, further "gentrifying" it. For example, in 1071, in the wake of the Norman Conquest of England, a large group of Anglo-Saxon notables emigrated in about 300 ships. They arrived in Constantinople in 1075. Some of them remained there, in the service of the emperor, while most went to Domapia and established "Nova Anglia." The wealthy and educated migrated to Byzantium if they could and so desired, and there were other migrations from England to Byzantium in the Middle Ages.[17]

THE GUARDIANS

Whenever I discuss civilizational collapse, I often encounter rejection, denial, and magical thinking. In the face of evidence, many people adamantly declare that it simply "can't happen here." Their arguments take a number of forms. One of note evinces a certain "Gnostic" mentality, which relates to QAnon and the

---

17—Jack Lindsay, *Byzantium Into Europe: The Story of Byzantium as the First Europe (326-1204 A.D.) and Its Further Contribution Till 1453 A.D.* (London: The Bodley Head, 1952), 294.

conspiracy theories of the American Right. In effect: *The world is run by highly intelligent, evil people. They are going to institute eugenics for themselves and create a super-race. World government is real; elite tyranny is imminent, and the rest of us might end up enslaved or exterminated.*[18] Or something to that effect.

How can one respond to this? First, there is no evidence whatsoever that "the elite" is doing this, so it is just religiously motivated speculation. Secondly, what evidence would falsify this hypothesis? If it cannot theoretically be falsified—which it seems it cannot be—it is not scientific and should be dismissed as speculation at best. Thirdly, we should ask, which is more probable: Post-industrial civilization is fundamentally different from all others—we have somehow escaped the cycles of world history? Or our civilization will collapse like all the others before it? In the end, post-industrial civilization has followed, and continues to follow, the precise same pattern as all other civilizations, and it has all the markers of being in "Winter," after which all previous civilizations met their ends. Fourthly, even if "the elite" is pursuing a secret eugenics policy, it wouldn't work. As we discussed, very high intelligence correlates with autism and thus low empathy) low empathy; the non-empathic mind excels at systematizing, which better allows you to solve problems. It also correlates with being hyper-sensitive to stimuli and even with asthma, because those who can take in more information, and be more sensitive to their world, will better make sense of it.[19] Breeding for super-

18—See, for example, Alex Jones (dir.), *Endgame*, InfoWars, 2009.

19—Ruth Karpinski, Audrey Kolb, Nicole Tetreault, *et al.*, "High Intelligence: A Risk Factor for Psychological and Physiological Overexcitabilities,"

high intelligence would thus eventually create a society full of people with serious psychological problems. Worse still, as people become more intelligent, their intelligence becomes narrower in focus, meaning that a super-intelligent person often has trouble looking after himself, and he is low in other weak correlates of IQ, social skills being a good example. These high-IQ autistic people are rather like Sheldon Cooper from *The Big Bang Theory*: he is brilliant with computers but can never find his keys.[20] A society full of people like this would fall apart and, low in instinct, such people would likely not breed much anyway. Societies can't function without the *hoi polloi*.

Why these conspiratorial arguments are popular is a fascinating issue. Due to increased meritocracy and centralization, our society has become increasingly cognitively stratified, with people tending to attain the position of which they are intellectually capable in a way that would not have been the case when society was more nepotistic.[21] This, in turn, leads to greater genetic stratification, and there is clear evidence, for example, of social class differences in dominant blood type.[22] This, in turn, would lead to distrust between social classes and people of different social classes decreasing interacting and seeing the world increasingly differently—in a way, becoming "races."

Intelligence, 66 (2018): 8-23.

20—Michael Woodley, "The Cognitive Differentiation-integration Effort Hypothesis: A Synthesis Between the Fitness Indicator and Life History Models of Human Intelligence," *Review of General Psychology*, 15 (2011): 228-245.

21—See Richard Herrnstein and Charles Murray, *The Bell Curve: Intelligence and Class Structure in American Life* (New York: Free Press, 1994).

22—C. Mascie-Taylor and I. McManus, "Blood Group and Socio-economic Class" *Nature* 309 (1984): 395–396.

Nevertheless, it is clearly simplistic to make a binary, essentialist division between "the elite" and "the rest," as if the two never cross-over. This takes its most extreme form in perceiving the elite as, somehow, a different species, something predicted, as discussed above, not just by declining trust levels but also by declining intelligence. These arguments are clearly the stuff of paranoid fantasy. As somebody who went to an "elite" university, I met plenty of students who were, without question, part of the British "upper crust." Indeed, I often met their parents as well, some of whom had not been born elite. I lived with, and was friends with, an Old Etonian who was the grandson of a baronet on one side and the great-grandson of a peer-of-the-realm on the other. He went on to be assistant private secretary to Prince Philip (1921-2021). He's not a lizard and, he has assured me, nor is Prince Philip.

A related argument is that the elite will halt societal collapse by changing the conditions that are causing dysgenics. But these have been known about for centuries, and this all-powerful managerial class surely knows what's happening, yet they have done nothing. Such people will exploit the collapse and ensure that they are insulated from the chaos—like African despots—but they show no evidence of doing anything about it. Moreover, the elite is becoming less intelligent along with the broader population, and have long been doing so. Thus, they are decreasingly able to do anything about it and are increasingly short-term in their outlook and strategy.

People who espouse views like the ones outlined above are, in many ways, the new Gnostics. They see the world as run by Satan or, in secular terms, by an evil cabal of super-intelligent people. The fact that this is an evolved cognitive bias should, itself, make us highly skeptical of it and of any hypotheses that appear to rationalize it. They are wild, unscientific speculations that reflects a paranoid personality where the world is, in effect, haunted by Demiurgic demons. All evidence indicates that the West is collapsing just as Classical civilization, and the Bronze Age, collapsed before it. And this will mean that the Woke will die off, just as the decadent types in Rome did not pass on their genes. Automation, Artificial Intelligence, or "robots" won't rescue us from this, as, eventually, we'll be too stupid to maintain these technologies.

Indeed, with the Woke gone, there might be a new "Zombie Apocalypse" of low IQ, selfish, impulsive White people, who would be constantly pillaging collectivist territories, like Vikings pillaging European cities. This situation could re-institute group-selection among both groups, especially as we would expect modern civilization to collapse into more Darwinian conditions among the individualists, whose world would be like parts of the Third World today. In this sense, it is not merely zombie movies that seem to prepare us for the future but the many popular films and books of "dystopia" in which some kind of "speciation," or at least profound separation among Whites, has taken place.

The film *Waterworld* (1995) foresees two castes of human.[23] Another work in this genre is a young-adult science-fiction novel, *The Guardians* (1970). Here, the England of the year 2052 is an authoritarian regime divided into two completely separate areas: the modern and overpopulated "Conurbs" and the wealthy "County"

23—Kevin Reynolds (Dir.), *Waterworld*, Universal Pictures, 1995.

of manors and rolling-hills, in essence, a romanticized, 19th-century vision of country life. The story follows a "Conurban" orphan who escapes into the "County," rather like escaping from a South American "favela", and journeys to the wealthy suburbs of Boston. Those who live in the County are group-oriented, while those who live in the Conurbs have a "spirit of freedom," seemingly a euphemism for "individualists," as low IQ people tend to be.[24] What this novel misses, however, is that under conditions of societal collapse, polities tend to break-up and become smaller as trust levels collapse due to decreasing intelligence, ethnic conflict and the lack of group-selection to hold polities together.[25]

These may be fairy tales for adults. And, like the original fairy tales, they help us negotiate the crucibles of evolution. And with modernization, they might tell us something important that they older tales missed. The crucible of evolution have moved from warfare to Wokeism; from measles to Marxism. We—the non-infected—find ourselves like the little gang of non-infected in *28 Days Later*. We must make our way to a safe area, find other non-infected, and keep the light of civilization burning.

24—John Christopher, *The Guardians* (London: Hamilton, 1970).

25—See Tatu Vanhanen, *Ethnic Conflicts: Their Biological Roots in Ethnic Nepotism* (London: Ulster Institute for Social Research, 2012).

INDEX

#

2D:4D Ratio 267
28 Days Later (film) 5, 10, 365

A

adrenal hyperplasia 191–192, 255
agency over-detection 43
Agreeableness. *See* psychology
alcohol abuse 191, 255
Alexithymia 273
alleles. *See* genes; *See also* mutation
Alt-Right 18, 79–80, 159, 171–172
altruism 34–35, 40, 67, 102, 135, 175–176, 204
Anglican Church 325
Anorexia 249, 260, 262, 263, 271
anti-natalism 71, 140, 312, 321
antisocial behavior 80, 163, 176, 265. *See also* psychology
Apostolou, Menelaos 134, 322–323
asthma 190, 253, 255, 361
atheism 48, 65–66, 80, 94–97, 100, 115, 118, 120, 142, 215, 225, 312
autism 74–75, 78, 80–81, 142, 192, 237, 257–261, 266–267, 269, 273
Autogynephilia. *See* transsexuality

B

Babbitt, Ashli 158
backlash, political 68, 330, 344, 349, 358
Balzac, Honoré de 231
Barash, David 197, 345
Benin 6
Bible, the
  New Testament 92, 227
  Old Testament 89, 92, 182, 212, 219–220, 226
Biden, Joe 158, 245
Big Five personality traits. *See* psychology
binding values. *See* Moral Foundations
birth control. *See* contraception
Black Lives Matter (BLM) 23, 77, 111–144, 147, 161–162, 168, 174
Blanchard, Ray 190, 195, 199, 213, 250–254, 256
Borderline Personality Disorder 75, 78, 194, 257, 260–266, 272–273, 341. *See also* psychology; *See also* antisocial behavior

Bororo 222
Boyer, Pascal 43, 48
Boyle, Danny 5
Brass Eye (television series) 334–335
British Aristocracy 217–219
Buddhism 209
Buttigieg, Peter 233
Byzantine Empire 360

C

Calhoun, John B. 304–306
Calvinism 230. *See also* Christianity; *See also* Protestant Reformation
Campaign for Homosexual Equality 339
Campbell, Duncan 122
Canada and Canadians 358–359
"cancel culture". *See* de-platforming
capitalism 8, 84, 230
Catholicism 99, 137, 207–208, 211
Causey, Kayla 198, 202
Charlottesville protest 159
Charlton, Bruce 36, 78, 193, 200, 289
Chauvin, Derek 116
child mortality 11, 23, 54, 140, 147, 200, 206, 223, 293, 355
Christianity 11, 91–92, 99–100, 102, 115, 117, 131–133, 139–140, 142, 145, 161, 215, 225–226, 239, 324. *See also* Bible, the; *See also* Protestant Reformation; *See also* Catholicism
Churchill, Winston 113, 217–218
Church of England 96, 141
civilization 222–233
"seasons" 225, 361
Clinton, Bill 155
Clinton, Hillary 148
Cochran, Gregory 36
cognitive dissonance 36, 45, 311, 335
Colston, Edward 114–115
computer modeling 15, 33, 35, 50–51, 204, 318
Consensus Effect 45
consent, sexual 232, 338, 340
conspiracy theories 18, 44–45, 80, 99, 128, 146–147, 151, 156–157, 170, 174, 180
contraception 167, 228, 352–353, 356
coronavirus. *See* Covid-19
Cortes, Herman 143
Covid-19 77, 112, 116, 132–133, 154, 160, 292
lockdowns 112
Cromwell, Thomas 139
crucible of evolution 11, 74, 276, 326
cuckolding 41, 49, 51, 189, 245–248
"cultural war" 358

D

Dawkins, Richard 125, 307
Dawn of the Dead (film) 8
"Deep State," the 153–154
democracy 18, 354–356
Democratic Socialists of
America (DSA) 243
de-platforming 84–86, 104–106
depression 13, 18–20, 49,
53–54, 57, 59, 65–66,
72–74, 78, 97, 118, 127,
132, 134, 138, 140, 169,
185, 191, 194, 199, 201,
208, 237, 255, 347
developmental instability 55,
66, 172, 177, 190, 192,
199, 202, 252, 255–256,
265, 269, 272–273, 283,
341
devil worship 91–92, 128, 157,
175, 363
*Diagnostic and Statistical
Manual of Mental
Disorders* 331
disgust instinct 183
Dolezal, Rachel 245
drug abuse 117, 191, 255, 314
Durham Inter-Collegiate
Christian Union 25
Durham University 25–26,
235, 277–278, 377
Dutton's Rule 64
Dworkin, Andrea 73
dysgenics 54, 363
dysphoria 13, 21–23, 57,
63–65, 101, 108, 182,
224–227, 249–250, 252,
256, 260, 262, 266–270,
273, 276–279, 323, 326,
328, 347, 351

E

Egypt, Ancient 223, 226
Eliade, Mircea 99
elite, the 166–167, 174, 180,
361–363
Eminem 336
empathy 40, 52, 67, 80–81,
120, 134–135, 171, 177,
192, 203, 218, 237,
258–259, 317, 327, 361
Epstein, Jeffrey 154, 180
erectile dysfunction 300, 307.
See also pornography,
internet
Escriva, St. Josemaria 208
ethnic groups 32–33, 88, 94,
101, 135, 354
ethnocentrism 15, 33, 35, 50,
87, 90, 93, 101, 147,
204, 212, 214, 216, 359
Europe 83–85, 92, 94, 99, 111,
137, 145, 208, 226, 276,
352, 360
eusocial 107, 140
evolutionary mismatch 13, 17,
57–62, 68, 74, 100–101,
108, 128, 138, 141, 224,
277, 288, 291, 297–298,
301, 319, 321–322, 324,
326, 346–347, 351–352,
355
evolution, Darwinian
group selection 30–36, 50, 53,

59, 87, 90–91, 94–95,
  101, 140, 164, 200,
  204–206, 210–211, 216,
  220–221, 232, 317–318,
  343, 345
 criticisms 34–37
 kin selection 31–34, 197, 220
 Multi-Level Selection Theory
  30, 34
 natural selection 25–82,
  94–97, 197
 sexual selection 27–29
 social selection 30–34

F

fairy tales 6–8, 365
feminism 65, 73, 261, 325–328
fertility 13–14, 25, 29, 49,
  51, 57, 60–61, 65–66,
  70–71, 95–100, 140,
  165, 170, 197, 228, 297,
  311, 319, 323, 326, 328,
  346, 351–352, 356–357
fetishes. See paraphilia
fibromyalgia 237, 255
Floyd, George 111, 116–117,
  161. See also Black Lives
  Matter (BLM)
Forstater, Maya 244–245, 275
Freud, Clement 179
Freud, Sigmund 230
Fukasawa, Maki 285

G

Galileo's Middle Finger 251–252
Gallup, Gordon 205–206,
  221–222, 342

Game Theory 46
gang rape. See rape
Gates, Bill 153
Gay Shaman Theory 210
Gay Uncles 197–198
Gender Dysphoria 235–283
 Autism 257
 Borderline Personality Disorder
  260
 environmental causes 269–273
 fetishism 256
 Narcissistic Personality
  Disorder 262–264
 Psychopathic Personality
  Disorder 265
 Rapid-Onset Gender
  Dysphoria 271
general factor of intelligence 39
genes 11, 13, 15, 21, 23,
  26–32, 37, 53, 54–59,
  69, 94, 98, 156, 165,
  178, 185, 193, 197,
  209, 221, 261, 279,
  306–307, 316–317, 319,
  328, 348, 351, 364. See
  also mutation
 alleles 26–27
gentrification 359
Glitter, Gary 338
Gnosticism 93–94, 102–103,
  157, 278, 360, 363
Goad, Jim 135, 324
God. See religion
Goetz, Aaron 198, 202
Gone With The Wind (film) 114
Gottfried, Paul 93, 102
Graham, Billy 123, 126,
  129–131, 160–161
Great Britain 5, 83, 96, 113–

114, 121–123, 129, 135, 137, 142, 160–161, 240, 309–310, 324, 329–333, 337–338, 353
Greece, Ancient 66, 206, 214–215, 221–223, 225, 318
group selection. *See* evolution, Darwinian
Guardians, The (novel) 364
Guardian, The (newspaper) 243, 339–340

H

Haidt, Jonathan 15–16, 47, 67–68, 105, 180, 342–343. *See also* Moral Foundations
Hain, Peter 339
Hamilton, Thomas 332
Hamilton, William 20, 31–32
Hannah, Sophie 285
Harman, Harriet 338
Harper, Stephen 331
Harris, Rolf 179
"Herbivore Men" 285–289, 311
Hinduism 209
"hive mind". *See* eusocial
homosexuality 181–234, 250–253, 270, 293, 342, 345
    "gay uncle" theory 197–199
    "Johnny Depp effect" 202–206
    lesbianism 187–192
    prohibition and repression 219–220

"Shaman" theory 207–210
"tops and bottoms" 199–200
Hose, Keith 339
human rights 347
"Human Zoo" 217, 307
hyperandrogenism 255
hypergamy 30, 51, 64, 198, 320, 325
Hypersexuality. *See* sexuality

I

iGen 308–309
impulse control 67, 102, 136, 167, 176, 191, 216
Incels (involuntary celibates) 313–314
inclusive fitness 31–33
individualism. *See* Moral Foundations
Industrial Revolution 11, 23, 51, 54, 92, 94, 147, 165, 167, 172, 200, 304
instinct 13, 60, 97, 183, 224, 352, 362
intelligence 15, 18–19, 39–40, 44, 59–60, 79, 88, 97, 147, 166–167, 177, 180, 189, 204–205, 210, 225, 228–229, 237, 262, 303, 326, 352–354, 357, 361–362, 365
    IQ 18–19, 39, 97, 162, 166–167, 190, 319–320, 352–353, 357, 362, 364–365
internet, the 10, 173–174, 271, 286, 289, 296, 299–302, 307, 309, 313

in vitro fertilization 293, 346
IQ. *See* intelligence
Islam 91, 209, 215, 226

J

Jackson, Michael 180
James, William 125
January 6 insurrection 18, 158,
    163, 358
Japan 285–289, 292, 302, 304,
    307–308, 318
Judaism 90–91

K

Kaltiala-Heino, Riittakerttu
    242
Kaulback, Ronald 237
Kennedy, John F. 146, 154
Kessler, Harry 218
Kim, Emily 211, 230–231
kin selection. *See* evolution,
    Darwinian
Klaits, Joseph 92
Koresh, David 22

L

Lawrence, D.H. 229
left-handedness 55, 66, 190–
    191, 199, 253, 267
Left (political) 16, 19, 61, 72,
    76–78, 84–85, 103, 105,
    130, 135–136, 170, 321
Lesbians 187–191
Levine, Rachel 245
libertarianism 84, 338
Life History Strategy 12,
    38–42, 68, 71, 74, 178,
    222, 261, 302–303, 356
Little Red Riding Hood 7
Littman, Lisa 270–271, 294
Luce, A.A. 278

M

Machiavellianism 19, 76,
    103, 140, 171. *See
    also* psychology; *See
    also* psychopathy and
    psychopathology
Major, John 329
Mandelson, Peter 233
mansplaining 84
MAPs (Minor Attracted
    Persons). *See* pedophilia
marriage 212, 226, 232, 287,
    295, 298, 324
Marxism 99–102, 131, 365
Maunder Minimum 93
McMillan, Neil 281–282
Meisenberg, Gerhard 226
memes and memetics 98, 306
memes, internet 150, 229, 309,
    331
menarche 255
Mesopotamia, Ancient 223
Metro 312
Miesen, Anna van der 259
Milgram Experiment, the 44
Millennials 308–309
Miller, Edward 203, 311
Miller, Geoffrey 29, 78
monogamy 315, 327
monotheism 89–92. *See
    also* religion; *See
    also* Judaism; *See*

also Christianity

monolatry 89

Moon landing 146, 174

Moral Foundations 17,
47–48, 67–69, 105, 162,
342–343. *See also* Haidt,
Jonathan

binding values 15, 17, 68–69,
162, 354–355

fairness 19, 69, 166, 342

individualism 16, 22, 33, 59,
67–71, 73–74, 76, 80,
93, 96, 100, 102–103,
105, 139, 165, 172, 175,
177, 278, 294, 323, 340,
343

sanctity 15, 22, 64, 67–68,
342

Morris, Chris 334

mortality salience 13, 43,
97–98, 108, 117–118,
120, 124–125, 130, 133,
137–138, 224–225

Mouse Utopia experiment
304–307

Mukwege, Denis 63

multiculturalism 103, 115,
133–135, 228, 343, 355

Multi-Level Selection.
See evolution, Darwinian

Muslims 9, 214, 301

mutation 11–12, 16, 19,
21–22, 26–27, 35,
55–57, 72–73, 81, 94,
108, 117, 142, 168–169,
190, 193, 201, 253, 292.
See also genes

N

Napoles, Desmond 330

Narcissism 19, 75–76, 103–
104, 171, 257, 262–264,
278. *See also* psychology

National Council of Civil
Liberties (NCCL 338

Neduva, Alexander 104

Neuroticism. *See* psychology

New Guinea 213–214

News of the World, The 333

nihilism 10, 20, 23, 26, 57, 80,
144

Nolan, Nicole 318

Norenzayan, Ara 14, 84, 89,
118, 143, 160

nurturing 13

O

obedience 15, 44, 67, 141,
344. *See also* Milgram
Experiment, the

obesity 55, 255, 292

Obsessive-Compulsive Disorder
177

Openness. *See* psychology

Operation Yewtree 179

Opus Dei 208

P

Paedophile Information
Exchange 338–339

Paedophile Information
Network, The 337–342

paganism 90, 99

Palmer, Rory 310, 313
Pape, Robert 158
paraphilia 192–193, 196,
    256–259, 265, 269–271,
    277, 331
patriarchy 51–52, 58, 74, 106,
    120, 134, 298, 317, 322,
    326
Pattern Over-Detection 43
Payne, Sarah 332
pedophilia 329–348
  MAPs (Minor Attracted
    Persons) 330–331
Pelosi, Nancy 116
Peterson, Jordan 7, 244
phenotype 29, 55, 297
Philo 219
Philosophy Now 279–281
Pinker, Steven 34
"Pizzagate" 148, 155, 163. *See
    also* QAnon
Plato 90, 218
polarization, political 153, 162,
    172–173, 180, 358
Post, Felix 79, 176–177
Post-Traumatic Stress Disorder
    127, 255
Predestination. *See* Calvinism
Prisoner's Dilemma, the 46
prohibiton and repression.
    See homosexuality
promiscuity. *See* sociosexuality
Protestant Reformation 137
psychology. *See also* Narcissism;
    See also psychopathy
    and psychopathology;
    See also Borderline
    Personality Disorder
Agreeableness 40–42, 52–53,

79, 102, 135, 313, 358
Conscientiousness 40–42,
    52–53, 79, 102, 135–
    136, 320, 356–357
Extraversion 40, 356
Neuroticism 40, 52, 65,
    76, 78, 102, 118–120,
    127–130, 132, 134–136,
    169, 201, 264, 357
Openness 40, 103–104
psychopathy and
    psychopathology 18–19,
    55, 57, 75, 79–80, 171,
    174, 257, 265–266,
    272–273, 341
Putnam, Robert 228, 345

Q

QAnon 145–180, 360. *See
    also* conspiracy theories

R

Race, Evolution, and Behavior
    (Rushton) 302
rape 28, 63, 106, 178–179,
    197, 282, 298, 349
  gang rape 178, 197, 298
Reagan, Ronald 153
religion 98–102. *See
    also* Christianity; *See
    also* Judaism; *See
    also* paganism
  intrinsic religiousness 118
  moral god 49, 53, 72, 84,
    87–90, 95, 98, 102, 131,
    168, 170
  replacement religion 100–101,

131, 156
variations 87–94
Right (political) 17–19, 72, 79, 95, 145–180, 361
Rome, Ancient 60, 66, 94, 206, 222, 225, 360, 364
Romero, Geroge 5–6, 8–9
Rushton, J. Philippe 6, 40, 62–63, 165, 178, 203, 224, 302–303, 355

S

Salter, Frank 32–33, 47, 95, 316
Sambia 213–214, 222
sanctity. See Moral Foundations
Satan. See devil worship
Savile, Jimmy 179, 338–339
schizophrenia 44, 49, 55, 57, 74, 80–81, 98, 126–127, 169–170, 208, 255
schizotpy spectrum 80
secularization thesis 161
Sex and Culture (Unwin) 227
sexuality
  Hypersexuality 257
  sexual development 289, 294, 319
  sociosexuality 175, 336
sexual selection. See natural selection
Shaun of the Dead 6
"Simps" 312–313
Sneyd-Kynnersley, Herbert 218–219
Snyder, Zack 9
social contagion 20, 270, 294
Social Epistasis Amplification

Model 56, 142, 274
socialization 13, 138, 305–306
Social Justice Warriors (SJWs) 10, 83–110, 309, 324
social media 25, 138, 145, 172–173, 271, 331
sociosexuality. See sexuality
Soros, George 155
Soshoku Danshi. 285–286
"Soy Boys" 309–312, 318
Spencer, Richard 86, 246
spiritual struggle 132
Spiteful Mutants 12–13, 21–23, 56, 98, 107, 139–142, 200, 275, 288–289, 294, 306–308, 323, 343, 347
  definition 14–19
  Spiteful Ideas 19–21
St. Paul 219
sublimation 211, 230–231
suburbs 359
suicide 55, 144, 154, 185, 191, 199. See also depression
Swinburne, Richard 239–240

T

taboo 182, 215, 226–227, 230–232, 296, 329
Taylor, James 275
technology 172
teen pregnancy 336
Telfer, CeCe 247
testosterone 176, 255, 257, 290–292, 301, 309, 311, 313, 327
Thomas, Lia 247
"tipping point" 74, 107,

141–142, 203
transsexuality 10, 23, 75,
    235–284, 346
  autogynephilic transsexuals
    250–251, 256–257,
    269–270
  homosexual transsexuality
    252–255
transvestitism 207, 256. *See
    also* transsexuality
Trucker protests (2022)
    358–359
Trump, Donald 103, 146, 149,
    152–156, 169, 172
Twenge, Jennifer 59, 308

U

United States 83–85, 111, 115,
    119, 129, 145–146, 152,
    154, 156–157, 162–164,
    207, 242–243, 247–248,
    359
Unwin, J.D. 227–228

V

"virtue signaling" 17, 19, 71,
    78, 96, 139, 313, 344

W

Waddell, Alexander and Andrea
    235–242, 277–283
Walker, Allyn 348
Waterworld 364
Weber, Max 230
Weinstein, Harvey 154, 180
Weiss, Bari 86

Welby, Justin 96
White flight 359
White Nationalism. *See* Alt-
    Right
Wilson, David Sloan 30, 224
Wilson, E.O. 62
Woke 9–10, 23, 26, 61, 66–67,
    84, 238, 276, 329,
    351–352, 364–365
Woodley of Menie, Michael 12,
    51, 60, 142, 167–168,
    225, 274, 305, 320, 354,
    358
World War I 122
World War Z (film) 9

Y

Yanomamö 222

Z

zombies 5–11, 22, 351–378
Zoomers. *See* iGen

ABOUT THE AUTHOR

EDWARD DUTTON is a researcher based in Oulu in northern Finland. Born in London in 1980, Dutton read Theology at Durham University, before completing a PhD in Religious Studies at Aberdeen University in 2006. This was developed into his first book: *Meeting Jesus at University: Rites of Passage and Student Evangelicals* (Ashgate, 2008). He was made Docent of the Anthropology of Religion and Finnish Culture at Oulu University in 2011. In 2012, however, Dutton made the move to evolutionary psychology and has never looked back. Since then, Dutton has published in leading psychology journals including *Intelligence, Personality and Individual Differences,* and *Journal of Biosocial Science.* He has also been a guest researcher in the Psychology Department at Umeå University in Sweden and is academic consultant to a research group in the Special Education Department at King Saud University in Riyadh, Saudi Arabia. In 2020, he was made Professor of Evolutionary Psychology at Asbiro University in Łódź, Poland. Dutton's research has been reported worldwide including in the *Daily Telegraph, The Sun, Le Monde,* and *Newsweek* and his books have been translated into various languages including Russian, Japanese, and German. Dutton can be found online at his award-winning channel "The Jolly Heretic."

CPSIA information can be obtained
at www.ICGtesting.com
Printed in the USA
BVHW051309260522
638205BV00018B/674